A BIBLIOGRAPHY OF
recreational mathematics

volume 3

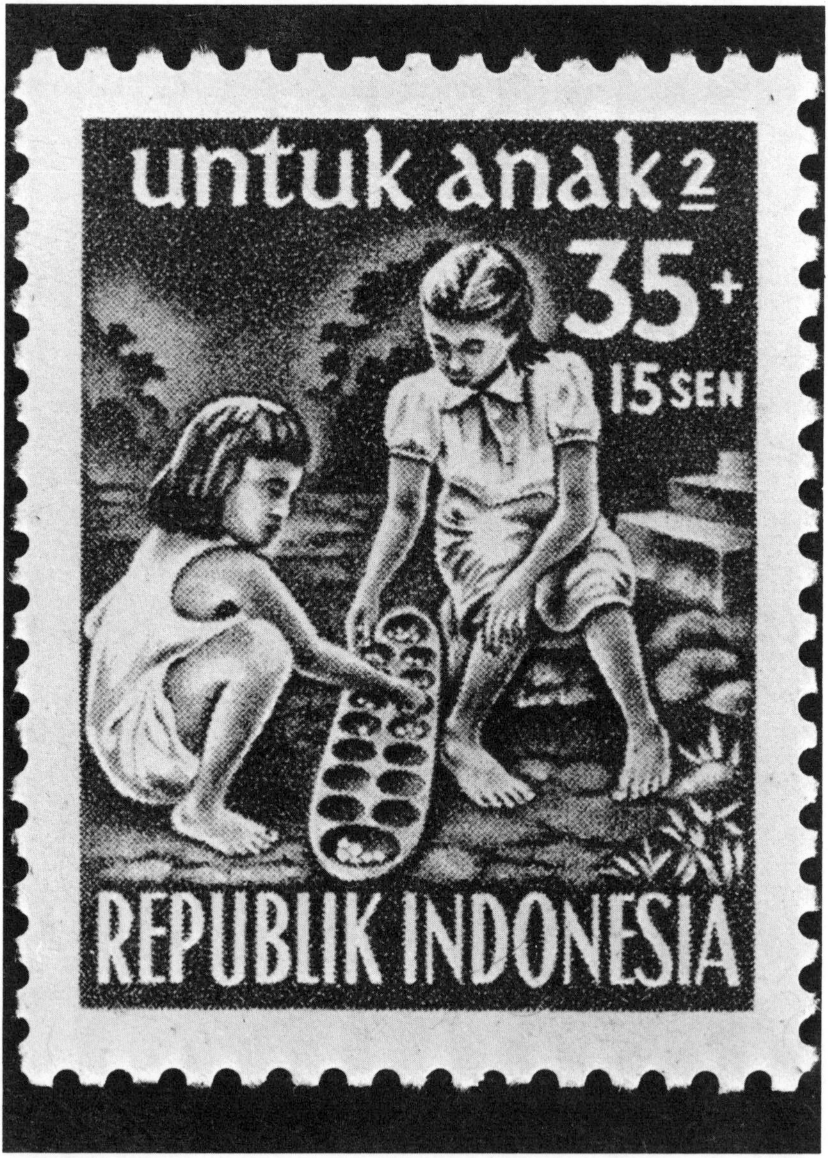
untuk anak2
35+
15 SEN
REPUBLIK INDONESIA

A BIBLIOGRAPHY OF
recreational mathematics

VOLUME
3

William L. Schaaf

Professor Emeritus
Brooklyn College
The City University of New York

NATIONAL COUNCIL OF TEACHERS OF MATHEMATICS
1906 Association Drive, Reston, Virginia 22091

Library of Congress Cataloging in Publication Data (Revised):

Schaaf, William Leonard, 1898–
    A bibliography of recreational mathematics.

    Vols. 2 and 3 lack edition statement.
    First-3d editions published under title: Recrea-
tional mathematics.
    1. Mathematical recreations—Bibliography.
I. Title.
Z6654.M3S32   016.7937'4   73-12168

Printed in the United States of America

Preface

Since the appearance of volume 2 in 1970, general interest in mathematical recreations has not abated. On the contrary, not only has the literature become more sophisticated, it has proliferated to amazing proportions. As Maxey Brooke suggests, it is like Alice: You have to keep running as hard as you can to stay in the same place. Thus the present volume is more than just an updating of the earlier monographs.

For the reader's convenience, the overall organization of the book has been retained, although there has been a notable rearrangement of subtopics in the interest of economy and greater clarity. Major changes include (1) the addition of two new sections on classroom games and recreational activities, which will doubtless appeal to teachers; (2) a chronological synopsis of Martin Gardner's popular column in *Scientific American*; and (3) a glossary of terms related to recreational mathematics.

As heretofore, some references have been listed under two different headings. Also, several hundred entries that were somehow previously overlooked have been belatedly included. Finally, a few items listed in the earlier volumes have been deliberately repeated here to enable the reader to retrieve related information concerning a given topic.

To acknowledge my indebtedness to many friends and correspondents would entail a lengthy list of names, and so I hereby express my gratitude to them all. My thanks are especially due to Maxey Brooke, Mannis Charosh, Martin Gardner, James A. H. Hunter, and Charles W. Trigg, whose help and suggestions have been invaluable. My thanks are also extended to the National Council of Teachers of Mathematics for its customary cooperation, and to my wife for her unflagging encouragement and patience.

William L. Schaaf

Boca Raton, Florida
April 1973

v

Contents

Problems

Problems worthy
of attack
prove their worth
by hitting back.

PIET HEIN
Grooks 1, p. 2 (1966)

Last Things First

Solutions to problems
are easy to find:
the problem's a great
contribution.
What is truly an art
is to wring from your mind
a problem to fit
a solution.

PIET HEIN
Grooks 3, p. 15 (1970)

Principal Abbreviations Used

A.M.M. = *American Mathematical Monthly*
A.T. = *Arithmetic Teacher*
Fib.Q. = *Fibonacci Quarterly*
J.R.M. = *Journal of Recreational Mathematics*
M.Gaz. = *Mathematical Gazette*
M.Mag. = *Mathematics Magazine*
M.S.J. = *Mathematics Student Journal*
M.T. = *Mathematics Teacher*
M.Tchg. = *Mathematics Teaching* (England)
NCTM = *National Council of Teachers of Mathematics*
N.M.M. = *National Mathematics Magazine*
P.M.E.J. = *Pi Mu Epsilon Journal*
R.M.M. = *Recreational Mathematics Magazine*
Sci.Am. = *Scientific American*
Sci.Mo. = *Scientific Monthly*
S.S.M. = *School Science and Mathematics*
Scrip.M. = *Scripta Mathematica*

Chapter 1

Arithmetical Recreations

1.1 Calendar Problems

Austin, A. K. A perpetual calendar. *M.Tchg.*, no. 56, p. 18; Autumn 1971.

Feser, Victor G. Annual sums. *J.R.M.* 5:252; Oct. 1972.

————. Product dates. *J.R.M.* 5:251–52; Oct. 1972.

Fredregill, Ernest J. *1000 Years: A Julian/Gregorian Perpetual Calendar.* New York: Exposition Press, 1970. 38 pp.

   Brief history of calendars and methods of construction.

Gardner, Martin. Birthday paradox. *Sci.Am.* Apr. 1957, p. 166.

————. Calendar problems. *Sci.Am.*, May 1967; Apr. 1969; May 1969.

————. Perverse month. *Sci.Am.*, Nov. 1969, p. 146; Feb. 1970, p. 114.

Heuer, C. V. *A.M.M.*, Aug.–Sept. 1963, p. 759.

   Friday the 13th.

Kravitz, Sidney. Abbreviated dates. *J.R.M.* 2:112; Apr. 1969.

Kravitz, Sidney, and Charles W. Trigg. Christmas falls on Sunday more often than once every seven years. [Problem 313.] *M.Mag.* 31:229–30; Mar. 1958.

Leetch, J. F. [Letter to the editor.] *M.T.* 63:684; Dec. 1970.

   On the frequency of occurrence of Friday the 13th.

Pai, B. Keshava R., and Monte Dernham. Years which have months with five Wednesdays. [Problem 389.] *M.Mag.* 33:236; Mar. 1960.

Poppe, Pam, and Betty Kruse. Note on the calendar. *Pentagon* 28:90–91; Spring 1969.

   Formula for expressing the day of the week as a function of the calendar date.

Prielipp, Robert. Calendar arithmetic. *A.T.* 16:69; Jan. 1969.

Rasof, Bernard. Continued fractions and "leap" years. *M.T.* 63:23–27; Jan. 1970.

Robinson, Raphael. Solution of the problem of the probability of Friday falling on the 13th. *A.M.M.* 40: 607; 1933.

Sanford, Vera. September hath XIX days. *M.T.* 45:336–39; May 1952.

   Historical discussion of older forms of the calendar; methods of calculating the calendar.

Stick, Marvin E. On what day were you born? *M.T.* 65:73–75; Jan. 1972.

Trigg, Charles W. Christmas Sunday. *M.Mag.* 31:229–30; Mar. 1958.

Wagner, John, and Robert McGinty. Superstitious? *M.T.* 65:503–5; Oct. 1972.

   Proof that there is at least one Friday the 13th in every year.

What Is the Date of Easter in 1970? *Pythagoras* (English ed.), vol. 2, no. 8, pp. 31–33; 1969–70.

   Gives Gauss's formula for determining the date of Easter.

1.2 Cryptarithms; Alphametics; Anagrams

Alphametics. [Problems 65, 68, 69, 103, 107, 109, 111.] *J.R.M.* 3:42–44, 48–50; Jan. 1970.

Alphametics. [Problems 93, 97, 100, 103, 107, 109, 111.] *J.R.M.* 3:234–37; Oct. 1970.
Alphametics. [Problems 140, 143, 146, 149.] *J.R.M.* 3:227–28; Oct. 1970.
Alphametics. [Problems 125, 127, 130, 133, 135, 137.] *J.R.M.* 4:146–48; Apr. 1971.
Alphametics. [Problems 187–92.] *J.R.M.* 4:283–84; Oct. 1971.
Alphametics. *J.R.M.* 5:63–64, 66, 68, 70, 71, 73; Jan. 1972.
Alphametics. *J.R.M.* 5:147–48; Apr. 1972.
Alphametics (without solutions). *J.R.M.* 5:227–28; July 1972.
Alphametics (J. A. H. Hunter, ed.). *J.R.M.* 5:289; Oct. 1972.
Alphametics. [Problems 203–9.] *J.R.M.* 5:301–4; Oct. 1972.
Card, Leslie E. A true alphametic. *J.R.M.* 4:75; Jan. 1971.
    (AN)[5] = EQUATION.
Demir, Huseyin, and Anton Glaser. Solution of UNITED + STATES = AMERICA in base eleven. [Problem 509.] *M.Mag.* 36:321; Nov. 1963.
Dudley, Underwood, and Charles W. Trigg. A doubly true addition. [Problem E1461.] *A.M.M.* 68:1006–7; Dec. 1961.
Gardner, Martin. Cryptarithms. *Sci.Am.* June 1959, p. 244; May 1959, p. 163; Jan. 1960, p. 156; Feb. 1960, p. 154; Oct. 1962, p. 126; Nov. 1962, p. 162; Nov. 1963, p. 156; Dec. 1963, p. 148; Jan. 1966, p. 114; Feb. 1966, p. 117; Mar. 1967, p. 124; Apr. 1967, p. 119; Oct. 1969, p. 127; Nov. 1969, p. 144; Feb. 1970, p. 112; Mar. 1970, p. 123; July 1971, p. 107.

Hunter, J. A. H. X/A plus Y/B plus $Z/C = \dfrac{XYZ}{ABC}$. *J.R.M.* 3:26; Apr. 1970.

Hunter, J. A. H., et al. A swinging alphametic. *M.Mag.* 44:166–68; May 1971.
Hunter, J. A. H., and Charles W. Trigg. A skeleton division. [Problem 710.] *M.Mag.* 42:160–61; May 1969.
————. Solution of DOUR + DONS + DON'T + STOP + DROP = OUTS. [Problem 719.] *M.Mag.* 42:268–69; Nov. 1969.
Prielipp, Robert W. Some famous mathematicians. *Pentagon*, vol. 31, no. 1, pp. 35–41; Fall 1972.
    Several interesting anagrams.
Tiner, John H., and J. A. H. Hunter. A cryptarithmic trick. [Problem 761.] *M.Mag.* 44:106–7; Mar. 1971.
    Solution of CHUCK + TRIGG + TURNS = TRICKS.
Trigg, Charles W. Anagrams. [Problem E1041.] *A.M.M.* 60:418–19; June 1953.
————. Atomistic chaos. *M.Mag.* 30:163–65; Jan. 1957.
————. Doubly true addition. *A.M.M.* 68:1006; Dec. 1961.
————. *Mathematical Quickies.* New York: McGraw-Hill Book Co., 1967.
    Cryptarithms. [Problems 19, 31, 80, 123, 173, 200, 223, 235, and 243.]
————. Names of mathematicians in timely anagrams. *M.Mag.* 34:244, 247; Mar. 1961.
————. Solution of IS/HE = .MADMADMAD . . . in base eleven. [Problem 3201.] *S.S.M.* 69:571–72; June 1969.
————. Solution of ME/SS = .PIPIPI . . . in base ten. [Problem 3284.] *S.S.M.* 71:178; Feb. 1971.
————. Solution of SI/HE = .CANCANCAN . . . in base eleven. [Problem 233.] *P.M.E.J.* 5:208; Spring 1971.
————. Solution of $(UNO)^2 + (TAN)^2 = (SEC)^2$. [Problem 3147.] *S.S.M.* 68:847; Dec. 1968.

————. Solution of VEXING = MATH without use of a computer. [Problem 614.] *M.Mag.* 40:168–69; May 1967.

Trigg, Charles W., M. Barnebey, and K. Wilke. Solution of SO/HE = .RANRANRAN . . . in bases nine and ten. [Problem 796.] *M.Mag.* 45:103; Mar. 1972.

Trigg, Charles W., and Elizabeth A. Calog. Solution of 3(BIDFOR) = 4(FORBID). [Problem 817.] *M.Mag.* 45:285; Nov. 1972.

Trigg, Charles W., and R. A. Carman. Solution of AM + PM = DAY in base six. [Problem 3424.] *S.S.M.* 72:573–74; June 1972.

Trigg, Charles W., and Herbert Leifer. Solution of ATOM + BOMB = CHAOS. [Problem 271.] *M.Mag.* 30:164–65; Jan. 1957.

Usiskin, Zalman, and J. A. H. Hunter. [Problem 810.] *M.Mag.* 45:230–31; Sept. 1972.
    An alphametic: TWO × SIX = TWELVE.

Wolf, Samual, and N. F. Nettheim. [Problem 714.] *M.Mag.* 42:216–18; Sept. 1969.
    Solution in base twelve of VIOLIN + VIOLIN + VIOLA + CELLO = QUARTET.

1.3   Determinants

Alfred, Brother U. Note on third order determinants. *Fib.Q.* 3:59–60; Feb. 1965.

Bicknell, Marjorie, and Verner E. Hoggatt. An investigation of nine-digit determinants. *M.Mag.* 36:147–52; May 1963.

Cohen, Joel E. Further properties of third order determinants. *M.Mag.* 35:304; Nov. 1962.

Trigg, Charles W. A census of nine-digit determinants. *M.Mag.* 36:153–56; May 1963.

————. An expansion of third order determinants. *M.Mag.* 35:234; Sept. 1962.

————. Nine-digit determinants equal to their principal diagonals. [Letter to the editor.] *M.T.* 56:521, 530; Nov. 1963.

————. Nine-digit determinants equal to 3. *J.R.M.* 3:157–59; July 1968.

————. A property of third order determinants. *M.Mag.* 35:78; Mar. 1962.

————. A theorem on determinants. *M.Mag.* 34:328; Sept. 1961.

————. Third order determinants invariant under element interchange. *Australian Mathematics Teacher* 18:40–41; July 1962.

————. Unique or no representation of integers by parent nine-digit determinants. *Boletin Matematico* [Buenos Aires] 35:121–22; Apr. 1963.

————. Unit-valued nine-digit determinants. *NABLA (Bulletin of the Malayan Mathematics Society)* 8:185–86; Dec. 1961.

————. Vanishing nine-digit determinants. *S.S.M.* 62:330–31; May 1962.

Trigg, Charles W., and D. C. B. Marsh. Probability that a determinant be even. [Problem E1512.] *A.M.M.* 70:93–94; Jan. 1963.

Wilson, W. W. Determinants. *M.Tchg.*, no. 51, pp. 6–8; Summer 1970.

1.4   Fallacies; Illegal Operations; Paradoxes

Bajaj, Prem N. A fallacy in limits. *J.R.M.* 4:135; Apr. 1971.
    The limits of a trigonometric expression arrived at in two different ways apparently "prove" that $\frac{1}{2} = \frac{2}{3}$.

Carman, Robert A. Mathematical misteaks. *M.T.* 64:109–15; Feb. 1971.

Carman, Robert A., and Herta Freitag. Illegal cancellations. [Problem 3236.] *S.S.M.* 70:263–64; Mar. 1970.

Manheim, Jerome H. True theorems from false conjectures. *M.T.* 65:231–36; Mar. 1972.
    Theoretical discussion of "illegal" cancellations and related processes.

Quast, W. G., and Richard Hunkler. "Comic" division. *M.T.* 64:345–47; Apr. 1971.

Silverman, David L. A pseudo-induction. *J.R.M.* 4:74; Jan. 1971.

Trigg, Charles W. Illegal cancellation in fractions with 3-digit denominators. [Problem 434.] *M.Mag.* 34:367–68; Sept.–Oct. 1961.

1.5   Four Fours; Four Digits; Related Problems

Bicknell, Marjorie, and Verner Hoggatt. 64 ways to write 64 using four 4's. *R.M.M.*, no. 14, pp. 13–15; Jan.–Feb. 1964.

Digital Diversions ("Rate Your Wits"). *J.R.M.* 3:45, 52; Jan. 1970.
    Problems similar to the four 4s.

Feser, Victor G. Integers expressed in repeated digits. *J.R.M.* 3:159–60; July 1970.

Freedman, Benedict. The four number game. *Scrip.M.* 14:35–47; 1948.

Gardner, Martin. Four 4's problem. *Sci.Am.* Jan. 1964, p. 122; Feb. 1964, p. 126.

The Hundred Problem

Fistie, G. *Sphinx;* Aug. 1935.
    A table of over 100 ways of writing 100 using the digits 1 through 9 in any order.

Gardner, Martin. Mathematical games. *Sci.Am.* 207:130–40, Oct. 1962; 207:151–64; Nov. 1962.
    Sum of 100 with the nine digits in reverse order.

Ley, W. For your information. *Galaxy Magazine*, vol. 19, no. 6, pp. 140-41; Aug. 1961.
    Sum of 100 from nine digits in forward order.

Madachy, J. S. *Mathematics on Vacation.* New York: Charles Scribner's Sons, 1966.
    Pages 157–59 give sums of 100 with digits both in forward and in reverse order.

———. Numbers, numbers, numbers. *R.M.M.*, no. 1, pp. 38–41; Feb. 1961.
    Sum of digits in forward order to give 100.

Patton, Robert L., Jr. The 100 problem revisited. *J.R.M.* 4:276–80; Oct. 1971.
    Bibliography; 7 references.

Resnick, M. Letters to the editor. *Sci.Am.* 208:10, 13; Jan. 1963.
    Solutions to the 100 problem, some with digits in forward order, some in reverse order.

1.6 Fractions; Farey Sequences

Algebra . . . Geometry. *Pythagoras* (English ed.), vol. 2, no. 9, pp. 58–62; 1969–70.

Curious properties of fractions resembling a Farey sequence, and their geometric interpretation.

Berenson, Lewis. A unit on unit fractions. *S.S.M.* 71:487–94; June 1971.

Blanch, Gertrude. Numerical evaluation of continued fractions. *SIAM Review,* Oct. 1964.

Frame, J. S. Continued fractions and matrices. *A.M.M.* 56:98–103; Feb. 1949.

Gardner, Martin. Fraction problem. *Sci.Am.* Jan. 1963, p. 138; Feb. 1963, p. 156.

Griffin, Harriett. Fractions in S-adic form. *M.T.* 64; 572–76; Oct. 1971.

Krinski, Sanford. The Farey series. *Mathematics Student* [Brooklyn Technical High School], vol. 21, no. 2, p. 3; Jan. 1953.

Moore, Charles G. *An Introduction to Continued Fractions.* Washington, D.C.: NCTM, 1964. 95 pp.

Excellent treatment of the properties and practical applications of continued fractions.

Penney, Walter. Egyptian fractions. [Problem 131.] *J.R.M.* 3:171; July 1970. Also, *J.R.M.* 4:290; Oct. 1971.

Rasof, Bernard. Continued fractions and "leap" years. *M.T.* 63:23–27; Jan. 1970.

Sherzer, Laurence. McKay's theorem. *M.T.* 66:229–30; Mar. 1973.

Given $a/b < c/d$, where a, b, c, and d are integers, then $(a + c)/(b + d)$ is between a/b and c/d.

Thomas, Paul D. Approximations to incommensurable numbers by ratios of positive integers. *M.Mag.* 36:281–89; Nov. 1963.

Wohlgemuth, Bernhardt. Egyptian fractions. *J.R.M.* 5:55–58; Jan. 1972.

1.7 Number Bases; Numeration

Amir-Moéz, Ali R. The magic of the base two. *S.S.M.* 71:335–38; Apr. 1971.

Barrett, M. J. A method for changing numerals in certain nondecimal bases to numerals in other certain nondecimal bases, directly. *A.T.* 15:453–54; May 1968.

Beiler, Albert H. *Recreations in the Theory of Numbers.* New York: Dover Publications, 1963.

Chapter 9: "Scales and Discords."

Bergman, George. A number system with an irrational base. *M.Mag.* 30:98–110; Dec. 1957.

Berlinghoff, William P. Numeration bases and infinity. *M.T.* 66:67–70; Jan. 1973.

Binary Codes. *Pythagoras* (English ed.), vol. 1, no. 4, pp. 70–74; 1968.

Brooke, Maxey. Is zero really necessary? *J.R.M.* 5:216–17; July 1972.

A comparison of multiplicative grouping systems and positional systems.

Brousseau, Brother Alfred. Palindromes by addition in base two. *M.Mag.* 42:254–56; Nov. 1969.

Brown, G. W. American dilemma: measuring up in the future: base 12 system. *S.S.M.* 71:435–56; May 1971.

Byrkit, Donald R. Changing bases—a method for squares. *S.S.M.* 71:513–17; June 1971.

Copley, G. N. Unidecimals and standard book numbers. *M.Tchg.*, no. 59, pp. 43–47; Summer 1972.
  Rather technical; discusses basimals with base eleven. Also an application of Pascal's triangle.
De Bruijn, N. G. On bases for the set of integers. *Publication Mathematics Debrecen* 1:232–42; 1950.
Dunkum, William. Another use for binary numerals. *A.T.* 17:225–26; Mar. 1970.
  Relation of binary notation to permutations and combinations.
Ellison, Alfred. The binary adder: a flow chart for the addition of binary numbers. *M.T.* 66:131–34; Feb. 1973.
Flaig, John. The theory of positional numeration. *Pentagon* 29:84–96; Spring 1970.
Gardner, Martin. The curious properties of the binary Gray code and how it can be used to solve puzzles. *Sci.Am.* 227:106–9; Aug. 1972.
———. "The Ternary System." In *Martin Gardner's Sixth Book of Mathematical Games from Scientific American*, pp. 104–12. San Francisco: W. H. Freeman & Co., 1971.
Glaser, Anton. *History of Binary and Other Nondecimal Numeration.* Southampton, Pa.: The Author (1237 Whitney Rd., Southampton, Pa. 18966), 1971. 196 pp. (Paper)
  Research monograph; comprehensive in scope. Excellent bibliography.
Grotelueschen, A. Structure and sequence in teaching number bases to adults. *Adult Education* 20:195–205; Summer 1970.
Hale, David, and Peter Wells. Base negative two. *M.Tchg.*, no. 60, pp. 32–33; Autumn 1972.
Hart, Maurice. Some work with children using multibase arithmetic blocks. *M.Tchg.*, no. 58, pp. 25–26; Spring 1972.
Jordan, James H. Small-digit representation of real numbers. *M.T.* 61:36–38; Jan. 1968.
Lenchner, Mitchell. The Lenchner base system. *M.S.J.*, vol. 19, no. 3, pp. 4–5; Mar. 1972.
Minné, Nels, and Herbert N. Johnson. It works for base ten and other bases too. *M.T.* 65:725–28; Dec. 1972.
O'Meara, D. J. A base for thought. *M.Tchg.*, no. 46, pp. 32–33; Spring 1969.
  Negative bases, etc.
Phillips, Eric. Bingo: the duodenary scale. *M.Tchg.*, no. 49, pp. 38–40; Winter 1969.
Portune, Robert G. A review of arithmetrickery. *M.S.J.*, vol. 19, no. 1, pp. 3–5; Nov. 1971.
  A humorous piece dealing with numeration systems.
Rosenblatt, Matthew. A modified ternary system. *Mathematics Bulletin* [Bronx High School of Science], 1959, pp. 7, 14.
Schaaf, William. Scales of notation. *M.T.* 47:415–17; Oct. 1954.
  Bibliography of 97 references to base 2, 8, 12, and to Nim.
Scopes, P. The hundred square. *M.Tchg.*, no. 50, pp. 69–71; Spring 1970.
  Diagrams for multiplication table in base ten as well as in other number bases.
Shurlow, H. J. Game of five. *A.T.* 10:290–91; May 1963.
  Game using base-five numeration.
Spickerman, W. R. Constructing base-*n* addition and multiplication tables. *S.S.M.* 69:771–72; Dec. 1969.

Swerdlow, Harold. A new idea on conversion from one base to another. *M.S.J.* vol. 20, no. 2, pp. 4–5; Dec. 1972.

Thébault, Victor, and G. W. Walker. Numbers having the same digits in two different systems of enumeration. [Problem 4240.] *A.M.M.* 55:508–9; Oct. 1948.

Thomason, G. To convert $N_{10} \rightarrow N_2$ on a hand calculating machine. *M.Tchg.*, no. 53, pp. 29–31; Winter 1970.

Thompson, G. A. Computers and the use of base two in the memory unit. *A.T.* 16:179–81; Mar. 1969.

Trigg, Charles W. "Other Number Bases." In *Mathematical Quickies.* New York: McGraw-Hill Book Co., 1967.
> Problems 47, 90, 112, 166, 235.

———. Terminal digits of MN $(M^2 - N^2)$ in the duodecimal system. *Duodecimal Bulletin* 14: 4X; Dec. 1960.

———. Terminal digits of MN $(M^2 - N^2)$ in the scale of 5. *Pentagon* 21:28–29; Fall 1961.

Twaddle, Richard D. A look at the base negative ten. *M.T.* 56:88–90; Feb. 1963.

Wardrop, R. F. Divisibility rules for numbers expressed in different bases. *A.T.* 19:218–20; Mar. 1972.

Wells, Chauncey. Using a negative base for number notation. *M.T.* 56:91–93; Feb. 1963.

Wessel, George. The base minus-ten numeration system. *S.S.M.* 68:701–6; Nov. 1968.

Willson, W. Wynne. Cheaper by the dozen. *M.Tchg.*, no. 26, pp. 62–64; Spring 1964.
> Arguments in favor of the duodecimal system.

Wiscamb, Margaret. "*b*-ary" fractions. *M.T.* 63:244–47; Mar. 1970.

Woo, Norman. A generalized base for integers. *M.T.* 66:169–70; Feb. 1973.
> 0's and 1's. *M.Tchg.*, no. 55, p. 35; Summer 1971.
> Note on binary notation and Pascal's triangle.

1.8 Number Mysticism; Numerology

Balliett, Mrs. L. Dow. *The Philosophy of Numbers: Their Tone and Colors.* Atlantic City, N.J., and London: The Author, 1908, 1925. 187 pp.
> Numerology.

Gardner, Martin. Dr. Matrix poses some heteroliteral puzzles while peddling perpetual motion in Houston. *Sci.Am.* 226:100–104; Feb. 1972.

———. Lessons from Dr. Matrix in chess and numerology. *Sci.Am.* 224:104–8; Jan. 1971.

———. A numeranalysis by Dr. Matrix of the lunar flight of Apollo II. *Sci.Am.* 221:126–30; Oct. 1969.
> Humor; numerology.

Kline, Morris. The harmony of the world. *M.Mag.* 27:127–39; 1953–54.

Shaw, James Byrnie. A chapter on the aesthetics of the quadratic. *M.T.* 21:121–34; Mar. 1928.

———. Irrational rhythms. *Sci.Mo.* 43:168–72; Aug. 1936.

———. Mystic harmony. *Scrip.M.* 8:69–77; June 1941.

———. Occult symmetry. *Scrip.M.* 9:129–38; Sept. 1943.
———. Shadow orders. *Scrip.M.* 12:241–58; Dec. 1946.

1.9   Number Pleasantries; Digital Oddities

Abbott, A. E. *Encyclopedia of Numbers.* London: Emerson Press, 1962.

Alfred, Brother U. Sums of squares of consecutive odd integers. *M.Mag.* 40:194–99; Sept. 1967.

Amir-Moéz, Ali R. Aboo-Bakkre Mohammad Al-Karkhi. *R.M.M.*, no. 10, pp. 45–46; Aug. 1962.

     Geometric aspects of number relations.

———. Ibn Bannaa. *R.M.M.*, no. 12, pp. 53–54; Dec. 1962.

     Number curiosities.

Barr, Stephen M., Underwood Dudley, and J. A. H. Hunter. Almost square integers. *J.R.M.* 4:145–46; Apr. 1971.

Bonyun, David A. The 1-4-8-9 and related problems. *J.R.M.* 5:218–24; July 1972.

Brooke, Maxey. Number please. *J.R.M.* 4:101–2; Apr. 1971.

     A note on the origin of numeral symbols.

Can You Handle a Googol? *R.M.M.*, no. 5, Oct. 1961.

Card, Leslie E. Some relatives of the integer 1089. *J.R.M.* 4:114; Apr. 1971.

Carman, Robert A., and Marilyn J. Carman. Number patterns. *A.T.* 17:637–39; Dec. 1970.

     Gives 40 examples of number patterns or pleasantries.

Carman, Robert, and Robert Prielipp. [Problem 3308.] *S.S.M.* 71:575–76; June 1971.

     To find an integer such that when its digits are rearranged in decreasing order from left to right, the difference between this number and its reverse is the original number.

Crouch, Ralph. *Coordinated Cross-Number Puzzles.* Spirit Masters. New York: McCormick-Mathers Publishing Co., 1970.

Davis, Chandler, and Donald Knuth. Number representations and dragon curves—I. *J.R.M.* 3:66–81; Apr. 1970.

deGuerre, Vernon, and R. A. Fairbairn. Automorphic numbers. *J.R.M.* 1:173–79; July 1968.

     A history of automorphic numbers; also tables of 1,000-digit automorphic numbers in bases six, ten, and twelve.

Dixon, J. A. Number squares. *M.Tchg.*, no. 57, pp. 38–40; Winter 1971.

Duncan, Donald C. Happy integers. *M.T.* 65:627–29; Nov. 1972.

Fairbairn, R. A. More on automorphic numbers. *J.R.M.* 2:170–74; July 1969. Also, *J.R.M.* 2:245; Oct. 1969.

Feser, Victor G. Some expressions for years. *J.R.M.* 5:197; July 1972.

Gardner, Martin. Automorphic numbers. *Sci.Am.* 218:122; Feb. 1968.

———. Cyclic numbers and their properties. *Sci.Am.* 222:121–24; Mar. 1970.

———. The magic number 12,345,679. *Sci.Am.* 222:126–27; Jan. 1970.

———. "Parity Checks." In *Martin Gardner's Sixth Book of Mathematical Games from Scientific American,* pp. 71–78. San Francisco: W. H. Freeman & Co., 1971.

Geldzahler, Barry. Powers of eleven by Pascal's triangle. *J.R.M.* 3:188; July 1970.

Goldenburg, E. Paul. Scrutinizing number charts. *A.T.* 17:645–53; Dec. 1970.
  Seeking number patterns and prime numbers by means of tables of numbers.
Goldberg, Michael, and George Eldredge. Nesting habits of the laddered parenthesis. *A.M.M.* 77:525–26; May 1970.
  Expressions such as $2^{(2^{2^{.^{.^{.^{2}}}}})}$.
Goodrich, Merton T. On squares in arithmetic progression. *M.Mag.* 39:87–88; Mar. 1966.
Goodwin, Norton. An unusual integer. *J.R.M.* 2:100–101; Apr. 1969.
  Curious properties of the number 1,089.
Gross, F. Cross-number. *M.Tchg.*, no. 46, p. 71; Spring 1969.
Hobbes, V. G. "An unusual integer"—a comment. *J.R.M.* 3:9; Jan. 1970.
Hunter, J. A. H. Curious factorizations. *J.R.M.* 4:252; Oct. 1971.
———. Double square differences. *J.R.M.* 4:105; Apr. 1971.
———. Double square sums. *J.R.M.* 4:103–4; Apr. 1971.
———. The end of three squares. *J.R.M.* 2:247; Oct. 1969.
———. *Figures Are Fun: Books 1–5*, with teacher's manual. Toronto: Copp Clark, 1959.
———. *Figures for Fun.* London: J. M. Dent & Sons, 1957.
———. Integer oddities. *J.R.M.* 2:146; July 1969.
———. Integer oddities. *J.R.M.* 2:248–49; Oct. 1969.
———. Integer oddities. *J.R.M.* 3:127–28; Apr. 1970.
———. Integer oddities: squares starting with 7777777. *J.R.M.* 3:126; Apr. 1970.
———. Integer oddities. *J.R.M.* 3:158, July 1970.
———. Integer oddities. *J.R.M.* 4:141; Apr. 1971.
———. Integer oddities. *J.R.M.* 5:143; Apr. 1972.
  Identities of the pattern
$$38791,19307 = (38791)^2 + (19307)^2 + 7$$
$$144369,351464 = (144369)^2 + (351464)^2 + 7$$
  and so on.
———. Interesting sums of two squares. *J.R.M.* 3:61; Jan. 1970.
———. *More Fun with Figures.* New York: Dover Publications, 1968. (Paper)
———. A note on sums of squares of consecutive odd integers. *M.Mag.* 42:145; May 1969.
———. Representation as sum of two squares. *J.R.M.* 3:186–87; July 1970.
———. Reversal products. *J.R.M.* 1:246; Oct. 1968.
———. Single square differences. *J.R.M.* 4:65; Jan. 1971.
———. Single square sums. *J.R.M.* 4:64–65; Jan. 1971.
———. Some polyautomorphic numbers. *J.R.M.* 5:27; Jan. 1972.
———. Squares ending with 0987654321. *J.R.M.* 2:205, 247; Oct. 1969.
———. Triple square differences. *J.R.M.* 4:191; July 1971.
———. Triple square sums. *J.R.M.* 4:190; July 1971.
Hunter, J. A. H., and E. P. Starke. A square number with five fours. [Problem 786.] *M.Mag.* 44:294; Nov. 1971.
Johnson, R. S., and Harry L. Nelson. The long . . . and the short of it. *J.R.M.* 5:285–86; Oct. 1972.
  Two cross-number puzzles.
Klosinski, L. F., and D. C. Smolarski. On the reversing of digits. *M.Mag.* 42:208–10; Sept. 1969.

Kordemsky, Boris. *The Moscow Puzzles*. New York: Charles Scribner's Sons, 1972.
    Number pleasantries: chapters 7, 13, and 14.
Lindon, J. A. Dee-dee consecutives. *J.R.M.* 2:21–24; Jan. 1969. Also, *J.R.M.* 3:40–41; Jan. 1970.
Luthar, R. S. On squares in arithmetic progression. *M.T.* 64:735; Dec. 1971.
Makowski, Andrzej. Curious factorizations. *J.R.M.* 3:257; Oct. 1970.
————. Remark on the paper "Sums of Squares of Consecutive Odd Integers" by Brother U. Alfred. *M.Mag.* 43:212–13; Sept. 1970.
Mathison, Sally. Mathematicalosterms. *A.T.* 16:64–65; Jan. 1969.
May, Kenneth O. Galileo sequences, a good dangling problem. *A.M.M.* 79:67–69; Jan. 1972.
    Discussion of the sequence
    $$\frac{1}{3} = \frac{1 + 3}{5 + 7} = \frac{1 + 3 + 5}{7 + 9 + 11} = \cdots.$$
Moessner, Alfred, and R. Baras. Numbers in reverse. *Scrip.M.* 8:78; June 1941.
————. [Problem 180.] *Sphinx* 4:12, 63–64; 1934.
Ondrejka, Rudolf. [Letter to the editor.] *J.R.M.* 4:151; Apr. 1971.
    List of number words (in various languages) that contain the same number of letters as the number itself.
————. Non-zero factors of 10^n. *R.M.M.*, no. 6, p. 59; Dec. 1961.
Perelman, Yakov. *Figures for Fun; Stories and Conundrums*. New York: Ungar, n.d. (Paper)
Plateau, Joseph A. F. *Sur une récréation arithmétique*. Brussels: F. Hayez, 1874.
Poole, George D. Integers and the sum of the factorials of their digits. *M.Mag.* 44:278–79; Nov. 1971.
Porges, A. A set of eight numbers. *A.M.M.* 52:379–83; Aug.–Sept. 1945.
Prielipp, Robert. Digital sums of perfect numbers and triangular numbers. *M.T.* 62:179–82; Mar. 1969.
————. [Problem 3311.] *S.S.M.* 71:577; June 1971.
    To find all the positive integers whose squares end with three equal positive integer digits.
Rosenberg, Edwin A., and Steven Rosenberg. Choose your favorite digit. *M.T.* 64:475; May 1971.
    Generalization of a multiplication trick that produces a string of nine consecutive identical digits.
Schlotterbeck, B. *Knacknüsse für Freunde des Rechnens*. Langensalza: Gressler, 1905. 211 pp.
Schneider, Louis. Have pennies—will travel. *R.M.M.*, no. 1, pp. 29–32; Feb. 1961.
    The classic chessboard grain-of-wheat problem interestingly revisited.
Scopes, P. The hundred square. *M.Tchg.*, no. 50, pp. 69–71; Spring 1970.
    A study of patterns on a 10 × 10 square numbered consecutively from 1 to 100.
Stewart, B. M. Sums of functions of digits. *Canadian Journal of Mathematics*, 12:374–89; 1960.
Thébault, Victor, and Charles W. Trigg. An interesting perfect cube. [Problem E808.] *A.M.M.* 55:583–84; Nov. 1948.

————. Two cubes which jointly contain all the digits. [Problem E377.] *A.M.M.* 47:178–79; Mar. 1940.

Tocquet, Robert. *The Magic of Numbers.* (Translation of the 1957 French ed.) New York: Wehman Bros., 1960. 160 pp.

Trigg, Charles W. Anagrams. *A.M.M.* 60:418–19; June 1953.

————. Equal products from integer pairs and their reverses. *J.R.M.* 3:180–81; July 1970.

————. A general reversal—subtraction. *J.R.M.* 4:58–59; Jan. 1971.

————. Integer solutions of $AB/(A + B)$. *M.Mag.* 34:119; Nov. 1960.

————. Names of mathematicians in timely anagrams. *M.Mag.* 34:244, 247; Mar. 1961.

————. The nature of $N = n(n + 1) - 1$. *M.Mag.* 36:120; Mar. 1963.

————. Number relationships involving cubes. *R.M.M.*, no. 9, pp. 44–46; June 1962.

Ramanujan's number, etc.

————. Permutations from 1961. *M.Mag.* 34:406; Nov. 1961.

————. Prime portions of 1961. *M.Mag.* 34:274; May 1961.

————. A rectified equality. *M.Mag.* 34:163; Jan. 1961.

$2967 = 17$ is rectified.

Trigg, Charles W., and W. R. MacHose. [Problem 207.] *Pentagon* 27:123–24; Spring 1968.

A unique three-digit number that equals twice the sum of the squares of its digits.

Trigg, Charles W., and E. C. Torbert, III. [Problem 212.] *Pentagon* 28:42–44; Fall 1968.

A unique three-digit number that is six times the sum of the fourth powers of its digits.

Trotter, Terrel, Jr. More about $P = N^2 + M^3$. *J.R.M.* 4:45–49; Jan. 1971.

Trotter, Terrel, Jr., and Irene Klaver. Number patterns from digit sums. *A.T.* 18:100–103; Feb. 1971.

What's the Limit? *J.R.M.* 3:42–43; Jan. 1970.

Yates, Robert C. Sums of powers of integers. *M.T.* 52:268–71; Apr. 1959.

1.10   Number Tricks; Calculating Prodigies

Barr, George. *Entertaining with Number Tricks.* New York: McGraw-Hill Book Co., 1971. 143 pp.

Branscome, C. E. Mental squaring. *R.M.M.*, no. 7, p. 23; Feb. 1962.

Burley, Ross A. "The Figure Friend" (lightning calculation supreme). Chicago: A. Nelmar Albino, 1941.

Reproduced from typewritten copy.

Butler, Joseph Reuben. *Easy Arithmetical Short Cuts and Tricks with Numbers.* Shawnee, Okla.: Bison Press, 1954.

Caro, Victor Eduardo. *Los Números; Su Historia, Sus Propriedades, Sus Mentiras y Verdades.* Bogotá: Editorial Minerva, 1937.

Cox, Alfred Bertram. *Figures Aren't Funny.* Adelaide, Australia: Rigby; and San Francisco: Tri-Ocean Books, 1966.

Goldman, Henry. *Arithmetical Amusements.* Chicago: Office Men's Record Co., 1895.

Harding, Lowry W. *Arithmeriddles*. Columbus, Ohio: Association for the Study of Educology, Ohio State University, 1961.

Jeffers, Verne G. Editorial feedback. *A.T.* 16:650–51; Dec. 1969.
Brief note on a number puzzle.

Lamb, Sydney H. *The Magic of Numbers*. New York: Arco Publishing Co., Arc Books, 1967.

Lean, John Udy. *Freaks of Figures*. Detroit: Udy Publishing Co., 1907.
"A unique collection of interesting arithmetical recreations and amusing mental diversions, suitable for parlor entertainments, social gatherings and the home circle, for old and young."

Lietzmann, Walther. *Sonderlinge im Reich der Zahlen*. Bonn: F. Dummler, 1954.

Long, Louis. *Du zéro à l'infini; jeux mathématiques à la portée de tous*. Avignon: Aubanel, 1959.

Nelson, A. H. More about an old number trick. *M.T.* 64:348; Apr. 1971.

Nixon, J. T. *Magic Sums*. Edinburgh and London: Oliver & Boyd, 1966.

Regnault, Jules Émile Joseph. *Les Calculateurs prodiges, l'art de jongler avec les nombres*. Paris: Payot, 1943.

Souza, Julio. *Diabruras da Matemática; Problemas Curiosos e Fantasias Aritméticas*. São Paulo: Edicao Saraiva, 1966.

Tahan, Malba [J. C. de Mello e Souza]. *O Homem Que Calculava*. Rio de Janeiro: Conquista, 1954. (Spanish translation, *El Hombre Que Calculaba*. Buenos Aires: Colegio.)

Troutman, Andria. Some mind reading fun. *Florida Council of Teachers of Mathematics Newsletter*, vol. 14, no. 1, p. 13; Fall 1971.
An interesting, simple trick with a set of 5 cards, each containing 16 numerals in square arrays.

Welch, John. *Mathematical Curiosities*. Athens, Ohio: The Author and the *Athens Messenger*, 1883.
"A series of puzzles, surprises, new rules and short cuts, including a cheap and novel form of interest table, or method of computing interest."

1.11 Repeating Decimals

Beiler, Albert H. *Recreations in the Theory of Numbers*. New York: Dover Publications, 1963.
Chapter 10: "Cycling towards Infinity."

Farrell, Peter. Recurring decimals. *R.M.M.*, no. 13, pp. 45–47; Feb. 1963.

Hall, Lucien T., Jr. Persuasive arguments: $.9999 \ldots = 1$. *M.T.* 64:749–50; Dec. 1971. See also, *M.T.* 65:709; Dec. 1972 (by Wayne Peterson).

Hilferty, Margaret M. Some convenient fractions for work with repeating decimals. *M.T.* 65:240–41; Mar. 1972.

Hutchinson, Margaret. Investigating the nature of periodic decimals. *M.T.* 65:325–27; Apr. 1972.

McLean, Robert C. A general formula for changing repeating decimals to common fractions. *S.S.M.* 72:552–54; June 1972.

Manchester, Mark. Decimal expansions of rational numbers. *M.T.* 65:698–702; Dec. 1972.
Using the computer to determine properties of repeating decimals.

Myers, W. G., and B. D. Wright. Periodic decimals. *M.S.J.*, vol. 18, no. 1, pp. 1–3; Nov. 1970.
Nygaard, P. H. Note on repeating decimals. [Letter to the editor.] *M.S.J.*, vol. 18, no. 3; Mar. 1971.
Seabloom, Edward. Rapid repeating decimal-fraction interchange. *M.T.* 60:42–44; Jan. 1967.
Schiller, J. K. A theorem in the decimal representation of rationals. *A.M.M.* 66:797; Oct. 1959.
Trigg, Charles W. Division of integers by transposition. *J.R.M.* 1:180–82; July 1968.

1.12 Story Problems

Crossed Ladders

Bennett, A. A. Crossed ladders. [Problem E433.] *A.M.M.* 48:268–69; Apr. 1941.
Gardner, Martin. Crossed-ladder problem. *Sci-Am.* 222:133–36; June 1970.
Graham, L. A. *Ingenious Mathematical Problems and Methods.* New York: Dover Publications, 1959.
    Problem 25: Crossed ladders.
———. *The Surprise Attack on Mathematical Problems.* New York: Dover Publications, 1968.
    Problem 6: Crossed ladders.
Janusz, Gerald. Crossed ladders. [Problem 5323.] *A.M.M.* 73:1125–27; Dec. 1966.
Sutcliff, Alan. Complete solution of the ladder problem in integers. *M.Gaz.* 47:133–36; May 1963.

False Coin and Weight Problems

Greenblatt, M. H. The "12 + 1" false coin problem. *J.R.M.* 3:34–35; Jan. 1970.
Hobbes, V. G. The false coin problem dissected and decently laid to rest. *J.R.M.* 4:28–32; Jan. 1971.
McIvor, Robert A. The "12 + 1" false coin problem—a comment. *J.R.M.* 4:24–25; Jan. 1971.
Roth, Ted. The false coin problem extended. *J.R.M.* 4:26–27; Jan. 1971.
Rowland, Timothy. A generalization of a well-known puzzle. *M.Tchg.*, no. 53, pp. 35–38; Winter 1970.
    Technical discussion of a generalization of Bachet's weight problem.
Williams, A. S. Ali's four weights. *A.T.* 7:209; Apr. 1960.
    Weight puzzle based on numbers in base three.

The Jeep Problem

Alway, G. C. Crossing the desert. *M.Gaz.* 41:209; 1957.
Fine, N. J. The jeep problem. *A.M.M.* 54:24–31; Jan. 1947.
Franklin, J. N. The range of a fleet of aircraft. *SIAM Journal on Applied Mathematics* 8:541–48; Sept. 1960.
Gale, David. Correction to "The Jeep Once More or Jeeper by the Dozen." *A.M.M.* 78:644–45; June–July 1971.

——. The jeep once more or jeeper by the dozen. *A.M.M.* 77:493–501; May 1970.

Helmer, O. A problem in logistics: the jeep problem. Project Rand Report no. Ra15015, Dec. 1947.

Phipps, C. G. The jeep problem; a more general solution. *A.M.M.* 54:458–62; Oct. 1947.

Pouring Problems

Bakst, Aaron. "The Container Problem." In *Mathematical Puzzles and Pastimes*, pp. 14–21. New York: D. Van Nostrand Co., 1954.

Court, Nathan Altshiller. "Pouring Problems: The Robot Method." In *Mathematics in Fun and in Earnest*, pp. 223–31. New York: Dial Press, 1958.

Coxeter, H. S. M., and S. L. Greizer. "The Three Jug Problem." In *Geometry Revisited*, pp. 89–93. New York: Random House, 1967.

Gardner, Martin. "Bouncing Balls in Polygons and Polyhedrons." In *Martin Gardner's Sixth Book of Mathematical Games from Scientific American*, pp. 29–38. San Francisco: W. H. Freeman & Co., 1971.

    Methods for solving liquid-measuring problems by means of directed graphs.

Knuth, Donald. Billiard balls in an equilateral triangle. *R.M.M.*, no. 14, pp. 20–23; Jan. 1964.

Madachy, Joseph. "Bouncing Billiard Balls." In *Mathematics on Vacation*, pp. 231–41. New York: Charles Scribner's Sons, 1966.

O'Beirne, T. H. "Jug and Bottle Department." In *Puzzles and Paradoxes*, pp. 49–75. New York and Oxford: Oxford University Press, 1965.

Tweedie, M. C. K. A graphical method of solving Tartaglian measuring puzzles. *M.Gaz.* 23:278–82; July 1939.

Pursuit Problems

Bernhart, A. Curves of general pursuit. *Scrip.M.* 24:189–206; 1959.

——. Curves of pursuit. *Scrip.M.* 20:125–41; 1954.

——. Curves of pursuit—II. *Scrip.M.* 23:49–65; 1957.

——. Polygons of pursuit. *Scrip.M.* 24:23–50; 1959.

Clapham, J. C. Playful mice. *R.M.M.*, no. 10, pp. 6–7; Aug. 1962.

    More about pursuit problems.

Klamkin, M. Cyclic pursuit or "The Three Bugs Problem." *A.M.M.* 78:631–39; June–July 1971.

Steinhaus, Hugo. *Mathematical Snapshots*. New York: Oxford University Press, 1969.

    Problem of the four pursuing dogs.

Miscellaneous Problems

Brown, B. H. The pasturage problem of Sir Isaac Newton. *A.M.M.* 33:155–57; 1926.

Budden, F. J. A problem. *M.Tchg.*, no. 51, pp. 52–53; Summer 1970.

    Solution of "story problems" involving compound proportion by means of matrices.

Byrkit, Donald R., and William M. Waters, Jr. Extension of the chain-cutting problem. *J.R.M.* 4:33–35; Jan. 1971.

Dickson, L. E. *History of the Theory of Numbers*, vol. 2, p. 342. New York: Chelsea Publishing Co., 1950.

Lessing's description of Archimedes' cattle problem in verse.

Dudley, Underwood. The first recreational mathematics book. *J.R.M.* 3:164–69; July 1970.

Knuth, Donald E. The Gamow-Stern elevator problem. *J.R.M.* 2:131–37; July 1969.

Lamb, David P. The minimum catastrophe problem. *M.S.J.*, no. 20, pp. 1–3; Dec. 1972.

Another look at the problem of the three houses and the three wells; generalization for N houses and M wells.

Rowe, R. Robinson. The vicious circle. *J.R.M.* 5:207–10; July 1972.

An imaginative problem about predatory animal populations; the solution involves differential equations and elementary iterative processes.

Sanford, Vera. An old problem with a modern twist. *M.T.* 45:119–20; Feb. 1952.

———. The problem of the lion in the well. *M.T.* 44:196–97; Mar. 1951.

The Three Wells Problem. *Pythagoras* (English ed.), vol. 1, no. 2, pp. 23, 39–41; 1968.

Chapter 2

Number Theory as Recreation

2.1 Amicable Numbers

Amicable numbers. *A.M.M.* 20:84; Jan. 1913.
Gives definitions of amicable number triples, quadruples, quintuples, sextuples, and k-tuples.

Bratley, P., F. Lunnon, and J. McKay. Amicable numbers and their distribution. *Mathematics of Computation* 22:677–78; July 1968.

Brown, B. H. A new pair of amicable numbers. *A.M.M.* 46:345; 1939.

Cohen, H. On amicable and sociable numbers. *Mathematics of Computation* 24:423–29; Apr. 1970.

Dickson, L. E. Amicable number triples. *A.M.M.* 20:84–92; Jan. 1913.

———. *History of the Theory of Numbers.* Washington, D.C.: Carnegie Institution of Washington, 1919.
Amicable numbers, including Euler's list, pp. 35–50.

Escott, E. B. Amicable numbers. *Scrip.M.* 12:61; 1946.
A list of the first 390 amicable pairs.

Faller, Laura T. Friendly numbers. [Letter to the editor.] *M.T.* 62:64–65; Jan. 1969.

Garcia, M. New amicable pairs. *Scrip.M.* 23:167–71; 1957.
Contains list of 162 pairs.

Gardner, Martin. A short treatise on the useless elegance of perfect numbers and amicable pairs. *Sci.Am.* 218:121–26; Mar. 1968.

Gerardin, A. M. Sur la détermination des nombres amiables. *Mathesis* 26:41–44; 1906.

Hagis, Peter. Lower bounds for relatively prime amicable numbers of opposite parity. *Mathematics of Computation* 24:963–68; Oct. 1970.

———. On relatively prime odd amicable numbers. *Mathematics of Computation* 23:539–43; 1969.

———. Relatively prime amicable numbers of opposite parity. *M.Mag.* 43:14–20; Jan. 1970.
Advanced discussion; standpoint of number theory.

———. Relatively prime amicable numbers with twenty-one prime divisors. *M.Mag.* 45:21–26; Jan. 1972.

Kanold, H.-J. Über befreundete Zahlen. *Mathematische Nachrichten* 9:243–48 and 10:99–111; 1953.

———. Über die Dichten der Mengen der vollkommenen und der befreundeten Zahlen. *Mathematische Zeitschrift* 61:180–85; 1954.

———. Untere Schranken für teilerfremde befreundete Zahlen. *Archiv der Mathematik* 4:399–401; 1953.

Lee, Elvin J. Amicable numbers and the bilinear Diophantine equation. *Mathematics of Computation* 22:181–87; Jan. 1968.

———. [Letter to the editor.] *M.T.* 62:452; Oct. 1969.

———. On divisibility by nine of the sums of even amicable pairs. *Mathematics of Computation* 23:545–48; July 1969.

Lee, Elvin J., and Joseph S. Madachy. The history and discovery of amicable numbers. *J.R.M.* 5:77–93, 153–73, 231–50; Apr.–July–Oct. 1972.

Very comprehensive; bibliography, 99 references.

Mason, T. E. On amicable numbers and their generalizations. *A.M.M.* 28:195–200; 1921.

Lists of amicable pairs, triples, quadruples, quintuples, and sextuples.

Poulet, P. De nouveaux amiables. *Sphinx* 4:134–35; 1934.

———. 43 new couples of amicable numbers. *Scrip.M.* 14:77; 1948.

Rolf, Howard L. Friendly numbers. [Letter to the editor.] *M.T.* 62:65; Jan. 1969.

Van der Waerden, B. L. *Science Awakening*, pp. 82–105. Groningen, Netherlands: P. Noordhoff, 1954.

Young, B. F. Another definition of amicable numbers and some of their relations to Dickson's amicables. *A.M.M.* 30:311; 1923.

2.2 Divisibility

Berenson, Lewis. A divisibility test for amateur discoverers. *A.T.* 17:39–41; Jan. 1970.

El-Nagger, Hisham. Divisibility. *M.Tchg.*, no. 54, pp. 20–21; Spring 1971.

Hunter, J. A. H. Cyclic transformations—divisibility. *J.R.M.* 3:190; July 1970.

Kennedy, Robert E. Divisibility by integers ending in 1, 3, 7, or 9. *M.T.* 64:137–38; Feb. 1971.

Kordemsky, Boris. *The Moscow Puzzles*. New York: Charles Scribner's Sons, 1972.

Chapter 11: "Divisibility," pp. 135–42.

Long, Calvin T. A simpler "7" divisibility rule. *M.T.* 64:473–75; May 1971.

Matthews, E. Rebecca. A simple "7" divisibility rule. *M.T.* 62:461–64; Oct. 1969.

Nilsson, Mark. A method of determining divisibility by seven. *M.S.J.*, vol. 17, no. 2, pp. 4–5; Jan. 1970.

Oliver, Charlene. Gus's magic numbers: a key to the divisibility test for primes. A.T. 19:183–89; Mar. 1972.

Rogers, Frank. Divisibility rule for seven. *A.T.* 16:63–64; Jan. 1969.

Singer, Richard. Modular arithmetic and divisibility criteria. *M.T.* 63:653–56; Dec. 1970.

Smith, Frank. Divisibility rules for the first fifteen primes. *A.T.* 18:85–87; Feb. 1971.

Trigg, Charles W. Division by transposition of digits. [Problem 3027.] *S.S.M.* 66:390–91; Apr. 1966.

————. Division of integers by transposition. *J.R.M.* 1:180–82; July 1968.
Torreyson, H. C., and Henry Snyder. Divisibility. [Problem 3091.] *S.S.M.* 67:658–59; Oct. 1967.
Wardrop, R. F. Divisibility rules for numbers expressed in different bases. *A.T.* 19:218–20; Mar. 1972.
Weaver, James. The nine test. *Exponent* 9:6–7; June 1967.
Weeks, C. J. Divisibility. *M.Tchg.*, no. 58, p. 29; Spring 1972.
    Proof that if $M = 10A + B$ is divisible by $N = 10C + D$, then $AD - BC$ is also divisible by N.
Wentworth, R. A. Lubienski. Divisibility explained by manipulation. *M.Tchg.*, no. 57, pp. 31–34; Winter 1971.
Whitaker, Buford. A new discovery. *Florida Council of Teachers of Mathematics Newsletter*, pp. 4–5; Summer 1971.
    A hitherto unknown procedure for finding the highest common factor by prime factorization.

2.3   Fibonacci and Lucas Numbers

Ainsworth, Nathan. An introduction to sequence: elementary school mathematics and science enrichment. *A.T.* 17:143–45; Feb. 1970.
    Relation of the Fibonacci sequence to phyllotaxis in nature.
Archibald, R. C. Fibonacci series. *A.M.M.* 25:235–38; 1918.
Bankoff, Leon. The Fibonacci arbelos. *Scrip.M.* 20:218; 1954.
Basil, Gordon. On the Fibonacci sequence. *M.Mag.* p. 104; Nov.–Dec. 1955.
Brooke, Maxey. Fibonacci fancy. *M.Mag.*, p. 218; Sept. 1962.
Brousseau, Alfred. *Fibonacci and Related Number Theoretic Tables.* San Jose, Calif.: The Fibonacci Association, 1972. 151 pp.
————. *Linear Recursion and Fibonacci Sequences.* San Jose, Calif.: The Fibonacci Association, 1971. 60 pp.
Burton, J. L. Fibonacci numbers and Lucas series. *A.M.M.*, p. 616; Oct. 1955.
Carman, Robert A. Fibonacci numbers. [Problem 3418.] *S.S.M.* 72:459–60; May 1972.
Curl, James C. Fibonacci numbers and the slow learner. *Fib.Q.* 6:266–74; Oct. 1968.
De Vol, David. Some properties of the Fibonacci sequence. *A.M.M.*, p. 142; Feb. 1951.
Dudley, Underwood. Fibolucas numbers. *J.R.M.* 2:97; Apr. 1969; and 3:47; Jan. 1970.
Garrett, Paul. Matrix eigenvalues: characteristic values. *M.S.J.*, vol. 18, no. 4, pp. 4–5; May 1971.
    Generating Fibonacci numbers by means of matrix equations.
Halberg, C. J. A., Jr. The Fibonacci operator. *A.M.M.*, p. 591; June–July 1961.
Hoggatt, V. E., Jr. *Fibonacci and Lucas Numbers.* Boston: Houghton Mifflin Co., 1969. 92 pp.
————. A type of periodicity for the Fibonacci numbers. *M.Mag.*, pp. 139–42; Jan.–Feb. 1955.
Horodam, A. F. Fibonacci number triples. *A.M.M.* 68:751–53; 1961.
————. A generalized Fibonacci sequence. *A.M.M.* 68:455–59; 1961.

Hunter, J. A. H., and Joseph Madachy. *Mathematical Diversions*. Princeton, N.J.: D. Van Nostrand Co., 1963.
Chapter 2: "From Paradox to Parastichy," pp. 12–22; properties of the Fibonacci series, the golden section, and phyllotaxis.

Huntley, H. E. *The Divine Proportion: A Study in Mathematical Beauty*. New York: Dover Publications, 1970.
Chapter 4, "Phi and Fi-Bonacci"; chapter 11, "The Fibonacci Numbers."

Just, Erwin. A note on the nth term of the Fibonacci sequence. *M.Mag.* 44:199; Sept. 1971.

Kay, D. C. Uniquely Fibonacci. [Problem E2272.] *A.M.M.* 78:1143; Dec. 1971.
Dissecting a square to form a rectangle with a net gain or loss of one square unit, based on the relations $x + y = z$ and $xz = y^2 \pm 1$, where $x = F_n$, $y = F_{n+1}$, and $z = F_{n+2}$.

Loftus, Sonja. Fibonacci numbers: fun and fundamentals for the slow learner. *A.T.* 17:204–8; Mar. 1970.

Nygaard, P. H. Fibonacci-type sequences. *M.T.* 63:671–72; Dec. 1970.

Prielipp, Robert. Some sums of Fibonacci numbers and $P*$ numbers. *Pentagon* 30:31–34; Fall 1970.

Rollett, A. P. Squares in the Fibonacci series. [Problem 5080.] *A.M.M.*, pp. 220–22; Feb. 1964.

Saunders, W. M. On convergence of the ratio of Fibonacci numbers. *A.M.M.*, p. 590; June–July 1961.

Shapiro, H. S. The Fibonacci sequence again. [Problem 1502.] *A.M.M.*, pp. 922–23; Nov. 1962.

Stanley, T. E. A note on the sequence of Fibonacci numbers. *M.Mag.* 44:19–22; Jan. 1971.

Wunderlich, M. On the non-existence of Fibonacci squares. *Mathematics of Computation*, pp. 455–57; Oct. 1936.

2.4 Figurate Numbers

Ball, W. W. R. Gnomic numbers. *M.Gaz.* 8:5–12; 1915.

Barron, J. P. Sums of reciprocals of figurate numbers. *M.Tchg.*, no. 53, pp. 39–41; Winter 1970.

Branfield, J. R. Find the mathematician. *M.Tchg.*, no. 47, pp. 4–6; Summer 1969.
A discussion of figurate numbers.

Carman, Robert A. Every triangular number is the sum of three triangular numbers. [Problem 3242.] *S.S.M.* 70:352; Apr. 1970.

Carman, Robert A., and Robert Prielipp. Consecutive pentagonal numbers. [Problem 3301.] *S.S.M.* 71:360; Apr. 1971. Also, [Problem 3383.] *S.S.M.* 71:749–50; Nov. 1971.

Carman, Robert A., Robert Prielipp, and N. J. Kuenzi. Square tetrahedral numbers. [Problem 3422.] *S.S.M.* 72:571–72; June 1972.

Carman, Robert A., and Charles W. Trigg. [Problem 3451.] *S.S.M.* 73:80; Jan. 1973.
Proof that no tetragonal number can end in 2, 3, 7, or 8.

Cohen, Daniel I. A., J. L. Pietenpol, and Charles W. Trigg. Polygonal numbers. [Problem 481.] *M.Mag.* 36:71; Jan. 1963.

Dickson, L. E. *History of the Theory of Numbers*, vol. 2, pp. 1–39. Washington, D.C.: Carnegie Institute of Washington, 1919.
Gnomic numbers and related topics.

Edmonds, George F. An intuitive approach to square numbers. *M.T.* 63:113–17; Feb. 1970.

Ellis, Wade. Sequences and progressions. *M.T.* 64:455–58; May 1971.
Reexamination of arithmetic and geometric progressions, with implications for polygonal numbers.

Fielker, David. Notes from a maths centre. *M.Tchg.*, no. 51, pp. 18–21; Summer 1970.

From Pythagoras to Taylor to Today. *M.S.J.*, vol. 5, no. 1, pp. 1–4; Mar. 1958.
Relation of figurate numbers to the calculus of finite differences.

Hansen, Rodney T. Arithmetic of pentagonal numbers. *Fib.Q.* 8:83–87; Feb. 1970.

Hervey, Margaret, and Bonnie Litwiller. Polygonal numbers: a study of patterns. *A.T.* 17:33–38; Jan. 1970.

Jones, B. R. Mathematics at a glance. *M.Tchg.*, no. 58, pp. 30–39; Spring 1972.
Discussion of the summation of finite sequences by diagrams; not strictly on figurate numbers but makes use of the gnomon concept.

Lichtenberg, Donovan R. [Letter to the editor.] *M.T.* 63:624; Nov. 1970.
A note on Pythagorean triples and figurate numbers.

Note on Polygonal Numbers. *Pentagon* 29:47–48; Fall 1969.

Piza, Pedro A. Sums of powers of triangular numbers. *Scrip.M.* 16:127; Mar. 1950.

Prielipp, Robert. Digital sums of perfect numbers and triangular numbers. *M.T.* 62:180; Mar. 1969.

Schröter, Rudolf. *Vom Netzwerk ganzer Zahlen; gezeichnete Zahlen.* Hamburg-Wandsbek: Claudius Buchhandlung, 1940.

Smith, Joe K. The nth polygonal number. *M.T.* 65:221–25; Mar. 1972.

Struyk, Adrian, and Charles W. Trigg. Maximum volume boxes with triangular number dimensions. [Problem 611.] *M.Mag.* 40:108–9; Mar. 1967.

Trigg, Charles W. A partition of triangular numbers. *M.Mag.* 43:106–7; Mar. 1970.

———. Tetrahedral numbers. [Problem 3177.] *S.S.M.* 69:175; Feb. 1969.

———. Triangular number of form $abcdef$ in which $def = 2abc$. [Problem 207.] *P.M.E.J.* 5:27; Fall 1969.

———. Triangular number that is permutation of nine distinct digits. [Problem 214.] *P.M.E.J.* 5:89; Spring 1970.

Trigg, Charles W., Donald Beans, and E. F. Schmeichel. Triangular numbers partitioned into three 3-digit primes. [Problem 735.] *M.Mag.* 43:106, 288–89; Mar., Nov. 1970.

Trigg, Charles W., and Jeanette Bickley. Tetrahedral number a permutation of nine consecutive digits. [Problem 258.] *P.M.E.J.* 5:345–47; Fall 1972.

Trigg, Charles W., and Herta Freitag. Proof that any triangular number greater than 3 is the sum of four triangular numbers. [Problem 3219.] *S.S.M.* 69: 835–38; Dec. 1969.

Trigg, Charles W., and N. F. Nettheim. Triangular number sectioned into three prime triads. [Problem 769.] *M.Mag.* 44:168; May 1971.

———. Triangular number which is a permutation of the ten digits. [Problem 805.] *M.Mag.* 45:171; May 1972.

Willerding, Margaret F. Figurate numbers. *S.S.M.* 72:151–58; Feb. 1972.
Bibliography.
Wulczyn, Gregory. Square pentagonal numbers. [Problem 3398.] *S.S.M.* 72:176–77; Feb. 1972.

2.5 Palindromes; Repunits and Repdigits

Anning, Norman. Fun with palindromes. *Scrip.M.* 22:227; Sept. 1956.
Beiler, Albert H. *Recreations in the Theory of Numbers.* New York: Dover Publications, 1963.
Chapter 11 deals with repunits; palindromic multigrades, p. 164; palindromic primes, pp. 222, 228.
Bernstein, Leon. Multiplicative twins and primitive roots. *Mathematische Zeitschrift* 105:49–58; 1968.
Brousseau, Brother Alfred. Palindromes by addition in base two. *M.Mag.* 42:254–56; Nov. 1969.
Brown, Gerald W. Applying "Madam I'm Adam" to mathematics: a discovery project. *A.T.* 19:549–51; Nov. 1972.
About palindromic numbers.
Card, Leslie E. Patterns in primes. *J.R.M.* 1:93–99; Apr. 1968.
———. More patterns in primes. *J.R.M.* 2:112–16; Apr. 1969.
Duncan, D. C. Sujet d'étude, no. 74. *Sphinx* [Brussels] 9:91–92; 1939.
Gabai, Hyman, and Daniel Coogan. On palindromes and palindromic primes. *M.Mag.* 42:252–54; Nov. 1969.
Gardner, Martin. Backward run numbers, letters, words and sentences. *Sci.Am.* 223:110–13; Aug. 1970.
Gives a number of good palindromes.
———. Mathematical games. *Sci.Am.* 210:120–28; Mar. 1964. Also, 210:114–20; June 1964.
Note on reprints.
Hansen, Rodney T. Modular palindromes. *M.Mag.* 44:208–12; Sept. 1971.
Kacyznski, T. J. Note on a problem of Alan Sutcliffe. *M.Mag.* 41:84–86; Mar. 1968.
Concerning palindromic numbers.
Lehmer, D. H. Sujet d'étude, no. 74. *Sphinx* [Brussels] 8:12–13; 1938.
Moser, Leo. Palindromic primes. *Scrip.M.* 16:127–28; Mar. 1950.
Moser, Leo, and E. P. Starke. Palindromes in progression. [Problem 231.] *M.Mag.* 29:110; Nov. 1955.
Piza, P. A., and Charles Fendall. Partitioning 166,665 into palindromes. [Problem 262.] *M.Mag.* 30:51–52; Sept. 1956.
Rebmann, Michael, and Frank Sentyrz. A note on palindromes by reversal-addition. *M.Mag.* 45:186–87; Sept. 1972.
Simmons, Gustavus J. On palindromic squares of nonpalindromic numbers. *J.R.M.* 5:11–19; Jan. 1972.
Bibliography.
———. Palindromic powers. *J.R.M.* 3:93–98; Apr. 1970.
Simmons, Gustavus J., and D. Rawlinson. Palindromic biquadrates. [Problem 70-8.] *SIAM Review* 12:287; 1970.

Sutcliffe, Alan. Integers that are multiplied when their digits are reversed. *M.Mag.* 39:282–87; Nov. 1966.

Trigg, Charles W. More on palindromes by reversal-addition. *M.Mag.* 45:184–86; Sept. 1972.

——. Palindromes by addition. *M.Mag.* 40:26–28; 1967.

——. Palindromic cubes. *M.Mag.* 34:214; Mar. 1961.

——. Palindromic cubes. *S.S.M.* 71:165–66; Feb. 1971.

——. Palindromic pentagonal numbers. [Problem 3248.] *S.S.M.* 70:471; May 1970.

——. Repeated palindromes which are triangular numbers. [Problem 240.] *P.M.E.J.* 5:244; Fall 1971.

——. Repdigits as the differences of patterned squares. *J.R.M.* 5:123–24; Apr. 1972.

——. Special palindromic primes. *J.R.M.* 4:169–70; July 1971.

Trigg, Charles W., and P. N. Nagara. A non-palindromic strobogram. [Problem 467.] *M.Mag.* 35:250; Sept. 1962.

Trigg, Charles W., and C. F. Pinzka. Palindromic numbers whose squares are composed of distinct digits. [Problem 478.] *M.Mag.* 35:314–15; Nov. 1962.

Trigg, Charles W., and Robert Prielipp. Palindromic triangular numbers. [Problems 3387 and 3413.] *S.S.M.* 71:84; Dec. 1971. Also, 72:358; Apr. 1972.
    Proof that in the system of numeration with base three, the set of palindromic triangular numbers is infinite.

Wulczyn, Gregory, and Charles W. Trigg. Palindromic pentagonal numbers in base five. [Problem 3440.] *S.S.M.* 72:838; Dec. 1972.

Yates, Samuel. Factors of repunits. *J.R.M.* 3:114–19; Apr. 1970. Bibliography.

——. More repunit riddles. *J.R.M.* 4:140–41, 155–56; Apr. 1971.

——. On repunit primes. [Letter to the editor.] *J.R.M.* 3:259; Oct. 1970.

——. Peculiar properties of repunits. *J.R.M.* 2:139–46; July 1969.

——. Repunit riddles. *J.R.M.* 4:19, 76–77; Jan. 1971.

——. Repunit riddles—set 3. *J.R.M.* 4:292, 299; Oct. 1971.

2.6   Perfect, Deficient, and Abundant Numbers

Baird, Mara. Perfect numbers in mod systems. *M.S.J.*, vol. 19, no. 2, pp. 3–4; Jan. 1972.

Benkoski, Stan. Are all weird numbers even? *A.M.M.* 79:774; Aug.–Sept. 1972.

Brauer, A. On the non-existence of odd perfect numbers of the form $p^{\alpha} \cdot q_1{}^2 \cdot q_2{}^2 \cdots q_{i-1}{}^2 \cdot q_i{}^4$. *Bulletin of the American Mathematical Society* 49:712–18; 1943.

Cramer, G. F. Extension of the theorem of Servais on perfect numbers. *A.M.M.* 48:17; 1941.

——. On almost perfect numbers. *A.M.M.* 48:133; 1941.

Dickson, L. E. Finiteness of odd perfect and primitive abundant numbers with n distinct prime factors. *American Journal of Mathematics* 35:413–22; 1913.

Franqui, B., and M. Garcia. 57 new multiply perfect numbers. *Scrip.M.* 20:169–71; 1954.

——. Some new multiply perfect numbers. *A.M.M.* 60:459–62; 1953.

Hunter, J. A. H. Perfect number "endings." *Fib.Q.* 4:82; Feb. 1966.

Kaplansky, I. Lucas' tests for Mersenne numbers. *A.M.M.* 52:188–90; 1945.

Karst, E. New factors of Mersenne numbers. *Mathematics of Computation,* p. 51; 1961.

Klarner, David A. Perfect number notes. *J.R.M.* 3:261; Oct. 1970.

Kourkoutis, Andrew. An amalgam of numbers. *Math Student* [Brooklyn Technical High School], pp. 15–16. Jan. 1969.
Discussion of triperfect and quadriperfect numbers, automorphic and amicable numbers, and so on.

Kraitchik, M. On the factorization of $2^n \pm 1$. *Scrip.M.*, Mar. 1952.

Kravitz, Sidney. Divisors of Mersenne numbers. $10,000 < p < 15,000$. *Mathematics of Computation,* pp. 292–93; July 1961.

Lehmer, D. H. On the factors of $2^n \pm 1$. *Bulletin of the American Mathematical Society* 53:164; Feb. 1947.

Levit, R. J. The non-existence of a certain type of odd perfect number. *Bulletin of the American Mathematical Society* 53:392–96; 1946.

McCarthy, Paul J. Odd perfect numbers. *Scrip.M.* 23:43–47; 1957.

———. Remarks concerning the non-existence of odd perfect numbers. *A.M.M.* 64:257–58; 1957.

McDaniel, Wayne L. The non-existence of odd perfect numbers of a certain form. *Archief der Mathematick* 21:52–53; 1970.

Molling, Joe. Perfect numbers. *M.S.J.*, vol. 18, no. 2, pp 1–3; Jan. 1971.

Ore, Oystein. *Number Theory and Its History.* New York: McGraw-Hill Book Co., 1948.
Observations on perfect numbers, pp. 91–94.

Perfect Numbers. *M.T.* 47:542; Dec. 1954.
Brief note on the sixteenth and seventeenth perfect numbers.

Prielipp, Robert W. Digital sums of perfect numbers and triangular numbers. *M.T.* 62:179–82; Mar. 1969.

———. Even perfect numbers modulo 12. *Pentagon* 31:78–79, 112; Spring 1972.

———. More about odd perfect numbers. *M.T.* 64:633; Nov. 1971.

———. Perfect numbers, abundant numbers, and deficient numbers. *M.T.* 63: 692–96; Dec. 1970.
Proofs of some of their properties.

Prielipp, Robert W., N. J. Kuenzi, and Charles W. Trigg. Deficient numbers. [Problem 3419.] *S.S.M.* 72:460; May 1972.

Problem E1755. [Solution.] *A.M.M.*, p. 203; Feb. 1966.
On perfect numbers.

Read, Cecil B. What is an abundant number? *S.S.M.* 72:249–51; Mar. 1972.

Riesel, H. A new Mersenne prime. *Mathematics of Computation* 12:60; Jan. 1958.

Scheffler, D., and R. Ondrejka. The numerical evaluation of the eighteenth perfect number. *Mathematics of Computation,* pp. 199–200; Apr. 1960.

Shapiro, Harold N. Note on a theorem of Dickson. *Bulletin of the American Mathematical Society* 55:450–52; 1949.

———. On primitive abundant numbers. *Communications on Pure and Applied Mathematics* 21:111–18; Mar. 1968.
Advanced discussion.

Sierpinski, W. On some unsolved problems of arithmetic. *Scrip.M.* 25:125–36; 1960.
———. Sur les nombres pseudoparfaits. *Mat. Vesnik.* 2:212–13; 1965.
Subbarao, M. V. Are there an infinity of unitary perfect numbers? *A.M.M.* 77:389–90; Apr. 1970.
Subbarao, M. V., and L. J. Warren. Unitary perfect numbers. *Canadian Mathematics Bulletin* 9:147–53; 1966.

2.7 Prime Numbers

Bateman, Paul T., and Marc E. Low. Prime numbers in arithmetic progression with difference 24. *A.M.M.* 72:139–43; Feb. 1965.
Bateman, Paul T., and Roger A. Horn. A heuristic asymptotic formula concerning the distribution of prime numbers. *Mathematics of Computation* 16:363–67; July 1962.
Berg, Murray, and John Walstrom. Right and left primes. *J.R.M.* 3:179; July 1970.
Bergerson, Howard. Prime sums. *J.R.M.* 4:70–71; Jan. 1971.
Buchman, A. L. Patterns in algorithms for determining whether large numbers are prime. *M.T.* 63:30–41; Jan. 1970.
   Bibliography.
Card, Leslie. Hexadecimal twin primes. *J.R.M.* 3:150; July 1970.
———. More twin prime curiosities. *J.R.M.* 3:191; July 1970.
———. Patterns in primes—addenda. *J.R.M.* 1:250–52; Oct. 1968.
———. Primes ending in three like digits. *J.R.M.* 2:195; Oct. 1969.
———. Reversible primes in hexadecimal form. *J.R.M.* 3:263; Oct. 1970.
Carman, Robert, et al. [Problem 3452.] To find three consecutive primes whose sum is a perfect square. *S.S.M.* 73:164; Feb. 1973.
Dubisch, Roy. The sieve of Eratosthenes. *A.T.* 18:236–37; Apr. 1971.
Gabai, Hyman, and Daniel Coogan. On palindromes and palindromic primes. *M.Mag.* 42:252–54; Nov. 1969.
Gardner, Martin. Mathematical games. *Sci.Am.* 222:121–24; Mar. 1970.
   Prime numbers.
———. "Patterns and Primes." In *Martin Gardner's Sixth Book of Mathematical Games from Scientific American,* pp. 79–90. San Francisco: W. H. Freeman & Co., 1971.
Green, R. E. Primes and recurring decimals. *M.Gaz.* 17:25; Feb. 1963.
Hawthorne, Frank. Prime factorization of numbers of the form $10^n + 1$. *New York State Mathematics Teachers Journal,* pp. 168–69; Oct. 1968.
Heinke, C. H. "Example from Arithmetic." In *The Teaching of Secondary School Mathematics,* pp. 337–58. 33d Yearbook of the NCTM. Washington, D.C.: NCTM, 1970.
Hervey, Margaret A., and Bonnie H. Litwiller. Graphical representation of multiples of the whole numbers. *A.T.* 18:47–48; Jan. 1971.
Hewitt, Frances. Patterns for discovery; prime and composite numbers. *A.T.* 12:136–38; Feb. 1966.
Hirsch, Joseph. Prime triplets. *M.T.* 62:467–71; Oct. 1969.

John, Brother Felix, and Charles W. Trigg. Factors of $N = 111 \ldots 11$. [Problem 3077.] *S.S.M.* 67:287; Mar. 1967.

Karst, Edgar. At least 10 primes in arithmetical progression. [Abstract.] *A.M.M.* 74:1034–35; 1967.

———. Lists of ten or more primes in arithmetical progression. *Scrip.M.* 28:313–17; Feb. 1970.
  Bibliography.

———. More primes in arithmetical progression. *J.R.M.* 3:99; Apr. 1970.

———. "Snowball" primes. *J.R.M.* 2:154; July 1969.

———. 12 to 16 primes in arithmetical progression. *J.R.M.* 2:214–15; Oct. 1969.

Kelley, J. L. "Number Systems of Arithmetic; Primes." In *Mathematics Education*, pp. 107–8. 69th Yearbook of the National Society for the Study of Education, pt. 1. Chicago: University of Chicago Press, 1970.

Kelly, Alice C. Permutation prime numbers. *J.R.M.* 3:36–38; Jan. 1970.

Krishnamurthy, E. V. An observation concerning the decimal periods of prime reciprocals. *J.R.M.* 2:212–13; Oct. 1969.

Krishnamurthy, E. V., and G. Komissar. On the distribution of primes congruent to modulo 40. *J.R.M.* 4:270–71; Oct. 1971.

Legard, A. R. Prime eights. *J.R.M.* 2:147–49; July 1969.

Lehmer, D. H. A note on primitive roots. *Scrip.M.* 26:117; 1963.

Letter from the Editor. *J.R.M.* 3:40–41; Jan. 1970.
  Properties of snowball primes.

Madachy, Joseph S. A consecutive-digit prime. *J.R.M.* 4:100; Apr. 1971.

———. Consecutive-digit primes—again. *J.R.M.* 5:253–54; Oct. 1972.

Moore, Thomas E. A note on the distribution of primes in arithmetic progressions. *J.R.M.* 5:253; Oct. 1972.

Moser, Leo. Palindromic primes. *Scrip.M.* 16:127–28; Mar. 1950.

Nelson, Harry L. Snowball primes. [Letter to the editor.] *J.R.M.* 3:258; Oct. 1970.

Niebaum, Jerome. Reversible primes. *Bulletin, Kansas Association of Teachers of Mathematics* 41:27–29; Apr. 1967.

Oliver, Charlene. Gus's magic number: a key to the divisibility test for primes. *A.T.* 19: 183–89; Mar. 1972.

Omejc, Eve. A different approach to the sieve of Eratosthenes. *A.T.* 19:192–96; Mar. 1972.

Ondrejka, Rudolph. Primes with 100 or more digits. *J.R.M.* 2:42–44; Jan. 1969.

———. Primes with 100 or more digits—addenda. *J.R.M.* 3:161–62; July 1970.

Prielipp, Robert. The arithmetic mean of a pair of twin primes cannot be a perfect nth power for $n > 2$. [Problem 3293.] *S.S.M.* 71:269; Mar. 1971.

———. The many pearls of number theory. *S.S.M.* 70:63–67; Jan. 1970.

Prielipp, Robert, et al. Concerning sets of consecutive primes with special properties. [Problem 3454.] *S.S.M.* 73:165 ; Feb. 1973.

Riesel, Hans. Lucasian criteria for the primality of $N = h \cdot 2^n - 1$. *Mathematics of Computation* 23:869–75; Oct. 1969.

Schafer, Dorothy. A graphic representation of prime and composite numbers. *A.T.* 17:654–56; Dec. 1970.
  Graphic interpretation of the least common multiple and the greatest common factor.

Shanks, Daniel. "Class Number, a Theory of Factorization, and Genera." In *Proceedings of Symposia in Pure Mathematics*, vol. 20, pp. 415–40. Providence, R.I.: American Mathematical Society, 1971.

———. A low density of primes. *J.R.M.* 4:272–75; Oct. 1971.

Shogren, Merle, and Richard Yates. A sieve for primes, $p > 5$. *M.T.* 59:24–28; Jan. 1966.

Silvey, Ina Mae, and Anina Christensen. Using prime numbers to teach mathematics in the elementary school. *S.S.M.* 71:247–56; Mar. 1971.

65-Digit Twin Primes. *J.R.M.* 3:257; Oct. 1970.

Smart, James R. Theorems for finite sets of primes. *M.T.* 63:307–10; Apr. 1970.

Smith, Frank. Divisibility rules for the first fifteen primes. *A.T.* 18:85–87; Feb. 1971.

Stenger, Donald J. Prime numbers from the multiplication table. *A.T.* 16:617–20; Dec. 1969.

Tahta, D. G. Pegboard primes. *M.Tchg.*, no. 59, pp. 4–7; Summer 1972.
Number theory and the sieving process of Eratosthenes.

Trigg, Charles W. Alternate primes in arithmetic progression. *M.Mag.* 35:42; Jan. 1962.

———. A close look at 37. *J.R.M.* 2:117–28; Apr. 1969.

———. Prime sums of primes with distinct digits. *J.R.M.* 2:149–50; July 1969.

———. Special palindromic primes. *J.R.M.* 4:169–70; July 1971.

Trigg, Charles W., et al. A prime sum. [Problem 700.] *M.Mag.* 42:98–99; Mar. 1969.

Walstrom, J. E., and Murray Berg. Prime primes. *M.Mag.* 42:232; Nov. 1969.

Whitaker, Buford. A new discovery. *Florida Council of Teachers of Mathematics Newsletter*, pp. 4–5; Summer 1971.
A hitherto unknown procedure for finding the highest common factor by prime factorization.

Yates, Samuel. Even and odd period lengths. *J.R.M.* 4:268–69; Oct. 1971.

———. Factors of repunits. *J.R.M.* 3:114–19; Apr. 1970.

———. Full-period primes. *J.R.M.* 3:221–25; Oct. 1970.

———. More repunit riddles. *J.R.M.* 4:140–41; 155–56; Apr. 1971.

———. On repunit primes. [Letter to the editor.] *J.R.M.* 3:259; Oct. 1970.

———. Peculiar properties of repunits. *J.R.M.* 2:139–46; July 1969.

———. Repunit riddles. *J.R.M.* 4:19, 76–77; Jan. 1971.

———. Repunit riddles—set 3. *J.R.M.* 4:292, 299; Oct. 1971.

Yates, Samuel, and G. R. Taylor. Table of period lengths of primes under 183,300. [Copy given to the editor of *J.R.M.*]

2.8   Recursive Operations; Bracelets; Digital Inversions

Isaacs, R. Iterates of fractional order. *Canadian Journal of Mathematics* 2:409–16; 1950.

Jordan, J. H. Self-producing sequences of digits. *A.M.M.* 71:61–64; 1964.

Kaprekar, D. R. Another solitaire game. *Scrip.M.* 15:244–45; Sept. 1949.

———. An interesting property of the number 6174. *Scrip.M.* 21:304; Dec. 1955.

———. *The New Constant 6174.* Devlali, India; Devlali Co., n.d. 42 pp. (Paper)

Krause, R. M., et al. Kaprekar's constant. [Problem E2222 (1970, p. 307).] *A.M.M.* 78:197–98; Feb. 1971.
   Bibliography; 8 references.
Nelson, Harry L. More on PDI's. *University of California Publication UCRL-7614*, 1 Dec. 1963.
   Discussion of perfect digital invariants.
Porges, Arthur. A set of eight numbers. *A.M.M.* 52:379–82; Aug. 1945.
   Repeated summing of the squared digits of N.
Schwartz, B. L. Finite bounds on digital invariants. *J.R.M.* 3:88–92; Apr. 1970.
———. Finiteness of a set of self-generating integers. *J.R.M.* 2:79–83; Apr. 1969.
Trigg, Charles W. Associated additive decimal digit bracelets. *Fib.Q.* 7:287–94; Oct. 1969.
———. A digital bracelet for 1971. *M.T.* 64:567–71; Oct. 1971.
———. Kaprekar's constant. [Generalization of problem E2222.] *A.M.M.* 78:197–98; Feb. 1971.
———. Kaprekar's routine with two-digit integers. *Fib.Q.* 9:189–93; Apr. 1971.
———. Kaprekar's routine with five-digit integers. *M.Mag.* 45:121–29; May 1972.
———. Predictive indices for Kaprekar's routine. *J.R.M.* 3:245–54; Oct. 1970. Also, 5:148; Apr. 1972.
———. A recursive operation on two-digit integers. *Fib.Q.* 3:90; Apr. 1965.

2.9   General Theory of Numbers

Baker, Betty L. The Koutsoures-Baker theorem. *M.S.J.*, vol. 20, no. 3, p. 5; Feb. 1973.
Barnett, I. A. The fascination of whole numbers. *M.T.* 64:103–8; Feb. 1971.
   Brief introductory discussion of primes, perfect numbers, and Pythagorean triples.
Bobker, Martin. Squares and other things. *M.Tchg.*, no. 59, p. 17; Summer 1972.
Brillhart, J., and J. L. Selfridge. Some factorizations of $2^n \pm 1$ and related results. *Mathematics of Computation* 21:87–96; Jan. 1967.
Brown, Stephen. Of "prime" concern: what domain? *M.T.* 58:402–7; May 1965.
Carman, Robert A. Mathematical misteaks. *M.T.* 64:109–15; Feb. 1971.
Carman, Robert, and Robert Prielipp. [Problem 3255.] *S.S.M.* 70:589; June 1970.
   Proof that the product of four consecutive integers can never be a perfect cube.
Dickson, Leonard Eugene. *History of the Theory of Numbers*. New York: Chelsea Publishing Co., 1952.
   Vol. 2, chap. 8, pp. 275–303: partitioning of integers into squares.
———. Notes on the theory of numbers. *A.M.M.* 18:109; 1911.
Duncan, David R., and Bonnie Litwiller. A pattern in number theory; example → generalization → proof. *M.T.* 64:661–64; Nov. 1971.
Ellison, W. J. Waring's problem. *A.M.M.* 78:10–36; Jan. 1971.
   Highly technical; extensive bibliography of nearly 150 references.
Gardner, Martin. Diophantine analysis and Fermat's "last theorem." *Sci.Am.* 223:117–19; July 1970. Also, 223:112; Aug. 1970.
   Includes Archimedes' cattle problem and the "Integral brick" problem.

Gillies, Donald. Three new Mersenne primes and a statistical theory. *Mathematics of Computation* 18:93–95; Jan. 1964.

Godino, Charles. *Elementary Topics in Number Theory.* Boston: Allyn & Bacon. 1971. 170 pp.

Greenblatt, M. H. Wilson's theorem. *J.R.M.* 4:88–89; Apr. 1971.

Griffin, Harriet. Discovering properties of the natural numbers. *A.T.* 12:627–32; Dec. 1965.

Griffin, William Raymond. Mersenne primes—the last three digits. *J.R.M.* 5:53–54; Jan. 1972.

Gross, H. I. Problem, a solution, and some commentary. *M.T.* 64:221–24; Mar. 1971.

Henry, Boyd. Modulo 7 arithmetic—a perfect example of field properties. *M.T.* 65:525–28; Oct. 1972.

Hervey, Margaret A., and B. H. Litwiller. Structure: a different look at L.C.M. and G.C.F. *S.S.M.* 70:713–19; Nov. 1970.

Himmelberger, Warren J. Puzzle problems and Diophantine equations. *M.T.* 66:136–38; Feb. 1973.

Hoffer, Alan R. What you always wanted to know about six but have been afraid to ask. *A.T.* 20:173–80; Mar. 1973.

Hunter, J. A. H., and Joseph Madachy. *Mathematical Diversions.* Princeton, N.J.: D. Van Nostrand Co., 1963.
    Chap. 6: "Diophantos and All That," pp. 52–64.

Jansson, Lars C., and Edward C. Beardslee. Conjecturing with Kaprekar. *M.Tchg.,* no. 61, pp. 31–33; Dec. 1972.

Just, Erwin. Fermat's theorem, special case. *M.Mag.* 45:109; Mar. 1972.

Kalman, Karl S. Diophantus and Diophantine equations. *Mathematical Log,* vol. 7, no. 2, pp. 2–3; Feb. 1963.

Kelley, J. L. Number systems of arithmetic; clock arithmetic. In *Mathematics Education,* pp. 108–13. 69th Yearbook of the National Society for the Study of Education, pt. 1. Chicago: University of Chicago Press, 1970.

Krishnamurthy, E. V. The ending two-digit pattern of 2^{p-1} $(2^p - 1)$. *J.R.M.* 4:187–89; July 1971.

Lehmer, D. H. The prime factors of consecutive integers. *A.M.M.,* vol. 72, no. 2, pt. 2, pp. 19–20; Feb. 1965.

LeVan, M. O. A triangle for partitions. *A.M.M.* 79:507–10; May 1972.
    On the number of ways in which a positive integer can be expressed as the sum of positive integers.

Love, Janet. Linear Diophantine equations and congruences. *Pentagon* 29:24–29, 48; Fall 1969.

Mann, Nathaniel III. Modulo systems: one more step. *M.T.* 65:207–9; Mar. 1972.

Merriel, D. Nim and natural numbers. *M.T.* 64:342–44; Apr. 1971.

Neuner, Albert R. A modulo line. *A.T.* 20:214–15; Mar. 1973.

Nymann, J. E. A note concerning the square-free integers. *A.M.M.* 79:63–65; Jan. 1972.

Polya, G. Heuristic reasoning in the theory of numbers. *A.M.M.* 66:357–84; 1959.

Prielipp, Robert. Many pearls of number theory. *S.S.M.* 70:63–67; Jan. 1970.

———. [Problem 3411.] *S.S.M.* 72:356; Apr. 1972.
    Proof that an odd prime number can be represented as the difference of two squares of positive integers in one and only one way.

Prielipp, Robert, et al. [Problem 3393.] *S.S.M.* 72:93; Jan. 1972.
If $x^2 + y^2 = z^2$, where x, y, and z are positive integers, and if $(y,z) = 1$ and y is even, prove that $z - y \equiv 1$ (mod 8) and $z + y \equiv 1$ (mod 8).

Reid, Constance. *From Zero to Infinity*. New York: Thomas Y. Crowell Co., 1955.
Fermat numbers: pp. 99–109.

Sierpinski, W. On some unsolved problems in arithmetic. *Scrip.M.* 25:129; June 1960.
On Fermat numbers.

Silverman, David L. A pair of Diophantine equations. *J.R.M.* 4:72–73; Jan. 1971.

Silverman, David L., and J. A. H. Hunter. Square partitions, solution. [Problem 533.] *M.Mag.* 37:201–2; May 1964.

Sowell, Katye O., and Jon P. McGuffey. Nondecimal slide rules—and their use in modular arithmetic. *M.T.* 64:467–72; May 1971.

Taylor, L. F. *Numbers*. London: Faber & Faber, 1970. 153 pp.
Includes a discussion of recurring decimals, series, prime numbers, Diophantine equations, finite arithmetic, and Fermat's theorem.

Trigg, Charles W. A close look at 37. *J.R.M.* 2:117–28; Apr. 1969.

———. Integers immune to partitioning into distinct squares. *J.R.M.* 3:124; Apr. 1970.

Trotter, Terrel, and Irene Klaver. Number patterns from digit sums. *A.T.* 18:100–103; Feb. 1971.
An introductory discussion of digital roots and casting out nines; based on experience with fourth-grade pupils.

Vandiver, H. S. On the theory of numbers. *A.M.M.* 67:47–50; 1960.

Wisner, Robert J. *A Panorama of Numbers*. Glenview, Ill.: Scott, Foresman & Co., 1970. 176 pp.
General introduction to number theory; primes, tests for divisibility; perfect numbers; modular arithmetic. An informal, recreational approach.

Zwier, Paul J. Multitudinous kinds of counting numbers and their generating functions. *M.T.* 63:61–21; Nov. 1970.

Chapter 3

Geometric Recreations

3.1   Curves: Their Properties and Construction

Anderson, Frank A. Translation of axes discovered through the overhead projector. *M.T.* 63:669–70; Dec. 1970.

Charosh, Mannis. *The Ellipse.* New York: Thomas Y. Crowell Co., 1971.
For young readers.

Condon, Richard. Harmonograph. *Engineering Opportunities,* vol. 6, no. 6, pp. 10–11; June 1968.
Mechanically described Lissajous figures.

Cooper, P. W. Conic sections . . . in geometry and literature. *Varsity Graduate* [University of Toronto], Summer 1966, p. 65 ff.

Coxeter, H. S. M. *Helices and Concho-spirals.* Nobel Symposium series, vol. 11, pp. 29–34. New York: John Wiley & Sons, Interscience, n.d.
Technical discussion.

Davis, Chandler, and Donald Knuth. Number representations and dragon curves—I. *J.R.M.* 3:66–81; Apr. 1970.

———. Number representations and dragon curves—II. *J.R.M.* 3:133–49; July 1970.

Felix, Lucienne. From Venn diagrams to Peano curves. *M.Tchg.,* no. 50, pp. 13–21; Spring 1970.
Peano curves derived from sequences of lines.

Dolan, W. W. Early sundials and the discovery of the conic sections. *M.Mag.* 45:8–12; 1972.

———. The ellipse in eighteenth century sundial design. *M.Mag.* 45:205–9; Sept. 1972.
Bibliography.

Gardner, Martin. [Curves, in *Scientific American.*]
Archimedean spiral: Apr. 1962, p. 156
Brachistochrone: July 1964, p. 112
Cardioid: Sept. 1970, p. 212
Catenary: Oct. 1961, p. 160
Circle (involute) : Apr. 1962, p. 156
Cyclical curves: Sept. 1970, pp. 210–18
Cycloid: July 1964, pp. 110–12, Aug. 1964, p. 99
Dragon curve: Mar. 1967, pp. 124–25; Apr. 1967, pp. 118–20; July 1967, p. 115
Ellipse: Feb. 1961, pp. 146–54
Epicycloid: Sept. 1970, p. 212
Equiangular spiral: Apr. 1962, p. 160
Logarithmic spiral: Aug. 1959, p. 125; Apr. 1962, p. 158

Nephroid: Sept. 1970, p. 216

Tautochrone: July 1964, p. 112

———. "The Cycloid: Helen of Geometry." In *Martin Gardner's Sixth Book of Mathematical Games from Scientific American,* pp. 127–34. San Francisco: W. H. Freeman & Co., 1971.

Gridgeman, N. T. Elliptic parallels. *M.T.* 63:481–85; Oct. 1970.

Grinstein, Louise S. Another look at the roses. *M.T.* 64:709–14; Dec. 1971.
   Discussion of rose curves (polar coordinates) and their construction. Bibliography.

Groasdale, Robert. A note on conicoids. *M.Tchg.,* no. 59, p. 12; Summer 1972.

Heard, T. J. Cycloid and cardioid lengths. *M.Tchg.,* no. 57, pp. 36–38; Winter 1971.

Hogben, E. Bottled sections. *M.Tchg.,* no. 50, p. 68; Spring 1970.
   Properties of conic sections shown visually.

Kanter, L. H. A note on the optical property of the hyperbola. *S.S.M.* 71:689–92; Nov. 1971.

———. A note on the optical property of the parabola. *S.S.M.* 71:403–6; May 1971.

Kennedy, Hubert C. The Witch of Agnesi—exorcised. *M.T.* 62:480–82; Oct. 1969.
   Bibliography.

Kepler, J. *The Six-cornered Snowflake.* (Translated by Colin Hardie.) New York: Oxford University Press, 1966.

King, Bruce W. Snowflake Curves. *M.T.* 57:219–22; Apr. 1964.

———. Some crinkled curves and prickly polyhedra. *M.Tchg.,* no. 57, pp. 43–45; Winter 1971.

Lalich, Marilyn. Geometric inversion. *Pentagon* 28:63–72; Spring 1969.

Leonard, Harold A. The whispering chamber. *M.S.J.,* vol. 19, no. 3, pp. 1–3; Mar. 1972.
   A simple proof of the ellipsoidal "whispering" phenomenon.

Lindstrom, Peter. Some curve sketching exercises. *S.S.M.* 72:726–29; Nov. 1972.

Lissajous Figures. *Pythagoras* (English ed.), vol. 2, no. 9, pp. 53–57; 1969–70.

Macmillan, R. H. The freedom of linkages. *M.Gaz.* 34:37; 1950.

Maletsky, Evan M. Conics from straight lines and circles. *M.T.* 66:243–46; Mar. 1973.

Miller, William A. A psychedelic approach to conic sections. *M.T.* 63:657–59; Dec. 1970.

Oakwood, Elliott F. Improving the witch. *M.T.* 63:667–68; Dec. 1970.
   Sidelight on the Witch of Agnesi.

Rajan, S. Construction of conics. *M.S.J.,* vol. 14, no. 1, pp. 3–6; Nov. 1966.

Ranucci, Ernest R. Curves from polygons. *M.Tchg,* no. 55, pp. 10–12; Summer 1971.

Rowe, R. Robinson. The mutuabola. *J.R.M.* 3:176–78; July 1970.
   Discussion of the graphs of $x^y = y^x$ and $x \log y = y \log x$.

Schneider, Joel E. A generalization of the Van Koch curve. *M.Mag.* 38:144–47; May 1965.

Shilgalis, Thomas W. Graphical solution of the equation $a^b = b^a$. *M.T.* 66:235; Mar. 1973.

Shwarger, Michael. Parametric construction of the coins. *M.T.* 65:105–9; Feb. 1972.

32   RECREATIONAL MATHEMATICS

The Spirograph. *Pythagoras* (English ed.), vol. 2, no. 10, pp. 67–69; 1969–70.
    Mechanically described Lissajous figures.
Stover, Donald W. *The Conics: A Geometric Approach.* Boston: Houghton
    Mifflin Co., 1971. 83 pp. (Paper)
Tilley, George C., et al. Concerning a square inscribed in an ellipse such that the
    square passes through its foci. [Problem 3453.] *S.S.M.* 73:165; Feb. 1973.
    Involves the golden ratio indirectly.
Van Koch's Snowflake Curve. *Pythagoras* (English ed.), vol. 2, no. 10, pp. 76–78;
    1969–70.
Wilde, Edwin F. Equations of polygons. *M.S.J.*, vol. 19, no. 2, pp. 1–3; Jan. 1972.

3.2   Curves of Constant Width

Dossey, John A. What—a roller with corners? *M.T.* 65:720–24; Dec. 1972.
Elliotte, Norma H. Rotation of convex curves in regular polygons. *Pentagon*
    29:3–12, 42; Fall 1969.
Evans, Leonard. On "rotating" ellipses inside triangles. *M.Mag.* 44:28–33; Jan.
    1971.
Gardner, Martin. Curves of constant width. *Sci.Am.* 208:148–56; Feb. 1963.
Hammer, P. C., and Andrew Sobezyk. Planar line families, I. *Proceedings of the
    American Mathematical Society* 4:226–33; Apr. 1953.
Kearsley, J. Curves of constant diameter. *M.Gaz.* 36:176–79; Sept. 1952.
Peterson, B. B. Do self-intersections characterize curves of constant width?
    A.M.M. 79:505–6; May 1972.
    Bibliography, 12 references.
Schneider, Joel E. A generalization of the Van Koch curve. *M.Mag.* 38:144–47;
    May 1965.
Shaw, Harry. Multipoint gauges. *American Machinist*, pp. 43–46, 173–75, 208–11;
    1931.

3.3   The Fourth Dimension

Abbas, Sallie W. Some investigations of *N*-dimensional geometries. *M.T.* 66:
    126–30; Feb. 1973.
Brooke, Maxey. How to make a magic tessarack. *R.M.M.*, no. 5, pp. 40–44; Oct.
    1961.
Brückner, Max. *Die Elemente der vierdimensionalen Geometrie, mit besonderer
    Berücksightigung der Polytope.* Zwickau, 1894.
Eckhart, Ludwig. *Four Dimensional Space.* Bloomington, Ind.: Indiana Uni-
    versity Press, 1968. 90 pp.
    Unusual approach: representing four dimensions in terms of descriptive
    geometry.
Gardner, Martin. "The Church of the Fourth Dimension." In *The Unexpected
    Hanging and Other Mathematical Diversions*, pp. 65–75. New York: Simon &
    Schuster, 1963.
Hess, Adrien L. Viewing diagrams in four dimensions. *M.T.* 64:247–48; Mar.
    1971.

Hess, Adrien L., and Carl Diekhans. The number of segments needed to extend a cube to *n* dimensions. *M.Mag.* 43:189–92; Sept. 1970.
Some characteristics of the tesseract.
Hinton, Charles Howard. *Scientific Romances.* n.p., 1886.
Problems of the fourth dimension.
Jouffret, Esprit. *Mélanges de géométrie à quatre dimensions.* n.p., 1906.
———. *Traité élémentaire de géométrie à quatre dimensions, et introduction à la géométrie à n dimensions.* n.p., 1903.
Marr, Richard F. *4-Dimensional Geometry.* New York: Houghton Mifflin Co., 1970. 41 pp.
Introduction to four-dimensional space by means of the 5-cube and the hypercube.
Sainte-Lague, André. "A Journey into the Fourth Dimension." In *Great Currents of Mathematical Thought,* pt. 1, bk. 2, edited by F. Le Lionnais. New York: Dover Publications, 1962.

3.4 Geometric Constructions; Mascheroni Constructions

Bold, Benjamin. *Famous Problems of Mathematics: A History of Constructions with Straight-Edge and Compasses.* New York: Van Nostrand Reinhold Co., 1969. 112 pp.
Court, N. A. Castillon's problem. *Scrip.M.* 20:118–20, 232–35; Mar.–June, 1954.
———. Fagano's problem. *Scrip.M.* 17:147–50; Mar.–June, 1951.
Gardner, Martin. Geometric constructions with a compass and a straightedge, and also with a compass alone. *Sci.Am.* 221:239–46, Sept. 1969; 221:130, Oct. 1969; 221:127, Dec. 1969.
———. Napoleon's problem. *Sci.Am.* 221:239–46, Sept. 1969; 221:130, Oct. 1969; 221:127, Dec. 1969.
Haley, James B., Jr. A rusty compass construction. *J.R.M.* 5:66–67; Jan. 1972.
Pedersen, Jean. Asymptotic Euclidean type constructions without Euclidean tools. *Fib.Q.* 9:199–216; Apr. 1971.
Bibliography.
Hess, Adrien L. Certain topics related to constructions with straight-edge and compasses. *M.Mag.* 29:217–21; Mar.–Apr. 1958.
Ransom, William R. Dürer's pentagon. *S.S.M.* 64:236–37; Mar. 1964.
———. A six-sided hexagon. *S.S.M.* 52:94; Feb. 1952.
Construction of an interesting model.
Rubenfeld, Rina, Howard Eves, and Michael Goldberg. A compass construction. *M.Mag.* 45:290–91; Nov. 1972.
How to construct a square, given two points as vertices, using a compass only.
Satterly, John. A problem with touching circles. *M.T.* 53:90–95; Feb. 1960.
Unusual construction problems; filling the plane with circles.
Stover, Donald W. A student's construction. *M.T.* 66:172; Feb. 1973.
Drawing a line parallel to a given line.
Trigg, Charles W. *Mathematical Quickies.* New York: McGraw-Hill Book Co., 1967.
Problem 248: "Napoleon's Problem."
Wernick, William. Geometric construction: the double straightedge. *M.T.* 64:697–704; Dec. 1971.

3.5   Geometric Problems and Theorems

The Arbelos. [Problem 333.] *M.S.J.*, vol. 18, no. 2, p. 7; Jan. 1971.

Archibald, R. C. Malfatti's problem. *Scrip.M.* 1:170–71; Sept. 1932.

Ault, J. C. Labelling the 13-point geometry. *J.R.M.* 4:60–63; Jan. 1971.

Amir-Moéz, Ali R. Proofs of the converse of the "isosceles triangle theorem." *Pentagon* 28:94–99; Spring 1969.

   Gives direct, indirect, algebraic, and analytic proofs, as suggested by Elisha Loomis.

Bankoff, Leon, and Jack Garfunkel. The heptagonal triangle. *M.Mag.* 46:7–19; Jan. 1973.

   The "modern geometry" of the regular heptagon and related triangles.

Baylis, D. John. The box and ladder problem. *M.Tchg.*, no. 54, p. 24; Spring 1971.

Brumfiel, Charles. A generalization of vux triangles. *M.T.* 65:171–74; Feb. 1972.

Bryant, V. W., and A. K. Austin. An inscribed equilateral triangle. *M.Tchg.*, no. 54, pp. 8–9; Spring 1971.

Burns, J. C. Morley's triangle. *M.Mag.* 43:210–11; Sept. 1970.

Cheney, Fitch. Vux triangles. *M.T.* 63:407–10; May 1970.

Collings, S. N. Chains of circles *M.Tchg.*, no. 54, pp. 25–26; Spring 1971.

   Problems in modern geometry.

———. Cyclic polygons and their Euler lines. *M.Gaz.* 51:108–14; 1967.

Coltharp, Forest L. Properties of polygonal regions. *A.T.* 19:117–22; Feb. 1972.

Court, N. A. The problem of Apollonius. *M.T.* 54:444–52; Oct. 1961.

Fermat's Problem and Plateau's Soap Films. *Pythagoras* (English ed.), vol. 2, no. 8, pp. 23–27; 1969–70.

Gardner, Martin. Elegant triangle theorems not to be found in Euclid. *Sci.Am.* 222:132–36; June 1970.

Giles, Geoff. Angles in polygons and polyhedra. *M.Tchg.*, no. 61, pp. 42–43; Dec. 1972.

Goldberg, Michael. The minimum path and the minimum motion of a moved line segment. *M.Mag.* 46:31–34; Jan. 1973.

Gore, Norman, and Sidney Penner. An absent-minded professor builds a kite. *M.T.* 66:184–85; Feb. 1973.

   Theorem concerning quadrilaterals.

Greenblatt, M. H. Wilson's theorem. *J.R.M.* 4:88–89; Apr. 1971.

May, Lola J. Patterns in geometry. *Grade Teacher* 89: 64–65; Apr. 1972.

Neidhardt, G. L., and V. Milenkovic. Morley's triangle. *M.Mag.* 42:87–88; 1969.

O'Connor, Susan M. Equilateral triangles and the parallelogram. *Pentagon* 29:73–83; Spring 1970.

Ogilvy, C. Stanley. *Excursions in Geometry*. New York: Oxford University Press, 1969. 178 pp.

Rabinowitz, Stanley, and D. J. Bordelon. The problem of Apollonius. [Problem 759.] *M.Mag.* 43:286–88; Nov. 1970.

Ranucci, Ernest R. The Weequahic configuration. *M.T.* 53:124–26; Feb. 1960.

   Visualization of three dimensions.

Raphael, Brother L. In search of the perfect scalene triangle. *M.T.* 66:57–60; Jan. 1973.

Rowe, R. Robinson. Primitive semi-inscribed quadrilaterals. *J.R.M.* 3:151–57; July 1970.

Scheid, Francis. Square circles. *M.T.* 54:307–12; May 1961.
Taxicab geometry, etc.

Sitomer, Harry, and Mindel Sitomer. *What Is Symmetry?* New York: Thomas Y. Crowell Co., 1970. 34 pp.

———. *Lines, Segments, Polygons.* New York: Thomas Y. Crowell Co., 1972. 33 pp.

Sivaramakrishnan, R., and Leon Bankoff. An angle bisector. *M.Mag.* 43:285–86; Nov. 1970.

Spickerman, W. R. An extension of Morley's theorem. *M.Mag.* 44:191–92; Sept. 1971.

Stanton, R. G., and H. C. Williams. The Morley triangle. *Ontario Secondary School Mathematical Bulletin;* Sept. 1965.

Tóth, Imre. Non-Euclidean geometry before Euclid. *Sci.Am.* 221:87–98; Nov. 1969.
Historical approach.

Viertel, William K., et al. Concerning the maximum volume for a minimum surface, or the minimum surface for a given volume; generalization for open top containers with regular polygonal bases. [Problem 3456.] *S.S.M.* 73:166–67; Feb. 1973.

Webster, R. J. Morley's triangle theorem. *M.Mag.* 43:209–10; Sept. 1970.

Wells, Peter. Symmetries of solids. *M.Tchg.,* no. 55, pp. 48–52; Summer 1971.

3.6 Geometric Recreations and Puzzles

Alspaugh, Carol Ann. Kaleidoscopic geometry. *A.T.* 17:116–17; Feb. 1970.
Simple experiments with mirror geometry.

Amir-Moéz, Ali R. Ibn Haitham. *R.M.M.,* no. 11, pp. 47–48; Oct. 1962.
Geometric problems.

Ballew, David W. The wheel of Aristotle. *M.T.* 65:507–9; Oct. 1972.
A geometric paradox.

Bankoff, Leon. A geometric curiosity. *J.R.M.* 2:130; July 1969.

Bankoff, Leon, and Charles W. Trigg. A circular billiard table. [Problem 184.] *M.Mag.* 38:184; May 1965.

Beard, R. S. Star geometry: Pythagoras, Fibonacci and Beard. *Fib.Q.* 4:70–72; Feb. 1966.

Bell, S. D. The Brown railway. *M.Tchg.,* no. 49, pp. 42–45; Winter 1969.
The geometry of laying out model-railway track.

Bird, M. T. Maximum rectangle inscribed in a triangle. *M.T.* 64:759–60; Dec. 1971.

Brandley, Michael. Square circles. *Pentagon* 30:8–15; Fall 1970.

Fielker, David S., and Josephine Mold. *Triangles.* London: Cambridge University Press, 1971. 32 pp. (Paper)
For young children; geoboard, Pick's theorem, Pascal's triangle, triangular numbers, and so on.

Freitag, Herta, and Robert Carman. [Problem 3313.] *S.S.M.* 71:578–79; June 1971.
On an infinite succession of circles within a square.

Gardner, Martin. Geometric fallacies: hidden errors pave the way to absurd conclusions. *Sci.Am.* 224:114–17; Apr. 1971.

——. Simplicity as a scientific concept: does nature keep her accounts on a thumbnail? *Sci.Am.* 221:118–21; Aug. 1969.
  Geometric recreations, pp. 119–20.

Giles, Geoffrey. Rotagrams. *M.Tchg.*, no. 53, pp. 4–5; Winter 1970.

Goldberg, Michael. The minimum path and the minimum motion of a moved line segment. *M.Mag.* 46:31–34; 1973.

——. Triangles in a square. [Problem 785.] *M.Mag.* 44:292–94; Nov. 1971.

Goldenberg, E. Paul. A puzzle. *M.Tchg.*, no. 52, pp. 23–24; Autumn 1970.
  A geometric diversion.

Hillman, T. P. Colors, geometric forms, art, and mathematics. *A.T.* 14:448–52; Oct. 1967.

An Investigation into the Patterns of Rotation of a Square. *M.Tchg.* no. 49, pp. 54–56; Winter 1969.

Jacobson, R. A., and K. L. Yocom. Shortest paths within polygons. *M.Mag.* 39:290–93; Nov. 1966.
  Methods that do not use algebra or calculus.

Krbek, Franz von. *Geometrische Plaudereien.* Leipzig: Teubner, 1966.

McClellan, John. Polyhedra enumeration. *J.R.M.* 2:2; Jan. 1969.

Marshall, A. G. Pick: with holes. *M.Tchg.*, no. 50, pp. 67–68; Spring 1970.
  Geoboard; Pick's theorem; area of irregular polygons.

Millington, J. M. The perimeter of regular polygons. *M.Tchg.*, no. 52, pp. 21–23; Autumn 1970.

Murrow, Gene. A geometric application of the "Shepherd's Principle." *M.T.* 64:756–58; Dec. 1971.
  General methods of counting the number of squares or rectangles in a given configuration.

NSF Class, University of California at Berkeley, et al. Nested equilateral triangles. [Problem 754.] *M.Mag.* 43:280–83; Nov. 1970.

Perel'man, I. I. *Unterhaltsame Geometrie; eine Sammlung allgemeinverständlicher geometrischer Aufgaben zur Unterhaltung und Übung.* Berlin: Volk & Wissen, 1954.

Pitts, Richard. Negative points. *R.M.M.*, no. 9, pp. 23–24; June 1962.
  Unusual use of combinatorics.

Piza, P.A. *Fermagoric Triangles.* San German, P.R., 1945. 153 pp. Also available from Stechert-Hafner Service Agency, 31 E. 10th St., New York, N.Y.

Ranucci, Ernest R. On skewed regular polygons. *M.T.* 63:219–22; Mar. 1970.

Schadler, Reuben A., and Dale G. Seymour. *Pic-a-Puzzle; A Book of Geometric Puzzle Patterns.* Palo Alto, Calif.: Creative Publications, 1970. 127 pp.

Schwartz, B. L. An oldie but goodie. *J.R.M.* 5:67–68; Jan. 1972.
  With five points in the plane no three of which are collinear, some four of them always constitute a convex quadrilateral.

Sibson, Robert. Puzzle. ["Topics," *M.Tchg.*, no. 52, by Paul Goldenberg.] *M.Tchg.*, no. 54, p. 11; Spring 1971.

Spielman, Bryan. Rigidity and framework models. *M.Tchg.*, no. 51, pp. 39–43; Summer 1970.
  Deals with linkages.

Stover, Donald. *Stereograms.* Boston: Houghton Mifflin Co., 1966.

Szczepanski, Ronald. Predictor polynomials. *M.T.* 65:267–71; Mar. 1972.
Application of the calculus of finite differences to problems involving geo-metrical configurations.
Trigg, Charles W. Bisection of Yin and Yang. *M.Mag.* 34:107–8; Nov. 1960.
———. Inscriptable hexagon in the three-square configuration. [Problem 3291.]
S.S.M. 71:268; Mar. 1971.
———. A three-square geometry problem. *J.R.M.* 4:90–99; Apr. 1971.
Vaughn, Ruth. Investigation of line crossing in a circle. *A.T.* 18:157–60; Mar. 1971.
Walter, Marion. A few steps down the path of a locus problem. *M.Tchg.*, no. 53, pp. 23–25; Winter 1970.
Walter, Marion, and Stephen Brown. What if not? *M.Tchg.*, no. 46, pp. 38–45; Spring 1969.
Use of a geoboard, lattice points, and so forth.
Wells, Celia. How many triangles are there in this figure? *M.Tchg.*, no. 54, pp. 27–29; Spring 1971.
Wells, Peter. Do we meet? A mathematical activity for secondary children. *M.Tchg.*, no. 60, pp. 19–21; Sept. 1972.

3.7 Lattices; Taxicab Geometry; Geoboard

Avital, Shmuel. Lattices in the secondary school. *M.Tchg.*, no. 55, pp. 44–48; Summer 1971.
Baker, Lyndon, Al Marshall, and Peter Wells. Dissections on a geoboard. *M.Tchg.*, no. 61, pp. 13–15; Dec. 1972.
Brown, T. C., and S. B. Maurer. Lattice points in color. [Problem E2251 (1970, p. 766).] *A.M.M.* 78:796; Sept. 1971.
Buckeye, D. A., W. A. Ewbank, and J. L. Ginther. *A Cloudburst of Math Lab Experiments.* Vols. 3 and 4. Troy, Mich.: Midwest Publications, 1971.
Includes work with a geoboard.
Byrkit, Donald R. Taxicab geometry—a non-Euclidean geometry of lattice points. *M.T.* 64:418–22; May 1971.
Dodridge, John A. A C.S.E. question and its development: possible routes on a lattice. *M.Tchg.*, no. 49, p. 25; Winter 1969.
Edwards, Melanie. Shapes with four sides. *M.Tchg.*, no. 49, pp. 40–42; Winter 1969.
Lattice problems.
Enders, Max. "Die Verwendung der Netze zum Aufbau einer Geometrie der Unterstufe." In *Der Mathematikunterricht*, vol. 1, pp. 29–76. Stuttgart: Ernst Klett Verlag, 1955.
Use of a simple square grid for beginning instruction in geometry.
Ewbank, William A. If Pythagoras had a geoboard. *M.T.* 66:215–21; Mar. 1973.
Fielker, David S. Notes from a maths centre. *M.Tchg.*, no. 51, pp. 18–21; Summer 1970.
Patterns on a pegboard.
Gardner, Martin. "The Lattice of Integers." In *Martin Gardner's Sixth Book of Mathematical Games from Scientific American*, pp. 208–19. San Francisco: W. H. Freeman & Co., 1971.

Golomb, Solomon. Paths on arrays of dots. *J.R.M.* 1:154–56, July 1968; 2:229–30, Oct. 1969.

Harkin, J. B. The limit concept on the geoboard. *M.T.* 65:13–17; Jan. 1972.
    Finding the area of a circle and an ellipse by using a geoboard.

Kenney, Margaret. Factor lattices. *M.T.* 63:647–51; Dec. 1970.

Liedtke, Warner, and Thomas E. Kieren. Geoboard geometry for preschool children. *A.T.* 17:123–27; Feb. 1970.

Marshall, A. G. Pick: with holes. *M.Tchg.*, no. 50, pp. 67–68; Spring 1970.
    An extension of Pick's theorem; deals with areas of polygons on a grid when the polygons have "holes" in them.

Niven, Ivan, and H. S. Zuckerman. Lattice points covered by plane figures. *A.M.M.* 74:354; 1967.

———. Lattice points and polygonal areas. *A.M.M.* 74:1195–200; Dec. 1967.
    A rigorous, technical analysis.

Odds, Frank C. Spirolaterals. *M.T.* 66:121–24; Feb. 1973.
    Geometric patterns generated according to specific rules.

Page, David. *Maneuvers on Lattices.* Newton, Mass.: Educational Development Corp., 1965.

Saunders, K. Starting points on a square lattice. *M.Tchg.*, no. 59, pp. 50–51; Summer 1972.

Swadener, Marc. "Activity board"—the board of many uses. *A.T.* 19:141–44; Feb. 1972.
    A modified geoboard.

Viggiano, Joseph. Dots and triangles. *J.R.M.* 4:157–63; July 1971.

Walter, Marion, and Stephen Brown. What if not? *M.Tchg.*, no. 46, pp. 38–45; Spring 1969.
    Geoboards and lattice points.

3.8   Optical Illusions

Attneave, Fred. Multistability in perception. *Sci.Am.* 225:62–71; Dec. 1971.
    Excellent article on optical illusions.

Deregowski, Jan B. Pictorial perception and culture. *Sci.Am.* 227:82–88; Nov. 1972.
    Interesting sidelights on perspective and optical illusions.

Gardner, Martin. Optical illusions, from figures that are undecideable to hot dogs that float. *Sci.Am.* 222:124–27; May 1970.

Gibson, C. E. *Scientific Experiments and Amusements.* London: Seeley, Service & Co., 1931.
    Optical illusions, pp. 29–50.

Schaap's Bookrack [and] the Pavillion of Thomas Nix. *Pythagoras* (English ed.), vol. 2, no. 12, pp. 111–17; 1969–70.
    Intriguing "impossible figures" and optical illusions.

Stong, C. L., ed. Generating visual illusions with two kinds of apparatus. *Sci.Am.* 224:110–14; Mar. 1971.

Chapter 4

Topological Recreations

4.1 Braids; Knots; Flexagons; Möbius Bands; String Figures

Ball, W. W. Rouse. *Fun with String Figures.* Reprint. New York: Dover Publications, 1970. 80 pp. (Paper)
Reprint of a work formerly entitled *An Introduction to String Figures;* Bibliography and glossary.
Elder, Barbara. Paths and knots as geometric groups. *Pentagon* 28:3–15; Fall 1968.
Engel, Douglas. How a flexible tetrahedral ring became a SPHINXX. *Pentagon* 31:83–90; Spring 1972.
Gardner, Martin. Knotty problems with a two-hole torus. *Sci.Am.* 227:102–6; Dec. 1972.
Helfman, Harry. *Fun with Your Fingers; Working with Sticks, Paper and Strings.* New York: William Morrow & Co., 1968.
For grades 3–6.
———. *Tricks with Your Fingers.* New York: William Morrow & Co., 1967.
Grades 4–6.
Helfman, Harry, and Elizabeth Helfman. *Strings on Your Fingers, How to Make String Figures.* New York: William Morrow & Co., 1965.
For children, ages 8–12.
Hennemann, Willard. Tying things together with braids. *A.T.* 17:640–44; Dec. 1970.
Introducing the structure of a number system by means of braid terminology.
Long, C. A. Zip the strip. *M.T.* 64:41; Jan. 1971.
Brief note on the Möbius strip.
Mathematics in a Knot. *Pythagoras* (English ed.), vol. 1, no. 3, pp. 49–53; 1968.
Matthews, Charles J. Some novel Möbius strips. *M.T.* 65:123–26; Feb. 1972.
Shaw, George Russell. *Knots, Useful and Ornamental.* New York: Macmillan Co., 1972. (Paper)
Singer, Robert, and Leonard Angel. Research in combinatorial topology concerning the relation of self-penetrations to Moebius twists. *M.S.J.*, vol. 10, no. 2, pp. 4–5; Jan. 1963.

4.2 Dissection Problems

Bankoff, Leon, and Donald Brown. A square dissection into 3 pieces in ratio 3:4:5. [Problem 232.] *M.Mag.* 29:110–12; Nov. 1955.
Bricard, R. Sur une question de géométrie relative aux polyèdres. *Nouvelles Annales de Mathématiques* 55:331–34; 1896.

Coffman, R. T., H. Demir, and Maxey Brooke. Dissecting a square into six pieces which form surface of a cube. [Problem 383.] *M.Mag.* 33:228–30; Mar. 1960.

Félix, Lucienne. From Venn diagrams to Peano curves. *M.Tchg.*, no. 50, pp. 13–21; Spring 1970.
Regions, boundaries, dissections, bijectivity, continuity, and so on; analytical as well as geometrical approaches.

Frederickson, Greg N. Assemblies of twelve-pointed stars. *J.R.M.* 5:128–32; Apr. 1972.

———. Polygon assemblies. *J.R.M.* 5:255–60; Oct. 1972.

———. Several star dissections. *J.R.M.* 5:22–26; Jan. 1972.

Freese, R. W., Ann K. Miller, and Zalman Usiskin. Can every triangle be divided into n triangles similar to it? *A.M.M.* 77:867–69; Oct. 1970.

Goldberg, Michael. Tetrahedra equivalent to cubes by dissection. *Elemente der Mathematik* 13:107–8; 1958.

———. Two more tetrahedra equivalent to cubes by dissection. *Elemente der Mathematik* 24:130–32; 1969. Also, correction, 25:48; 1970.
Bibliography.

Hill, M. J. M. Determination of the volume of certain species of tetrahedrons. *Proceedings of the London Mathematical Society* 27:39–52; 1896.

Hollands, R. D. Developing a problem. *M.Tchg.*, no. 50, pp. 64–66; Spring 1970.
Filling a rectangle with similar rectangles.

Kay, D. C. Uniquely Fibonacci. [Problem E2272.] *A.M.M.* 78:1143; Dec. 1971.
Dissecting a square to form a rectangle with a net gain or loss of one square unit.

Kordemsky, Boris. *The Moscow Puzzles.* New York: Charles Scribner's Sons, 1972.
Chapter 4: "Measure Seven Times Before You Cut," pp. 59–68. (Dissections)

Lenhard, H. C. Über fünf neue Tetraeder, die einem Würfel aquivalent sind. *Elemente der Mathematik* 17:108–9; 1962.

Lindgren, Harry. Assembling two polygons into one. *J.R.M.* 2:178–80; July 1969.

———. A dissection problem by Sam Lloyd. *J.R.M.* 3:54–55; Jan. 1970.

———. H^2 problem. *R.M.M.*, no. 6, p. 38; Dec. 1961.

———. *Recreational Problems in Geometric Dissections and How to Solve Them.* New York: Dover Publications, 1971. 184 pp. (Paper)
Revised and enlarged edition of the first (1964) edition entitled *Geometric Dissections.*

Marshall, A. G. Certain dissections of polygons. *M.Tchg.*, no. 49, p. 24; Winter 1969.

Mathematics Staff, University of Chicago. On the transformation of any rectangle into a square. *M.S.J.*, vol. 4, no. 1, pp. 1–2; Mar. 1957.

———. On transforming a hexagon into a square. *M.S.J.*, vol. 4, no. 2, pp. 1–2; May 1957.

———. On transforming rectangles into squares. *M.S.J.*, vol. 3, no. 4, pp. 1–2; Dec. 1956.

———. A problem on the cutting of squares. *M.S.J.*, vol. 3, no. 2, pp. 1–2, Apr. 1956; vol. 3, no. 3, pp. 1–2, Oct. 1956.

Meyer, Andrea L. The movable figures. *Pentagon* 27:86–95; Spring 1968.

Sydler, J. P. Conditions nécessaires et suffisantes pour l'équivalence des polyèdres de l'espace euclidien à trois dimensions. *Commentari Mathematici Helvetici* 40:43–80; 1965.
———. Sur les tétraèdres équivalents à un cube. *Elemente der Mathematik* 11:78–81; 1956.
Trigg, Charles W. Bisection of Yin and Yang. *M.Mag.* 34:107–8; Nov. 1960.
———. Dissection of surface of dodecahedron. [Problem 635.] *M.Mag.* 42:50–51; Jan. 1969.
Trigg, Charles W., and Kenneth Kramer. Cubes from pyramids. [Problem E1640.] *A.M.M.* 71:800; Sept. 1964.
Usiskin, Zalman, and Stanley Wayment. Partitioning a triangle into 5 triangles similar to it. *M.Mag.* 45:37–42; Jan. 1972.
Wakui, Koh. Making a square. *J.R.M.* 3:44; Jan. 1970. Also, 4:75; Jan. 1971.

4.3 Graphs; Networks

Anderson, Sabra S. *Graph Theory and Finite Combinatorics*. Chicago: Markham Publishing Co., 1970. 180 pp.
    Advanced treatment; extensive bibliography.
Bellman, Richard, Kenneth L. Cooke, and Jo Ann Lockett. *Algorithms, Graphs and Computers*. New York: Academic Press, 1970.
Biggs, Norman. An edge-colouring problem. *A.M.M.* 79:1018–20; Nov. 1972.
Bostwick, C. W. [Problem E1321.] *A.M.M.* 65:446; 1958. Also, 66:141–42; 1959.
Branfield, John R. Teaching matrices via networks. *M.T.* 65:561–66; Oct. 1972.
The Bridges of Königsberg Revisited. *M.S.J.*, vol. 20, no. 3, p. 4; Feb. 1973.
Bush, Mary T. Seeking little Eulers. *A.T.* 19:105–7; Feb. 1972.
    An activity approach to simple networks.
Cartwright, D., and F. Harary. The number of lines in a digraph of each connectedness category. *SIAM Review* 3:309–14; 1961.
Cohoon, D. K. The no-touch puzzle and some generalizations. *M.Mag.* 45:261–65; Nov. 1972.
Deventer, J. V. *The Many Facets of Graph Theory*. Lecture Notes in Mathematics, vol. 110. New York: Springer-Verlag, n.d.
Dirac, G. A. Circuits in critical graphs. *Monatsh. Math.* 59:178–87; 1955.
———. Some theorems on abstract graphs. *Proceedings of the London Mathematical Society*, ser. 3, vol. 2, pp. 69–81; 1952.
Elder, Barbara. Paths and knots as geometric groups. *Pentagon* 28:3–15; Fall 1968.
Euler, Leonhard. The Koenigsberg bridges. *Sci.Am.* 189:66–70; July 1953.
    Reprint of the original classical memoir of Euler.
Frank, Howard, and Ivan Frisch. Network analysis. *Sci.Am.* 223:94–103; July 1970.
    Theory of networks applied to industrial flow problems.
Gardner, Martin. The graceful graphs of Solomon Golomb, or how to number a graph parsimoniously. *Sci.Am.* 226:108–12; Mar. 1972. Also, 226:104; Apr. 1972.

42   RECREATIONAL MATHEMATICS

———. "Graph Theory." In *Martin Gardner's Sixth Book of Mathematical Games from Scientific American,* pp. 91–103; San Francisco: W. H. Freeman & Co., 1971.

Goodman, A. W. On sets of acquaintances and strangers at any party. *A.M.M.* 66:778–83; 1959.

Graham, R. L. Closed Hamiltonian circuits. *J.R.M.* 5:68–69; Jan. 1972.

Hadwiger, H. Über eine Klassifikation der Streckenkomplexe. *Viertelischer. Naturforsch. Gesell. Zurich* 88:133–42; 1943.

———. Ungelöste Probleme. *Elemente der Mathematik* 12:61–62; 1957. Also, 13:127–28; 1958.

Halin, R. Bemerkungen über ebene Graphen. *Mathematische Annalen* 153:38–46; 1964.

Harary, Frank. A complementary problem on non-planar graphs. *M.Mag.* 35:301–4; 1962.

———. *Graph Theory.* Reading Pa.: Addison-Wesley Publishing Co., 1969.

———. The two-triangle case of the acquaintance graph. *M.Mag.* 45:130–35; May 1972.

Harary, Frank, and Bennet Manvel. Trees. *Scrip.M.* 28:327–33; Feb. 1970.

Harary, Frank, R. Z. Norman, and D. Cartwright. *Structural Models: An Introduction to the Theory of Directed Graphs.* New York: John Wiley & Sons, 1965.

Harary, Frank, and W. T. Tutte. A dual form of Kuratowski's theorem. *Canadian Mathematics Bulletin* 8:17–20, 373; 1965.

Kaldenberg, Judy. Communication networks using matrices. *Pentagon* 27:71–81; Spring 1968.

Kelly, J. B., and L. M. Kelly. Paths and circuits in critical graphs. *American Journal of Mathematics* 76:786–92; 1954.

Kennedy, Joe. The traveling salesman problem. *M.T.* 65: 601; Nov. 1972.

Klee, Victor. What is the maximum length of a d-dimensional snake? *A.M.M.* 77:63–65; Jan. 1970.
    Bibliography.

König, D. *Theorie der endlichen und unendlichen Graphen.* Leipzig: Teubner, 1936.

Laible, Jon M. Try graph theory for a change. *M.T.* 63:557–62; Nov. 1970.

Lamb, David. The minimum catastrophe problem. *M.S.J.,* vol. 20, no. 2, pp. 1–3; Dec. 1972.
    The problem of the three wells, etc.

Lorden, G. Blue-empty chromatic graphs. *A.M.M.* 69:114–20; 1962.

Marathe, C. R. On the dual of a trivalent map. *A.M.M.* 68:448–55; 1961.

McClellan, John. The general's interrupted tour. *J.R.M.* 3:27–30; Jan. 1970.

Menon, V. The isomorphism between graphs and their adjoint graphs. *Canadian Mathematics Bulletin* 8:7–15; 1965.

———. On repeated interchange graphs. *A.M.M.* 13:986–89; 1966.

Meyer, Walter. Garbage collection, Sunday strolls, and soldering problems. *M.T.* 65:307–9; Apr. 1972.
    Soap-film configurations and Euler circuits.

Mycielski, Jan, and Robert Singleton. Minimum number of vertices in a four-chromatic graph. [Problem 5786.] *A.M.M.* 79:525–27; May 1972.

Nordhaus, E., and J. Gaddum. On complementary graphs. *A.M.M.* 63:175–77; 1956.

Papy, Frédérique, and Georges Papy. *Graph Games*. New York: Thomas Y. Crowell Co., 1971. 33 pp.
For young readers.

Parsons, T. D. On planar graphs. *A.M.M.* 78:176–78; Feb. 1971.
Bibliography.

Picard, Anthony J. Some observations on graphing in modular systems. *M.T.* 64:459–66; May 1971.
Relation of graphing to number theory, modular arithmetic, and the geometry of certain higher-order curves.

Posa, L. A theorem concerning Hamiltonian lines. *Publ. Math. Inst. Hungar. Acad. Sci.* 7:225–26; 1962.

Ranucci, Ernest R. Schlegel diagrams. *J.R.M.* 4:106–13; Apr. 1971.

Read, Ronald C., ed. *Graph Theory and Computing*. New York: Academic Press, 1972.

Rowe, R. Robinson. Random hops on polyhedral edges and other networks. *J.R.M.* 4:124–34; Apr. 1971.

Sauve, L. On chromatic graphs. *A.M.M.* 68:107–11; 1961.

Schwartz, B. L. Defining the interchange of a loop. *M.Mag.* 43:141–43; May 1970.

———. On interchange graphs. *Pacific Journal of Mathematics* 27:393–96; 1968.

Schwenk, A. J. Acquaintance graph party problem. *A.M.M.* 79:1113–17; Dec. 1972.

Trigg, Charles W. Concerning unicursal routes along the edges of a cube. [Problem 3455.] *S.S.M.* 73:165–66; Feb. 1973.

Tutte, W. T. *The Connectivity of Graphs*. Toronto: Toronto University Press, 1967.

———. The factors of graphs. *Canadian Journal of Mathematics* 4:314; 1952.

———. A non-Hamiltonian graph. *Canadian Mathematics Bulletin* 3:1–5; 1960.

———. *Proof Techniques in Graph Theory*. New York: Academic Press, 1969.

Whitney, H. Congruent graphs and the connectivity of graphs. *American Journal of Mathematics* 54:150–68; 1932.

———. Isomorphic graphs. *American Journal of Mathematics* 55:245–54; 1933.

———. Planar graphs. *Fund. Math.* 21:73–84; 1933.

———. A theorem on graphs. *Annals of Mathematics* 32:378–90; 1931.

Wilf, H. S. The eigenvalues of a graph and its chromatic number. *Journal of the London Mathematical Society* 42:330–32; 1967.

Winn, C. E. On the minimum number of polygons in an irreducible map. *American Journal of Mathematics* 62:406–16; 1940.

Woodrow, D. Linear graphs. *M.Tchg.*, no. 52, pp. 14–19; Autumn 1970.

4.4 Map Coloring

Aarts, J. M., and J. A. de Groot. A case of coloration in the four color problem. *Nieuw. Arch. Wisk.* 11:10–18; 1963.

Bernhart, A. Six-rings in minimal five-color maps. *American Journal of Mathematics* 69:391–412; 1947.

———. Another reducible edge configuration. *American Journal of Mathematics* 70:144–46; 1948.

Birkhoff, G. D. A determinant formula for the number of ways of colouring a map. *Annals of Mathematics* 14:42–46; 1912.

———. On the number of ways of coloring a map. *Proceedings of the Edinburgh Mathematical Society* 2:83–91; 1930.

———. On the polynomial expressions for the number of ways of coloring a map. *Ann. Scuola Norm. Sup. Pisa* 2:85–103; 1934.

———. The reducibility of maps. *American Journal of Mathematics* 35:115–28; 1913.

Birkhoff, G. D., and D. Lewis. Chromatic polynomials. *Transactions of the American Mathematical Society* 60:355–451; 1946.

Carlitz, L. The number of colored graphs. *Canadian Journal of Mathematics* 15:304–12; 1963.

Cartwright, D., and F. Harary. On the coloring of signed graphs. *Elemente der Mathematik* 23:85–89; 1968.

Chartrand, G., and D. Geller. Uniquely colorable planar graphs. *Journal of Combinatorial Theory* 6:271–78; 1969.

Choinacki, C. A. A contribution to the four color problem. *American Journal of Mathematics* 64:36–54; 1942.

Chuard, J. Les réseaux cubiques et le problème des quatre couleurs. *Mém. Soc. Vaudoise Sci. Nat.*, no. 25, 4:41–101; 1932.

Cohen, Daniel I. A., et al. Planar maps of convex countries. [Problem E1726.] *A.M.M.* 72:904; Oct. 1965.

Descartes, B. [Problem 4526.] *A.M.M.* 61:352; 1954.

Descartes, B., and R. Descartes. La coloration des cartes. *Eureka* 31:29–31; 1968.

Dirac, G. A. Map colour theorems related to the Heawood colour formula. *Journal of the London Mathematical Society* 31:460–71; 1956.

———. Note on the colouring of graphs. *Mathematische Zeitschrift.* 54:347–53; 1951.

———. On the structure of 5- and 6-chromatic abstract graphs. *J. für Math.* 214:43–52; 1964.

———. A property of 4-chromatic graphs and some remarks on critical graphs. *Journal of the London Mathematical Society* 27:85–92; 1952.

———. The structure of *k*-chromatic graphs. *Fund. Math.* 40:42–55; 1953.

———. A theorem of R. L. Brooks and a conjecture of H. Hadwiger. *Proceedings of the London Mathematical Society* 7:161–95; 1957.

———. Theorems related to the four colour conjecture. *Journal of the London Mathematical Society* 29:143–49; 1954.

———. Trennende Knotenpunktmengen und Reduzibilität abstrakter Graphen mit Anwendung auf das Vierfarbenproblem. *J. für Math.* 204:116–31; 1960.

Dirac, G. A., and P. J. Heawood. Map-colour theorems. *Journal of the London Mathematical Society* 38:263–77; 1963.

Erdos, P., and A. Hajnal. On chromatic numbers of graphs and set-systems. *Acta Math. Acad. Sci. Hungar.* 171:61–99; 1966.

Errera, A. *Du coloriage des cartes.* Ixelles, Belgium, 1921.

———. Une contribution au problème des quatres couleurs. *Bulletin de la Société Mathématique de France* 53:42; 1925.

Ershov, A. P., and G. I. Kozhukhin. Estimates of the chromatic number of connected graphs. *Dokl. Akad. Nauk.* 142:270–73; 1962. Also, *Trans.Soviet Math.* 3:50–53; 1962.

Finck, H. J., and H. Sachs. Über eine von H. S. Wilf angegebene Schranke für die chromatische Zahl endlicher Graphen. *Mathematische Nachrichten* 39:373–86; 1969.

Franklin, P. The four color problem. *American Journal of Mathematics* 44:225–36; 1922.

———. The four color problem. *Scrip.M.* 6:149–56, 197–210; 1939.

———. Note on the four color problem. *Journal of Mathematics and Physics* 16:172–84; 1938.

Grünbaum, B. Grötzch's theorem on 3-colorings. *Michigan Mathematics Journal* 10:303–10; 1963.

Halin, R. On a theorem of Wagner related to the four-color problem, homomorphisms. (German.) *Mathematische Annulen* 153:47–62; 1964.

Harary, F., S. T. Hedetniemi, and R. W. Robinson. Uniquely colorable graphs. *Journal of Combinatorial Theory*, vol. 6, Apr. 1969.

Heawood, P. J. Failures in congruences connected with the four-colour map theorem. *Proceedings of the London Mathematical Society* 40:189–202; 1936.

———. Map-color theorem. *Proceedings of the London Mathematical Society*, ser. 2, vol. 51, pp. 161–75; 1950. Also, *Mathematical Reviews* 11:43; 1950.

———. Map-colour theorems. *Quarterly Journal of Mathematics, Oxford*, series 24, pp. 332–38; 1890.

———. Note on a correction in a paper on map-congruences. *Journal of the London Mathematical Society* 18:160–67; 1943. Also, 19:18–22; 1944.

———. On extended congruences connected with the four-colour map theorem. *Proceedings of the London Mathematical Society* 33:252–86; 1932.

———. On the four-colour map theorem. *Quarterly Journal of Mathematics* 29:270–85; 1898.

Kempe, A. B. On the geographical problem of the four colors. *American Journal of Mathematics* 2:193–200; 1879.

Map Conjecture in Three Dimensions. *J.R.M.* 5:65; Jan. 1972.

Minty, G. J. A theorem on *n*-coloring the points of a linear graph. *A.M.M.* 69:623–24; 1962.

Ore, Oystein, and G. J. Stemple. Numerical calculations on the four-color problem. *Journal of Combinatorial Theory* 8:65–78; 1970.

Planar Maps of Convex Countries. [Problem E1726.] *A.M.M.* 72:904; Oct. 1965. Disproves that every planar map of convex countries can be colored with three colors.

Read, R. C. The number of *k*-coloured graphs. *Canadian Journal of Mathematics* 12:410–14; 1960.

Reynolds, C. N. On the problem of coloring maps in four colors. *Annals of Mathematics*, ser. 2, vol. 28, pp. 1–15, 477–92; 1926–27.

Saaty, Thomas L. Thirteen colorful variations on Guthri four-color conjecture. *A.M.M.* 79:2–43; Jan. 1972. Comprehensive survey; extensive bibliography of some 140 references.

Thomas, Joseph Miller. *The Four-Color Theorem*. Rev. ed. The Author, 7151 Crittenden St., Philadelphia, Pa. 19119; 1972. 9 pp. Bibliography.

Tutte, W. T. On the algebraic theory of graph colorings. *Journal of Combinatorial Theory*, vol. 1; June 1966.

———. On the enumeration of four-colored maps. *SIAM Journal of Applied Mathematics*, pp. 454–60; Mar. 1969.

Whitney, H. The coloring of graphs. *Annals of Mathematics* 33:688–718; 1932.

———. A numerical equivalent of the four-color map problem. *Montash. Math. und Physic.*, pp. 207–13; 1937.

Winn, C. E. A case of coloration in the four-color problem. *American Journal of Mathematics* 59:515–28; 1937.

———. On certain reductions in the four-color problem. *Journal of Mathematics and Physics* 16:159–71; 1938.

Wright, E. Counting colored graphs. *Canadian Journal of Mathematics* 13:683–93; 1961.

Youngs, J. W. T. "The Heawood Map-colouring Conjecture." In *Graph Theory and Theoretical Physics*, edited by F. Harary, pp. 313–54. London: Academic Press, 1967.

4.5   Mazes and Labyrinths

Culliney, Jay. Conjectures concerning the structure of mazes. *M.S.J.*, vol. 12, no. 4, pp. 4–6; May 1965.

Davidson, B. A maze problem. *M.Tchg.*, no. 50, pp. 72–75; Spring 1970.
A maze based on a grid of squares; programming a digital computer to find a route through such a maze.

Fraenkel, A. S. Economic traversal of labyrinths. *M.Mag.* 43:125–30; May 1970. Correction, 44:12; Jan. 1971.

Hartwick, Harry. *The Amazing Maze.* New York: E. P. Dutton & Co., 1969. 39 pp.
For young readers, ages 8–12.

Massmann, H. F. *Wunderpreise und Irrgarten.* Leipzig: Basse, 1844.
Mathematics of mazes.

Matthews, W. H. *Mazes and Labyrinths: Their History and Development.* New York: Dover Publications, 1970. 254 pp. (Paper)
Reprint of the London 1922 edition. An authoritative work, historical rather than mathematical emphasis, very readable; bibliography.

Tarry, G. Le problème des labyrinthes. *Nouvelles Annales de Mathématique*, ser. 3, vol. 14, pp. 187–90; 1895.

4.6   Paper Folding; Origami

Barr, Stephen, and C. L. Baker. Cube formation. *R.M.M.*, no. 9, p. 47; June 1962.

Brissenden, T. H. A paper-folding game about bicimals. *M.Tchg.*, no. 61, p. 42; Dec. 1972.

Dickoff, Steven S. Paper folding and cutting a set of tangram pieces. *A.T.* 18:250–52; Apr. 1971.

Engel, Douglas. How a flexible tetrahedral ring became a SPHINXX. *Pentagon* 31:83–90; Spring 1972.

Fell's Guide to Papercraft, Tricks, Games and Puzzles, by Walter B. Gibson. New York: Frederick Fells, 1963. 125 pp.

Gardner, Martin. The combinatorial richness of folding a piece of paper. *Sci.Am.* 224:110–14; May 1971.

——. Mathematical games: the plaiting of Plato's polyhedrons and the asymmetrical Yin-Yang-Lee. *Sci.Am.* 225:204–12; Sept. 1971.

——. On cutting and folding a 3-inch square to cover the largest possible cube. *Sci.Am.* 218:124–26; Mar. 1968.

Gibson, Walter B. *Fell's Guide to Papercraft, Tricks, Games and Puzzles.* New York: Frederick Fells, 1963. 125 pp.

Grant, Nicholas, and Alexander Tobin. Let them fold. *A.T.* 19:420–25; Oct. 1972.

Harbin, Robert. *New Adventures in Origami.* New York: Funk & Wagnalls, 1972. (Paper)

Lulli, Henry. Editorial feedback. *A.T.* 16:579–80; Nov. 1969.
    Folding paper cubes.

Lunnon, W. F. Mult-dimensional map-folding. *Computer Journal* [British Computer Society, London], vol. 14, no. 1, pp. 75–80; Feb. 1971.

Madachy, Joseph S. Bisection by folding. *J.R.M.* 3:231–32; Oct. 1970.

McClain, Ernest G. Pythagorean paper folding: a study in tuning and temperament. *M.T.* 63:233–37; Mar. 1970.

Pederson, Jean J. Asymptotic Euclidean-type constructions without Euclidean tools. *Fib.Q.* 9:199–216; Apr. 1971.

——. Some whimsical geometry. *M.T.* 65:513–21; Oct. 1972.
    Methods of approximating certain regular polygons by folding paper strips.

Phillips, Jo. *Right Angles: Paper-Folding Geometry.* New York: Thomas Y. Crowell Co., 1972.
    For beginners; grades K–3.

Randlett, Samuel. *The Best of Origami.* New York: E. P. Dutton & Co., 1963.

Robinson, Raphael, and Charles W. Trigg. Folding a rectangle into six congruent triangles. [Problem 139.] *A.M.M.* 42:451; Aug. 1935.

Rowe, R. Robinson. Carroll's paper-folding pillow-problem. *J.R.M.* 4:192–98; July 1971.

Scopes, P. G. Paper folding, the square root of two, and metric paper. *M.Tchg.*, no. 60, pp. 30–31; Sept. 1972.

Shreeve, Richard I. Plaited cubes. *M.Tchg.*, no. 61, p. 45; Dec. 1972.

Trigg, Charles W. A collapsible model of a tetrahedron. *M.S.J.*, no. 2, p. 1; Feb. 1955.

——. Collapsible models of the regular octahedron. *M.T.* 65:530–33; Oct. 1972.

——. Cutting an inscriptable octagon into two pieces which fold into a cube. [Problem 3063.] *S.S.M.* 67:105–6; Jan. 1967.

——. The eleven nets of a cube. [Problem 3426.] *S.S.M.* 72:574–75; June 1972.

——. Folding a rectangular card. [Problem 3181.] *S.S.M.* 69:176–77; Feb. 1969.

——. Folding tetrahedra. *A.M.M.* 58:39–40; Jan. 1951.

——. Geometry of paper folding. II. Tetrahedral models. *S.S.M.* 54:683–89; Dec. 1954.

Trigg, Charles W., and Alan Wayne. Folding a rectangle. [Problem 2916.] *S.S.M.* 64:241; Mar. 1964.

Vanderpool, Donald L. Regular polygons from knotted strips. *R.M.M.*, no. 10, pp. 3–4; Aug. 1962.

Williams, Ned, and Robert Harbin. *Origami: The Art of Paperfolding.* New York: Funk & Wagnalls, 1969. 186 pp.

Witt, Sarah M. A snip of the scissors. *A.T.* 18:496–99; Nov. 1971.

4.7   Polyhedrons; Platonic and Archimedean Solids

Alexandrov, A. D. *Konvexe Polyeder.* Berlin: Akademie Verlag, 1958.

Bobker, Martin. Colouring polyhedra. *M.Tchg.*, no. 59, pp. 15–16; Summer 1972.

Born, Richard, and Charles W. Trigg. Christmas tree ornaments from nine colored cubes. [Problem 3087.] *S.S.M.* 67:457–58; May 1967.

Bradford, Owen. Polyhedra of any dimension. *S.S.M.* 60:589–92; Nov. 1960.

Cussons, C. W., and H. S. M. Coxeter. Mathematical models. *Encyclopedia Britannica* 14:1087–91; 1966.

Demir, Huseyin, and Charles W. Trigg. Resistance in a cube. [Problem 407.] *M.Mag.* 34:115–16; Nov. 1960.

Engel, Douglas A. How a flexible tetrahedral ring becomes a SPHINXX. *Pentagon* 31:83–90; Spring 1972.

———. Polyhedron mousetraps. *J.R.M.* 4:55–57; Jan. 1971.

Federico, P. J. The melancholy octahedron. *M.Mag.* 45:30–36; Jan. 1972. Discussion of the polyhedron on Dürer's famous engraving *Melencolia;* bibliography.

Field, Richard, Jr. Fleas on Platonic solids. *J.R.M.* 2:160–61; July 1969. Also, 4:142–43; Apr. 1971.

For the Handyman. *Pythagoras* (English ed.), vol. 1, no. 1, pp. 9–12; 1968. Patterns for making regular and semiregular solids.

Gardner, Martin. A numeranalysis by Dr. Matrix of the lunar flight of Apollo II. *Sci.Am.* 221:126–30; Oct. 1969.

———. The plaiting of Plato's polyhedrons and the asymmetrical Yin-Yang-Lee. *Sci.Am.* 225:204–12; Sept. 1971.

———. "Polyiamonds." In *Martin Gardner's Sixth Book of Mathematical Games from Scientific American,* pp. 173–82. San Francisco: W. H. Freeman & Co., 1971.

———. "Tetrahedrons." In *Martin Gardner's Sixth Book of Mathematical Games from Scientific American,* pp. 183–94. San Francisco: W. H. Freeman & Co., 1971.

Goldberg, Michael. The space-filling pentahedra. *Journal of Combinatorial Theory* 13:437–43; Nov. 1972.

Hahn, H. S., and Joseph Konhauser. Solid with surface at fixed distance from surface of tetrahedron. [Problem 709.] *M.Mag.* 42:159–60; May 1969.

Hall, H. T., and Charles W. Trigg. Tetrahedron pushed through a soda straw. [Problem 598.] *M.Mag.* 38:132–33; Mar. 1966.

Holden, Alan. *Shapes, Space and Symmetry.* New York: Columbia University Press, 1971. 200 pp. A sophisticated exposition of relations between the five Platonic solids and the four Kepler-Poinsot solids; excellent photography.

Johnson, Norman W. Convex polyhedra with regular faces. *Canadian Journal of Mathematics* 18:169–200; 1966. Bibliography.

Levitt, Norman. The group of the tetrahedron. *Mathematics Bulletin* [Bronx High School of Science], p. 4 ff; 1959.

Laycock, Mary. *Straw Polyhedra Kit.* Creative Publications, P.O. Box 328, Palo Alto, Calif. 94302; 1972.
An activity kit, together with descriptive booklet for constructing the five regular polyhedron models.

Lulli, Henry. Polyhedra construction. *A.T.* 19:127–30; Feb. 1972.

Lyusternik, L. A. *Convex Figures and Polyhedra.* (Translated from the Russian.) Boston: D. C. Heath & Co., 1966. (Paper)

McClellan, John. The maxigon. *J.R.M.* 3:58–60; Jan. 1970.

———. Polyhedra enumeration. *J.R.M.* 2:2; Jan. 1969.

———. Polyhedra proliferation. *J.R.M.* 1:152; July 1968. Also, *J.R.M.* 3:46; Jan. 1970.

———. Problem of the hidden faces. [Problem 31.] *J.R.M.* 1:54; July 1968. Also, *J.R.M.* 4:175–78; July 1971.

McPhee, G. J., and W. Skelding. Colouring polyhedra. *M.Tchg.*, no. 59, pp. 15–16; Summer 1972.

Mold, Josephine. *Cubes.* London: Cambridge University Press, 1969. 32 pp.

———. *Solid Models.* London: Cambridge University Press, 1969. 32 pp.

Pfeiffer, George A. Geometric solids. *Encyclopedia Britannica* 20:941–45; 1966.

Read, Cecil B., and Charles W. Trigg. On Euler's formula for simple closed polyhedra. [Problem 3294.] *S.S.M.* 71:270; Mar. 1971.

Ryan, Sister M. Kara. Probability and the Platonic solids. *M.T.* 64:621–24; Nov. 1971.

Schloff, Charles E. Rolling tetrahedrons. *A.T.* 19:657–59; Dec. 1972.

Silverman, David L. The flea on the pyramid. *J.R.M.* 2:160; July 1969. Also, 4:142; Apr. 1971.

Steinitz, E., and H. Rademacher. *Vorlesungen über die Theorie der Polyeder.* Berlin: Springer, 1934.

Stengel, Carol Elizabeth. A look at regular and semiregular polyhedra. *M.T.* 65:713–19; Dec. 1972.

Stoker, J. J. Uniqueness theorems for polyhedra. *Proceedings of the National Academy of Science, U.S.A.* 55:1398–404; 1966.

Stover, Donald W. *Mosaics.* Boston: Houghton Mifflin Co., 1966. 34 pp. (Paper) Polygons, polyhedra, mosaics; bibliography.

Trigg, Charles W. A collapsible model of a tetrahedron. *M.S.J.*, no. 2, p. 1; Feb. 1955.

———. Collapsible models of isosceles tetrahedrons. *M.T.* 66:109–12; Feb. 1973.

———. Collapsible models of the regular octahedron. *M.T.* 65:530–33; Oct. 1972.

———. Colored faces of regular polyhedrons. [Problem 2965.] *S.S.M.* 65:190; Feb. 1965.

———. Folding tetrahedra. *A.M.M.* 58:39–40; Jan. 1951.

———. Geometry of paper folding. II. Tetrahedral models. *S.S.M.* 54:683–89; Dec. 1954.

———. A model of a tetrahedron. *Mathematics Student* [India], vol. 31, pp. 15–16; Jan. 1963.

———. Passing a regular tetrahedron through a circular ring. [Problem 231.] *P.M.E.J.* 5:144–45; Fall 1970.

————. "Polyhedrons." In *Mathematical Quickies*. New York: McGraw-Hill Book Co., 1967. Problems 18, 42, 82, 113, 114, 140, 148, 177, 188, 209, 210, 220, 221, 240.

————. [Problem 3312.] *S.S.M.* 71:577–78; June 1971. If two congruent regular tetrahedrons are inscribed in a unit cube, what is their common volume and what portion of the cube is not included in the tetrahedrons?

————. [Problem 3426.] *S.S.M.* 72:574–75; June 1972. Folding a pattern of six connected squares into a cube in eleven different ways.

————. Properties of the cuboctahedron. [Problem 3304.] *S.S.M.* 71:459; May 1971.

————. Properties of the truncated cube. [Problem 2897.] *S.S.M.* 63:774–75; Dec. 1963.

————. Properties of the truncated icosahedron. [Problem 3038.] *S.S.M.* 66:595–96; June 1966.

————. Rolling a cube onto a plane. [Problem 244.] *P.M.E.J.* 5:247–48; Fall 1971.

————. The soda straw. *M.Mag.* 39:132; Mar. 1966.

————. Solid with surface at fixed distance from surface of a cube. [Problem 3394.] *S.S.M.* 72:94; Jan. 1972.

————. Tetrahedron from an envelope. *Los Angeles Mathematics Newsletter*, vol. 2, p. 1; Jan. 1955.

————. Tetrahedron rolled onto a plane. *J.R.M.* 3:82–87; Apr. 1970.

————. Tetrahedrons inscribed in a cube. [Problem 3312.] *S.S.M.* 71:577–78; June 1971.

Trigg, Charles W., and Leon Bankhoff. Ratio of volumes of equiedged regular tetrahedron and regular octahedron. [Problem 390.] *M.Mag.* 33:297; May 1960.

Trigg, Charles W., and Aaron Buchman. Planes trisecting space diagonal of a cube. [Problem 3197.] *S.S.M.* 69:469; May 1969.

Trigg, Charles W., and R. J. Cormier. Two hexahedra. [Problem E1531.] *A.M.M.* 70:442; Apr. 1963.

Trigg, Charles W., and Sidney Spital. Sections of an octahedron. [Problem 582.] *M.Mag.* 38:320; Nov. 1965.

Wardrop, R. F. A look at nets of cubes. *A.T.* 17:127–28; Feb. 1970.

Wenninger, Magnus J. *Polyhedron Models*. New York: Cambridge University Press, 1971. 207 pp.

————. Spherical tessellation and polyhedra. *Summation* [New York City, Association of Teachers of Mathematics], vol. 13, no. 2, pp. 19–24; Nov. 1967.

Zalgaller, V. A. *Convex Polyhedra with Regular Faces*. New York: Plenum Publishing Corp., Consultants Bureau, 1969.

4.8   Polytopes; Irregular Polyhedrons

Alexandrov, A. D. A theorem on convex polyhedra. (In Russian.) *Trudy Mat. Inst. Steklov., Sect. Math.* 4:87; 1933.

Beck, Anatole, Michael Bleicher, and Donald Crowe. *Excursions into Mathematics*. New York: Worth Publishers, 1969. 489 pp. Chapter 1: "Polyhedra."

Bolker, E. D. A class of convex bodies. *Transactions of the American Mathematical Society* 145:323–45; 1969.
Advanced technical discussion.
———. The zonoid problem. *A.M.M.* 78:529–31; May 1971.
Bibliography.
Chilton, Bruce L. Shadows of four-dimensional polytopes. *M.Mag.* 44:269–73; Nov. 1971.
Coxeter, H. S. M. *Twisted Honeycombs.* American Mathematical Society, Conference Board of the Mathematical Sciences, Regional Conference Series in Mathematics, no 4. Providence, R.I.: American Mathematical Society, 1970. 47 pp.
Gilbert, Edgar N. The ways to build a box. *M.T.* 64:689–95; Dec. 1971.
Grünbaum, B. *Convex Polytopes.* New York: John Wiley & Sons, Interscience Publishers, 1967.
Hahn, H. S., and Michael Goldberg. Some nonregular polyhedra. *A.M.M.* 76:1067–70; 1969.
Jennings, Donald E. An intuitive approach to pierced polygons. *M.T.* 63:311–12; Apr. 1970.
Karcher, Hermann. Remarks on polyhedra with given dihedral angles. *Communications on Pure and Applied Mathematics* 21:169–74; Mar. 1968.
Advanced discussion.
King, Bruce W. Some crinkled curves and prickly polyhedra. *M.Tchg.*, no. 57, pp. 43–45; Winter 1971.
McClellan, John. The maxigon. *J.R.M.* 3:58–60; Jan. 1970.
———. The question of allomorphs. *J.R.M.* 4:115–23; Apr. 1971.
McMullen, P. The maximum number of faces of a convex polytope. *Mathematika* 17:179–84; 1970.
Mann, J. E. "Discovering" special polyhedra. *M.Tchg.*, no. 49, pp. 48–49; Winter 1969.
Stewart, B. M. *Adventures among the Toroids.* Okemos, Mich.: The Author, 4494 Wausau Rd., Okemos, Mich. 48864, 1970. 206 pp. (Paper)
Expository and recreational material dealing with accordion polyhedra, knotted toroids, and so on.
Stoker, J. J. Geometrical problems concerning polyhedra in the large. *Communications on Pure and Applied Mathematics* 21:119–68; Mar. 1968.
Elaborate, advanced discussion; bibliography.

4.9   Polyominoes; Polyiamonds; Rep-tiles

Bouwkamp, C. J. Simultaneous 4 × 5 and 4 × 10 pentomino rectangles. *J.R.M.* 3:125; Apr. 1970.
Cooke, Charles J. Polyominoes. *M.Tchg.*, no. 48, pp. 34–35; Autumn 1969.
Gardner, Martin. The graceful graphs of Solomon Golomb, or how to number a graph parsimoniously. *Sci.Am.* 226:108–12; Mar. 1972. Also, 226:104; Apr. 1972.
Klarner, Donald A. Packing a rectangle with congruent *N*-ominoes. *Journal of Combinatorial Theory* 7:107–15; Sept. 1969.
———. Some results concerning polyominoes. *Fib.Q.* 3:9–20; Feb. 1965.
Bibliography.

Madachy, Joseph S. Pentominoes—some solved and unsolved problems. *J.R.M.* 2:181–88; July 1969.

Patton, Robert L. Notes on the computer solution of the Twenty Problem. *J.R.M.* 3:214–20; Oct. 1970.

Patton, Robert L., and Joseph S. Madachy. The Twenty Problem—a limited solution. *J.R.M.* 3:207–13; Oct. 1970.

Penney, Walter. The double cross. *J.R.M.* 4:73–74; Jan. 1971.

Philpott, Wade E. Domino and superdomino recreations: parts 1, 2 and 3. *J.R.M.* 4:2–18, 79–87, 229–43; Jan., Apr., Oct. 1971.
Bibliography.

———. Domino and superdomino recreations: part 4. *J.R.M.* 5:102–22; Apr. 1972.
Domino-tromino rectangle patterns and related topics; bibliography.

———. Domino and superdomino recreations: part 5. *J.R.M.* 5:177–96; July 1972.

Risueño, M. Los polióminos—II. *Ciencia Nueva,* no. 4, pp. 15–18; 1970.

Torbijn, Ir. P. J. Polyiamonds. *J.R.M.* 2:216–27; Oct. 1969.

Trigg, Charles W. A hexagonal configuration. *M.Mag.* 35:70; Mar. 1962.

———. On a problem of Dudeney's. *J.R.M.* 3:182–85; July 1970.
Analysis of the problem of the sixteen sheep in relation to polyominoes.

———. Two tromino tessellations. *M.Mag.* 35:176; May 1962.

4.10   Soma Cubes; Polycubes

Barclay, Tim. Pattern blocks. *M.Tchg.,* no. 49, pp. 51–53; Winter 1969.

Bouwkamp, C. J. *Catalogue of Solutions of the Rectangular 3 × 4 × 5 Solid Pentomino Problem.* Eindhoven, Netherlands: Technische Hogeschool Eindhoven, 1967. 310 pp.

———. A new solid pentomino problem. *J.R.M.* 4:179–86; July 1971.

———. Packing a rectangular box with the twelve solid pentominoes. *Journal of Combinatorial Theory,* vol. 7, no. 3, pp. 278–80; Nov. 1969.

Bouwkamp, C. J., and D. A. Klarner. Packing a box with *y*-pentacubes. *J.R.M.* 3:10–26; Jan. 1970.

Conway, J. H. A living Soma classic. *Soma Addict* [Newsletter], vol. 2, no. 2; 1972.
Presents Conway's SOMAP.

Dorie, Joseph E. Soma architecture takes new turns: angles and openings! *Soma Addict* [Newsletter], vol. 2, no. 2; 1972.

Fielker, David. *Cubes.* London: Cambridge University Press, 1970.
Brief booklet for young readers; suggestive ideas.

Gardner, Martin. Pleasurable problems with polycubes. *Sci.Am.* 227:176–82; Sept. 1972. Also, 227:112, 112B; Oct. 1972.

———. Soma cubes. *Sci.Am.* Sept. 1958, p. 102; Oct. 1958, p. 129; July 1969, p. 119; Sept. 1969, p. 246.

Hein, Piet. *Soma.* Parker Bros., 190 Bridge St., Salem, Mass. 01970; 1969. 56 pp.

Verbakel, J. M. M. The *F*-pentacube problem. *J.R.M.* 5:20–21; Jan. 1972.

Wagner, N. R. Constructions with pentacubes. *J.R.M.* 5:266–68; Oct. 1972.
Wilson, Marguerite. *Soma Puzzle Solutions.* Palo Alto, Calif.: Creative Publications, 1973.

4.11 Squared Rectangles; Squaring the Square

Hollands, R. D. Developing a problem. *M.Tchg.*, no. 50, pp. 64–66; Spring 1970.
   Discussion of squared squares, etc.
Trigg, Charles W. Five rectangles that form a square. *J.R.M.* 3:56–57; Jan. 1970.

4.12 Tangrams

Allen, Charles E. Mission—tangrams. [Activities.] *M.T.* 66:143–46; Feb. 1973.
Dickoff, Steven S. Paper folding and cutting a set of tangram pieces. *A.T.* 18:250–52; Apr. 1971.
Fletcher, David, and Joseph Ibbotson. *Geometry with a Tangram.* (Pamphlet.) Selective Educational Equipment, 3 Bridge St., Newton, Mass. 02195.
   Interesting applications of the tangram puzzle.
Jenkins, Lee, and Peggy McLean. *It's a Tangram World.* Mind/Matter Corp., P.O. Box 345, Danbury, Conn. 06810.
   Suitable for grades 3–8.
Keller, C. Modern education meets Chinese puzzle; result, tangrams! *Pennsylvania School Journal* 117:312–13; Jan. 1969.
Li, H. Y., and Sibley S. Morrill. *I Ching Games of Duke Tan of Chou and C. C. Tung.* Cadleon Press, 1971. 138 pp.
   Interesting treatment of tangrams.
Tangrams (K–8). Part of equipment to accompany "Attribute Games and Problems Materials." *Elementary Science Study Units.* Manchester, Mo.: McGraw-Hill Book Co., Webster Div., 1967.
   A 7-piece tangram set for use with about 70 different geometric arrangements; on cards.

4.13 Tessellations; Packing Problems

Ball, Derek G. A different order of reptiles. *M.Tchg.*, no. 60, 44–45; Sept. 1972.
Bleicher, M. N., and L. Fejes-Tóth. Two-dimensional honeycombs. *A.M.M.* 72:969–73; Nov. 1965.
   Discussion of cells analogous to those of the bee.
Boerdijk, A. H. Some remarks concerning close packing of equal spheres. *Philip's Research Reports* 7:303–13; 1952.
Boorman, Phil. Irregular hexagon tessellations. *M.Tchg.*, no. 55, pp. 23–24; Summer 1971.
Bouwkamp, C. J. Packing a rectangular box with the twelve solid pentominoes. *Journal of Combinatorial Theory*, vol. 7, no. 3, pp. 278–80; Nov. 1969.

Coxeter, H. S. M. The problem of packing a number of equal nonoverlapping circles on a sphere. *Transactions of the New York Academy of Sciences* 24:320–31; 1962.

Davies, H. L. "Packings of Spherical Triangles and Tetrahedra." In *Proceedings of the Colloquium on Convexity*, pp. 42–51. Copenhagen, 1965.

Dunn, James A. More about tessellating hexagons. *M.Tchg.*, no. 55, pp. 22–23; Summer 1971.

Fejes-Tóth, L. *Lagerungen in der Ebene, auf der Kegel und im Raum*. Berlin: Springer, 1953.

———. A problem concerning sphere-packings and sphere-coverings. *A.M.M.* 79:62–63; Jan. 1972.

———. Über eine Abschätzung des kurzesten Abstandes zweier Punkte eines auf einer Kugelflache liegenden Punktsystems. *Jaheresbericht Deut. Math. Verein* 53:66–68; 1943.

Fyfe, R. M. Is it maths? *M.Tchg.*, no. 56, pp. 36–37; Autumn 1971. Designs based on combinations of polygons.

Goldberg, Michael. Axially symmetric packing of equal circles on a sphere. *Annales Univ. Sci. Budapest., Sect. Math.* 10:37–48; 1967. Bibliography.

———. Axially symmetric packing of equal circles on a sphere: II. *Annales Univ. Sci. Budapest., Sect. Math.* 12:137–42; 1969. Bibliography.

———. An improved packing of 33 equal circles on a sphere. *Elemente der Mathematik* 22:110–12; 1967.

———. Maximizing the smallest triangle made by N points in a square. *M.Mag.* 45:135–44; May 1972.

———. On the densest packing of equal spheres in a cube. *M.Mag.* 44:199–208; Sept. 1971.

———. The packing of equal circles in a square. *M.Mag.* 43:24–30; Jan. 1970. Bibliography.

———. Packing of 18 equal circles on a sphere. *Elemente der Mathematik* 20:59–61; 1965.

———. Packing of 14, 16, 17 and 20 circles in a circle. *M.Mag.* 44:134–39; May 1971.

———. Packing of 19 equal circles on a sphere. *Elemente der Mathematik* 22:108–10; 1967.

———. Packing of 33 equal circles on a sphere. *Elemente der Mathematik* 18:99–100; 1963.

———. The space-filling pentahedra. *Journal of Combinatorial Theory* 13:437–43; Nov. 1972. Bibliography.

Golomb, Solomon. Replicating figures in the plane. *M.Gaz.* 48:403–12; Dec. 1964.

———. Tiling with polyominoes. *Journal of Combinatorial Theory* 1:280–96; 1966.

Gridgeman, N. T. Latin-square tiling. *M.T.* 64:358–60; Apr. 1971.

Grossman, H. D. Fun with lattice points. *Scrip.M.*, pp. 157–59; June 1948.

Heesch, Heinrich. *Reguläres Parkettierungsproblem*. Cologne and Opladen: Westdeutscher Verlag, 1968. 96 pp.

Kershner, R. B. The law of sines and law of cosines for polygons. *M.Mag.* 44:150–53; May 1971.

———. On paving the plane. *A.M.M.* 75:839–44; Oct. 1968.

Proof that there are only three types of convex hexagons and eight types of convex pentagons that can form tessellation patterns.

Kravitz, Sidney. Packing of circles. *Engineering Materials and Design* [London], pp. 875–76; June 1969.

Kung, S. H. L. [Problem 745.] *M.Mag.* 43:170–71; 1970.

Leech, J. Equilibrium of sets of particles on a sphere. *M.Gaz.* 41:81–90; 1957.

Meyer, Rochelle Wilson. Mutession: a new tiling relationship among planar polygons. *M.Tchg.*, no. 56, pp. 24–27; Autumn 1971.

Excellent, original discussion.

Mold, Josephine. *Tessellations.* London: Cambridge University Press, 1969. 32 pp.

Tiling, polyominoes, polyiamonds; for young readers. Bibliography.

Morris, H. M. J. Tessellating hexagons. *M.Tchg.*, no. 54, pp. 26–27; Spring 1971.

Pirl, Udo. Der Mindesabstand von *n* in der Einheitskreisscheibe gelegenen Punkten. *Mathematische Nachrichten* 40: 111–24; 1969.

Ranucci, Ernest R. Space-filling in two dimensions. *M.T.* 64:587–93; Nov. 1971.

Reeve, J. E., and J. A. Tyrrell. Maestro puzzles. *M.Gaz.* 45:97–99; May 1961.

Puzzles related to the packing of a given set of figures to form a certain figure.

Robinson, R. M. Arrangement of 24 points on a sphere. *Mathematische Annalen* 144:17–48; 1961.

Roth, K. F. On a problem of Heilbronn. *Journal of the London Mathematical Society* 26:198–204; 1951.

Schaer, J. The densest packing of nine circles in a square. *Canadian Mathematics Bulletin* 8:273–77; 1965.

———. On the densest packing of spheres in a cube. *Canadian Mathematics Bulletin* 9:265–70, 271–74, 275–80; 1966.

———. On the packing of ten equal circles in a square. *M.Mag.* 44:139–40; May 1971.

Schaer, J., and A. Meir. On a geometric extremum problem. *Canadian Mathematics Bulletin* 8:21–27; 1965.

Scheid, F. Some packing problem. *A.M.M.* 67:231–35; 1960.

Schütte, K., and B. L. van der Waerden. Auf welcher Kugel haben 5, 6, 7, 8 oder 9 Punkte mit mindesabstand Eins Platz? *Mathematische Annalen* 123:96–124; 1951.

Schwartz, B. L. Separating points in a square. *J.R.M.* 3:195–204; Oct. 1970.

Silverman, David L. A max-min problem. [Problem 88.] *J.R.M.* 2:161–62; July 1969. Also, 4:143–44. Apr. 1971.

Silverman, David L., and Harry L. Nelson. Another grid problem. *J.R.M.* 4:144–45; Apr. 1971.

Sommerville, D. M. Y. Division of space by congruent triangles and tetrahedra. *Proceedings of the Edinburgh Royal Society* 43:85–116; 1923.

———. Space-filling tetrahedra in Euclidean space. *Proceedings of the Edinburgh Mathematical Society* 41:49–57; 1923.

Stover, Donald. *Mosaics.* Boston: Houghton Mifflin Co., 1966.

Strohmajer, J. Über die Verteilung von Punkten auf der Kugel. *Annales Univ. Sci. Budapest, Sect. Math.* 6:49–53; 1963.
Trigg, Charles W. A hexagonal configuration. *M.Mag.* 35:70; Mar. 1962.
———. *Mathematical Quickies.* New York: McGraw-Hill Book Co., 1967.
    Problem 251: Packing cylinders.
———. Two tromino tessellations. *M.Mag.* 35:176; May 1962.
van der Waerden, B. L. Punkte auf der Kugel, Drei Zusätze. *Mathematische Annalen* 125:213–22; 1952.
Wenninger, M. J. Spherical tessellation and polyhedra. *Summation* [New York City, Association of Teachers of Mathematics], vol. 13, no. 2, pp. 19–24; Nov. 1967.

4.14   Topological Amusements

Engel, Douglas. Can space be overtwisted? *M.T.* 61:571–74; Oct. 1968.
Froman, Robert. *Rubber Bands, Baseballs and Doughnuts: A Book about Topology.* New York: Thomas Y. Crowell Co., 1972.
    For beginners, grades 1–4.
Gardner, Martin. Asymmetry. ["Mathematical Games."] *Sci.Am.,* May 1962.
———. "Klein Bottles and Other Surfaces." In *Martin Gardner's Sixth Book of Mathematical Games from Scientific American,* pp. 9–18. San Francisco: W. H. Freeman & Co., 1971.
———. Knotty problems with a two-hole torus. *Sci.Am.* 227:102–6; Dec. 1972. Also, 228:112–14; Jan. 1973.
———. A topological problem with a new twist. *Sci.Am.* 226:100–104; Apr. 1972. Also, 226:114; May 1972.
Goldberg, Michael. Stability configurations of electrons on a sphere. *Mathematics of Computation* 23:785–86; 1969.
Hunter, J. A. H., and Joseph Madachy. *Mathematical Diversions.* Princeton, N.J.: D. Van Nostrand, 1963.
    Chapter 4: "Topological Delights," pp. 35–47.
Ranucci, Ernest R. Aspects of combinatorial geometry. *S.S.M.* 70:338–44; Apr. 1970.
———. Topology—through the alphabet. *M.T.* 65:687–90; Dec. 1972.
Stewart, B. M. *Adventures among the Toroids.* Okemos, Mich.: The Author, 4494 Wausau Rd., Okemos, Mich. 48864; 1970. 206 pp.
    A study of two-dimensional polyhedra that are spheres with handles.
Topological Woggles. *M.Tchg.,* no. 54, p. 27; Spring 1971.
    How to make a Boy Scout plaited-leather insignia (woggle) out of one strip of leather.
Weir, A. J. Problems of teaching topology in schools. *M.Gaz.,* pp. 119–26; May 1968.

Chapter 5

Magic Squares and Related Configurations

5.1 Magic Squares

Adkins, Bryce. Adapting magic squares to classroom use. *A.T.* 10:498–500; Dec. 1963.

Agnew, Elizabeth. Two problems on magic squares. *M.Mag.* 44:13–15; Jan. 1971.

Apostol, T. M., and H. S. Zuckerman. On magic squares constructed by the uniform step method. *Proceedings of the American Mathematical Society* 2:557–65; 1951.

Arnott, David. Magic squares. *M.Tchg.*, no. 48, pp. 26–30; Autumn 1969.

Cappon, John. Easy construction of magic squares for classroom use. *A.T.* 12:100–105; Feb. 1965.

Cohen, Daniel, and F. D. Parker. Divisibility of determinant of magic square. [Problem 553.] *M.Mag.* 38:56; Jan. 1965.

Dixon, J. A. Number squares. *M.Tchg.*, no. 57, pp. 38–40; Winter 1971.

Feldman, Richard W. Benjamin Franklin and mathematics. *M.T.* 52:125–27; Feb. 1959.

Field, Richard S., Jr., and Charles W. Trigg. Primagic squares. *J.R.M.* 4:149; Apr. 1971.

Freitag, Herta, and Arthur Freitag. The magic of a square. *M.T.* 63:5–14; Jan. 1970.
  Good discussion of the construction of 4 × 4 magic squares.

Froelich, Effie. Now what? *A.T.* 14:225–27; Mar. 1967.
  Using magic squares.

Gardner, Martin. Magic square for the new year. *M.T.* 61:18; Jan. 1968.

Gorts, Jeannie. Magic square patterns. *A.T.* 16:314–16; Apr. 1969.

Hammond, Robert C. Device for practice with common denominators and addition of unlike fractions. *A.T.* 8:373; Nov. 1961.
  Uses magic squares.

Hewitt, Frances. 4 × 4 magic squares. *A.T.* 9:392–95; Nov. 1962.

Hudson, Carolyn Brauer. On pandiagonal magic squares of order $6t \pm 1$. *M.Mag.* 45:94–96; Mar. 1972.

Hunter, J. A. H. Construction of odd-order diabolic magic squares. *J.R.M.* 2:175–77; July 1969.

Hunter, J. A. H., and Joseph Madachy. *Mathematical Diversions.* Princeton, N.J.: D. Van Nostrand Co., 1963.
  Chapter 3: "Mystic Arrays," pp. 23–34; brief treatment of magic squares and Latin squares.
Hunter, J. A. H., and R. Robinson Rowe. It's magic. *J.R.M.* 4:147; Apr. 1971.
  A magic square of consecutive integers whose magic constant is twice the square of the smallest integer in the array.
Jacobs, Charles J. A reexamination of the Franklin square. *M.T.* 64:55–62; Jan. 1971.
Johnson, C. R. A matrix theoretic construction of magic squares. *A.M.M.* 79:1004–6; Nov. 1972.
  A method for constructing magic squares of any odd order, as well as an extension for certain even orders.
Kordemsky, Boris. *The Moscow Puzzles.* New York: Charles Scribner's Sons, 1972.
  Chapter 12: "Cross Sums and Magic Squares," pp. 143–56.
Kothari, L. S. Notes on magic squares. *A.M.M.* 70:412–14; Apr. 1963.
Kozniuk, Dale. Fun with magic squares. *R.M.M.*, no. 14, pp. 50–52; Jan.–Feb. 1964.
Madachy, Joseph, ed. A 4 × 4 magic square using primes in arithmetical progression. *J.R.M.* 2:215; Oct. 1969.
Maletsky, Evan M. Manipulating magic squares. *M.T.* 65:729–32; Dec. 1972.
  Suggestions for the junior high school level.
Matthews, E. Try magic squares. *Instructor* 77:98; Jan. 1968.
May, Lola J. Enrichment games get pupils to think. *Grade Teacher* 83:53–54; May 1966.
  Using magic squares.
McCombs, Wayne. Four-by-four magic square for the new year. *A.T.* 17:79–80; Jan. 1970.
Munger, Ralph. An algebraic treatment of magic squares. *M.T.* 66:101–7; Feb. 1973.
Muth, C. About magic squares. *Baltimore Bulletin of Education* 34:17–19; June 1957.
Ondrejka, Rudolf, and J. A. H. Hunter. Magic squares. *J.R.M.* 2:233–34; Oct. 1969.
  Geometric magic squares; for "Errata," see *J.R.M.* 3:63; Jan. 1970.
Pagni, David L. Magic squares: would you believe . . .? *M.T.* 65:135, 189; Feb. 1972.
  Derivation of the formula for the "magic constant" of a normal magic square.
Peterson, Marcie. A class of 5 × 5 magic squares with a 3 × 3 magic center. *P.M.E.J.* 5:227; Fall 1971.
Portier, B. *Le Carré diabolique de 9 et son dérivé le carré satanique de 9: le carré cabalistique de 8.* 2 vols. Algiers, 1902.
Reissig, Rolf. *Die Pandiagonalen Quadrate vierte Ordnung.* Berlin: Akademie-Verlag, 1952. 54 pp.
Rosenfeld, Azriel, and R. B. Eggleton. Arithmagic squares. [Problem E1729.] *A.M.M.* 72:906–7; Oct. 1965.

Scheffler, Hermann. *Die magische Figuren; allgemeine Lösung und Erweiterung eines aus dem Altherthume Stammenden Problems.* Wiesbaden: M. Sändig, 1968.

Schulz, Charles E. Pattern analysis in magic squares. *A.T.* 10:214–15; Apr. 1963.
  Limited to 3 × 3 squares.

Scott, Robert. The third order magic square. *M.Mag.* 36:263; Sept. 1963.

Sharp, Richard M., and Seymour Metzner. *Magic Squares, Levels A–E.* Columbus, Ohio: Charles E. Merrill Publishing Co., 1972. 40 pp.

Silverman, David L. An enumeration problem. [Problem 139.] *J.R.M.* 3:226–27; Oct. 1970.
  Brief note on "magic domino squares."

Stern, Erich. *Resumé de contributions à une théorie générale mathématique des carrés magiques.* Brussels: Librairie du "Sphinx," 1937. 11 pp.

———. *Über irreguläre pandiagonale Lateinische Quadrate mit Primzahlseitenlänge.* Gröningen, Netherlands: P. Noordhoff, 1938. 15 pp.

Strum, Robert C. Some comments on "A Class of 5 × 5 Magic Squares." *P.M.E.J.* 5:279–80; Spring 1972.

Trigg, Charles W. [Problem 3446.] *S.S.M.* 73:77–78; Jan. 1973.
  Square arrays of the nine positive digits.

———. Another type of third order magic square. *S.S.M.* 70:467; May 1970.

———. A doubly magic square with remarkable subsidiaries. *J.R.M.* 4:171–74; July 1971. Also, 5:148; Apr. 1972.

———. Fifth order concentric magic squares. *J.R.M.* 4:42–44; Jan. 1971.

———. A 5 × 5 magic square with cyclic permutations of 1, 2, 3, 4, 5. [Problem 2893.] *S.S.M.* 63:691–92; Nov. 1963.

———. Magic squares with nonagonal and decagonal elements. *J.R.M.* 5:203–4; July 1972.

———. Magic squares with polygonal elements. *S.S.M.* 71:195–97; Mar. 1971.

———. A property of third order gnomon-magic squares. *M.Mag.* 43:70; Mar. 1970.

———. Squares with the form *abcabc*. *J.R.M.* 5:277–78; Oct. 1972.

———. Third order magic squares with prime elements. [Problem 3437.] *S.S.M.* 72:745; Nov. 1972.

Walker, G. W., and Charles W. Trigg. The mathematician and the jester. [Problem E791.] *A.M.M.* 55:429–30; Sept. 1948.

5.2   The Magic Knight's Tour

Barwell, Brian R. Arrows and circuits. *J.R.M.* 2:196–204; Oct. 1969.

Frankel, Edward. Fibonacci numbers as paths of a rook on a chessboard. *Fib.Q.* 8:538–41; Dec. 1970.

Knuth, Donald E. Uncrossed knight's tours. *J.R.M.* 2:154–55; July 1969.

Luke, Dorman. "Yoicks!" "tallyho!" shades of King Arthur. *R.M.M.*, no. 12, pp. 13–15; Dec. 1962.
  Magic knight's tour.

Stewart, Ian. Solid knight's tours. *J.R.M.* 4:1; Jan. 1971.

Trigg, Charles W. Knight's tours into non-magic squares. *J.R.M.* 3:3–8; Jan. 1970.
———. 3 × 3 matrices from knight's moves. *M.Mag.* 36:36; Jan. 1963.

5.3   Antimagic Squares; Heterosquares

Duncan, Dewey, and Charles W. Trigg. On heterosquares. [Problem 84.] *M.Mag.* 44:236–37; Sept. 1971.
Gardner, Martin. Antimagic squares. *Sci.Am.*, p. 164; Jan. 1961.
NaNagara, Prasert. On heterosquares. [Problem 84.] *M.Mag.* 39:255–56; 1966.
Pinzka, C. F. Heterosquares. *M.Mag.* 38:250–52; 1965.
Trigg, Charles W. Antimagic squares with sums in arithmetic progression. *J.R.M.* 5:278–80; Oct. 1972.
———. Knight's tours into non-magic squares. *J.R.M.* 3:3–8; Jan. 1970.
———. 108 third order almost heterosquares including 74 antimagic squares. *M.Mag.* 44:236–37; Sept. 1971.
———. A remarkable group of antimagic squares. *M.Mag.* 44:13; Jan. 1971.
———. The sums of third order antimagic squares. *J.R.M.* 2:250–54; Oct. 1969.

5.4   Magic Triangles and Other Plane Figures

Cohen, D. I. A. Comment on "A Magic Pentagram." *M.Mag.* 37:49–50; Jan. 1964.
Dongre, N. M. More about magic star polygons. *A.M.M.* 78:1025; Nov. 1971.
Lemke, Paul, and Charles W. Trigg. The magic hexagon. [Problem 824.] *M.Mag.* 46:44–45; Jan. 1973.
Philpott, Wade E. Domino magic squares. *J.R.M.* 4:84–87; Apr. 1971.
Silverman, David L. An enumeration problem. *J.R.M.* 3:226–27; Oct. 1970.
   A problem concerning magic domino squares.
Trigg, Charles W. A magic pentagram for 1962. *M.Mag.* 35:228; Sept. 1962.
———. Triangles with balanced perimeters. *J.R.M.* 3:255–56; Oct. 1970.
———. Triangular arrangements of numbered disks. *M.T.* 65:157–61; Feb. 1972.
———. A unique magic hexagon. *R.M.M.*, no. 14, pp. 40–43; Jan.–Feb. 1964.
Trotter, Terrel, Jr. Normal magic triangles of order *n*. *J.R.M.* 5:28–32; Jan. 1972.

5.5   Magic and Antimagic Solids

Hendricks, John Robert. The pan-3-agonal magic cube. *J.R.M.* 5:51–52; Jan. 1972.
———. The pan-3-agonal magic cube of order 5. *J.R.M.* 5:205–6; July 1972.
———. The third-order magic cube complete. *J.R.M.* 5:43–50; Jan. 1972.
Trigg, Charles W. Edge-antimagic tetrahedrons with rotating triads. *J.R.M.* 5:40–42; Jan. 1972.
———. Edge-magic and edge-antimagic tetrahedrons. *J.R.M.* 4:253–59; Oct. 1971.
———. Magic tetrahedra. *M.Gaz.* 54:148–49; May 1970.

5.6 Latin Squares and Euler Squares

Chowla, S., P. Erdös, and E. G. Strauss. On the maximal number of pairwise orthogonal Latin squares of a given order. *Canadian Journal of Mathematics* 12:204–8; 1960.

Gridgeman, N. T. Latin squares under restriction, and a jumboization. *J.R.M.* 5:198–202; July 1972.

——. Latin-square tiling. *M.T.* 64:358–60; Apr. 1971.

——. Magic squares embedded in a Latin square. *J.R.M.* 5:250; Oct. 1972.

Stern, Erich. *Über irreguläre pandiagonale Lateinische Quadrate mit Primzahlseitenlänge.* Gröningen, Netherlands: P. Noordhoff, 1938. 15 pp.

Trigg, Charles W. Fifth order Latin squares. [Problem 2893.] *S.S.M.* 63:691–92; Nov. 1963.

Chapter 6

Pythagorean Recreations

6.1 Pythagorean Theorem

Brown, Stephen, and Marion Walter. What-if-not? *M.Tchg.*, no. 51, pp. 9–17; Summer 1970.
An unusual discussion of the Pythagorean theorem.
Buchman, Aaron. An experimental approach to the Pythagorean theorem. *A.T.* 17:129–32; Feb. 1970.
Charosh, Mannis. On the equation $x^2 + y^2 = z^2$. *A.M.M.* 46:228; 1939.
Cliburn, Cecil. A new look at the Pythagorean theorem. *Pentagon*, vol. 30, no. 2, pp. 89–96; Spring 1971.
Cozens, W. H. Pythagorean dissections. *R.M.M.* no. 6, pp. 23–24; Dec. 1961.
Eagle, J. Edwin. Helping students to see the patterns. *M.T.* 64:315–22; Apr. 1971.
Discussion of the Pythagorean and related theorems.
Finney, Ross L. Dynamic proofs of Euclidean theorems. *M.Mag.* 43:177–85; Sept. 1970.
Gardner, Martin. Pythagorean theorem. ["Mathematical Games."] *Sci.Am.* Oct. 1964; Nov. 1964; June 1960.
―――. "The Pythagorean Theorem." In *Martin Gardner's Sixth Book of Mathematical Games from Scientific American*, pp. 152–62. San Francisco;, W. H. Freeman & Co., 1971.
Gass, Gregg. Garfield's proof of the Pythagorean theorem. *Pentagon* 28:88–89; Spring 1969.
Gummer, C. F. Discussions. *A.M.M.* 29:397; 1922.
Harrell, Ned [Letter to the editor.] *M.T.* 63:704, 708; Dec. 1970.
Proofs of the Pythagorean theorem.
Jones, Philip S. A note on the Pythagorean theorem. *M.T.* 43:278; Oct. 1950.
―――. The Pythagorean theorem. *M.T.* 43:162; Apr. 1950.
Jordan, John Q., and John M. O'Malley, Jr. An implication of the Pythagorean theorem. *M.Mag.* 43:186–89; Sept. 1970.
Lietzmann, Walther. *Der Pythagoreische Lehrsatz*. Leipzig: Teubner, 1968. 110 pp. (Paper)
Ninth edition of a popular monograph first published in 1912; includes a history of the Pythagorean theorem, several types of proofs, Pythagorean triples, and related material.
Mathematics Staff, University of Chicago. A generalization of the Pythagorean theorem. *M.S.J.*, vol. 2, no. 2; Apr. 1955.
―――. More on the cutting of squares. *M.S.J.*, vol. 3, no. 3, pp. 1–2; Oct. 1956.
A dissection that proves the Pythagorean theorem.

——. Three algebraic questions connected with Pythagoras' theorem. *M.T.* 49:250; 1956.

——. Three algebraic questions connected with Pythagoras' theorem. *M.S.J.*, vol. 2, no. 4; Dec. 1955. Conclusion, vol. 3, no. 2; Apr. 1956.

Sayili, A. Thabit ibn Qurra's generalization of the Pythagorean theorem. *Isis* 51:35–37; 1960.

Schaaf, William L. The theorem of Pythagoras. *M.T.* 44:585–88; Dec. 1951. Bibliography.

Sell, W. On integral solutions of $A^2 + B^2 = C^2$. *A.M.M.* 43:481; 1936.

Shannon, A. G., and A. F. Horadam. A generalized Pythagorean theorem. *Fib.Q.* 9:307–12; May 1971. Bibliography.

Shloming, Robert. Thabit ibn Qurra and the Pythagorean theorem. *M.T.* 63:519–28; Oct. 1970.

Silverman, David L. A wrong triangle. *J.R.M.* 4:73; Jan. 1971.

Sullivan, John J. Confirming the Pythagorean theorem. *A.T.* 18:115–16; Feb. 1971.

Yanney, B. F., and J. Calderheath. New and old proofs of the Pythagorean theorem. *A.M.M.* 3:65, 110, 169, 299; 1903.

6.2 Pythagorean Triples

Arpaia, Pasquale J. Discoveries in mathematics—Pythagorean triples. *M.T.* 65: 463–65; May 1972.
Interesting proofs of relations between the numbers of Pythagorean triples.

——. A generating property of Pythagorean triples. *M.Mag.* 44:26–27; Jan. 1971.

Ballantine, J. P., and O. F. Brown. Pythogorean sets of numbers. *A.M.M.* 45:298; 1938.

Brandley, Michael. On primitive Pythagorean triples. *Pentagon* 31:71–75; Spring 1972.
A new method of finding all primitive Pythagorean triples.

Brixey, John C. Pythagorean numbers. *Oklahoma University Mathematics Letter*, vol. 5, no. 2, p. 3; Dec. 1955.

Cohen, Ernst M. Complete Diophantine solution of the Pythagorean triple $(a,b = a + 1,c)$. *Fib.Q.* 8:402–5; Oct. 1970.

Dent, B. M. Pythagoras in integers. *M.Tchg.* no. 53, p. 41; Winter 1970.

Farmer, Frank. A new look at Pythagorean triplets. *M.S.J.*, vol. 19, no. 4, p. 4; May 1972.
A neat procedure for finding triplets involving very large numbers.

Hart, Philip J. Pythagorean numbers. *M.T.* 47:16–21; Jan. 1954.

How Many Different Pythagorean Triples Exist in Which 60 Represents One of the Two Lesser Integers? [Problem 321.] *M.S.J.*, vol. 17, no. 4, p. 6; May 1970.

Jones, Philip S. Pythagorean numbers. *M.T.* 45:269; Apr. 1952.

Kubota, K. K. Pythagorean triples in unique factorization domains. *A.M.M.* 79:503–5; May 1972.

Lichtenberg, Donovan R. [Letter to the editor.] *M.T.* 63:624; Nov. 1970. A note on Pythagorean triples and figurate numbers.
Oliver, B. M. The pattern of Pythagorean numbers. *M.T.* 64:449–54; May 1971. A unique study of the map of the integers a and b that represent primitive solutions of $a^2 + b^2 = c^2$, where c is an integer.
Oliver, S. Ron. Cubic quadruples from Pythagorean triples. *Pentagon* 28:73–76; Spring 1969.
Pythagorean Triangles. *Pythagoras* (English ed.), vol. 1, no. 2, pp. 30–32; 1968.
Sexhauer, N. Pythagorean triples over Gaussian domains. *A.M.M.* 73:829–34; 1966. Also, *A.M.M.* 75:278–79; 1968.
Subbarao, M. V. Perfect triangles. *A.M.M.* 78:384–85; Apr. 1971.
Talbot, W. R. Pythagorean triples. *A.M.M.* 56:402; 1949.
Teigen, M. G., and D. W. Hadwin. On generating Pythagorean triples. *A.M.M.* 78:378–79; Apr. 1971.
Trigg, Charles W. Pythagorean triangles. *A.M.M.* 57:329; May 1952.
Umansky, Harlan. Pythagoras revisited. *Fib.Q.* 9:83–84; Feb. 1971.
Zoll, Jeffery. A formula for determining Pythagorean triples containing a given number. *M.S.J.* 18:4–5; Jan. 1971.

6.3   Pythagorean Relationships

Brooke, Maxey, M. Darnham, and J. A. H. Hunter. Pythagorean triangles with cubic perimeters. [Problem 495.] *M.Mag.* 36:198–99; May 1963.
Byrkit, Donald, and Charles W. Trigg. [Problem 3258.] *S.S.M.* 70:591; June 1970.
    Solution of the problem of finding the eight right triangles that have 65 as the length of one of the sides.
Cheney, Fitch. Vux triangles. *M.T.* 63:407–10; May 1970.
    Relation of primitive Pythagorean triangles to triangles in which the measure of one angle is double that of another angle of the triangle.
Cheney, W. F., Jr., and Charles W. Trigg. Primitive Pythagorean triangles with the same incircle. [Problem E30.] *A.M.M.* 47:240–41; Apr. 1940.
Gardner, Martin. Pythagorean square. *Sci.Am.*, p. 114; Nov. 1971; p. 90, Dec. 1971.
Gowing, R. Pythagorean in-circles. *M.Tchg.*, no. 55, pp. 20–21; Summer 1971.
Gündel, Bernhard. *Pythagoras im Urlaub; ein Büchlein für nachdenkliche Leute, u.s.w.* Frankfurt am Main: M. Diesterweg, 1964.
Hall, Gary D. A Pythagorean puzzle. *A.T.* 19:67–70; Jan. 1972.
McArlde, Edward. The "cosine rule." *J.R.M.* 3:122–23; Apr. 1970.
Prielipp, Robert. The area of a Pythagorean triangle and the number six. *M.T.* 62:547–48; Nov. 1969.
Ransom, W. R., and Charles W. Trigg. Pythagorean triangles with sides < 100. [Problem 986.] *A.M.M.* 59:329–30; May 1952.
Rowe, R. Robinson. Chains of integrally circumscript squares. *J.R.M.* 5:33–35; Jan. 1972.
Trigg, Charles W. If $z > x > y$ are sides of a primitive Pythagorean triangle, then x and $x - y$ cannot be legs of another Pythagorean triangle. [Problem 257.] *P.M.E.J.* 5:305–7; Spring 1972.

──────. Pythagorean triangles with equal perimeters. *A.M.M.* 56:632; Nov. 1949.

──────. Pythagorean triangles with the same prime inradius. [Problem 3381.] *S.S.M.* 71:749; Nov. 1971.

──────. The ten digits in the smallest Pythagorean triangle. *J.R.M.* 5:206; July 1972.

──────. Terminal digits of MN ($M^2 - N^2$) in the duodecimal system. *Duodecimal Bulletin* 14: 4X; Dec. 1960.
The expression MN ($M^2 - N^2$) represents the area of a primitive Pythagorean triangle.

──────. Terminal digits of MN ($M^2 - N^2$) in the scale of five. *Pentagon* 21:28–39; Fall 1961.

──────. Terminal digits of MN ($M^2 - N^2$) in the scale of seven. *R.M.M.* no. 3, pp. 17–20; June 1961.

──────. Terminal digits of MN ($M^2 - N^2$) in the scale of ten. *M.Mag.* 34:159–60, 233–35; Jan.–Mar. 1961.

──────. X Pythagorean triangles with shortest equal perimeters; $X = 2, 3, \ldots,$ 10. *A.M.M.* 56:632–33; Nov. 1949.

Trigg, Charles W., and W. L. Mrozek. One side of Pythagorean triangle divisible by 5. [Problem 3069.] *S.S.M.* 67:204; Feb. 1967.

6.4   Heronic Triangles; Figures with Integer Dimensions

Carlson, John R. Determination of Heronian triangles. *Fib.Q.* 8:499–506; Dec. 1970.

Carman, Robert A., et al. What is the smallest positive integer that can be a side of five Pythagorean triangles? [Problem 3392.] *S.S.M.* 72:92–93; Jan. 1972.

Dapkus, Frank, and J. W. Wilson. A smallest partition. [Problem 830.] *M.Mag.* 46:50–51; Jan. 1973.
To find a right triangle with the smallest area which can be partitioned into two triangles with all integral sides.

Freitag, Herta T., and Charles W. Trigg. Rectangular prisms with equal volume and surface measures. [Problem 3385.] *S.S.M.* 71:751; Nov. 1971.

Groups of Rational Right Triangles Whose Hypotenuses Are Consecutive Numbers Less Than 1000. *Scrip.M.* 14:33–34; 1948.

Lieber, Michael, M. V. Tamhanker, and Suryanarayana. Triangles whose sides are consecutive integers. [Problem E1773.] *A.M.M.* 73:344–45; May 1966.

Parker, John. Heron's formula. *M.Tchg.*, no. 53; Winter 1970.

Phelps, R. R., and N. J. Fine. Perfect triangles. [Problem E1168.] *A.A.M.* 63:43–44; Jan. 1956.

Seiler, James G., and E. P. Starke. Heronic triangles, solution. [Problem 699.] *M.Mag.* 42:98; Mar. 1969.

Seiler, James G., and Charles W. Trigg. Heronic triangles. [Problem 699.] *M.Mag.* 43:172–73; May 1970. Also, *M.Mag.*, Sept. 1968, p. 212; and Mar. 1969, p. 98.

Trigg, Charles W. Heron triangles with three-digit sides involving distinct digits. *J.R.M.* 3:120–21; Apr. 1970. Also, *M.Mag.* 43:172–73; May 1970.

———. If x and y are legs of a primitive Pythagorean triangle, then x and $(x - y)$ cannot be the legs of another Pythagorean triangle. [Problem 257.] *P.M.E.J.* 5:305–7; Spring 1972.

Waters, William M., Jr. Notes on an extension of Pythagorean triplets in arithmetic progression. *M.T.* 62:633–35; Dec. 1969.

Recreations in Antiquity

7.1 Computation of Pi (π)

Field, Leeds K. *Mathematics, Minus and Plus.* New York: Pageant Press, 1953.
15 pp.
   A "proof" that $\pi = 3.0$ and not 3.1416; also, a novel approach to the problem
   of duplicating a cube.
Knuth, Donald E. *Art of Computer Programming.* Vol. 2, n.p., 1971.
   Page 248: Computation of π carried to 500,000 places in 1967 by Jean
   Guilloud.
Maier, Bruce. Comparison between various methods for determining pi with re-
   spect to running time in a computer. *S.S.M.* 72:777–81; Dec. 1972.
Nanjundiah, T. S. On Huygens' approximation to π. *M.Mag.* 44:221–23; Sept.
   1971.
Shanks, Daniel, and J. W. Wrench, Jr. Calculation of π to 100,000 decimals.
   Mathematics of Computation 16:76–99; Jan. 1962.
   Full printing of the first 100,000 decimal places.
Smithson, Thomas W. An Eulerian development for pi. *M.T.* 63:597–608; Nov.
   1970.
   Use of infinite series in computing the value of π.
Te Selle, David W. Pi, polygons, and a computer. *M.T.* 63:128–32; Feb. 1970.
   Applying the modern computer to Archimedes' method of computing π.
Trigg, Charles W. $\pi/4$ in terms of arccots from an n-square configuration.
   [Problem 243.] *P.M.E.J.* 5:246–47; Fall 1971.

7.2 History of Pi; e, π, and i

Allen, Arnold O. e^π or π^e? *J.R.M.* 2:255–56; Oct. 1969.
Archibald, R. C. Note on the value of i^i. *Scrip.M.* 2:293: 1934.
Beckmann, Petr. *A History of π.* Boulder, Colo.: Western Publishing Co., Golden
   Press, 1970. 190 pp.
———. *A History of π (pi).* 2d ed. Boulder, Colo.: Western Publishing Co.,
   Golden Press, 1971. 196 pp.
   Popular treatment.
A Complex Curiosity. *J.R.M.* 2:159; July 1969. Also, 3:111; Apr. 1970.
   Proof that the ith root of i is a real number equal to 4.8104773809 · · · · .
Davis, Philip J., and William G. Chinn. *3.1416 and All That.* New York: Simon
   & Schuster, 1969.
Dudley, U. π, i: 1832–1879. *M.Mag.* 35:153–54; 1962.

Gardner, Martin. "The Transcendental Number *e*." In *The Unexpected Hanging and Other Mathematical Diversions*, pp. 34–42. New York: Simon & Schuster, 1963.
Halsted, G. B. Pi in Asia. *A.M.M.* 15:84; 1908.
Kelisky, R. P. The numbers generated by exp. (arc tan x). *Duke Mathematical Journal*, pp. 569–81; Dec. 1959.
Mitchell, U. G. The number pi. *A.M.M.* 26:209–12; 1919.
Oliver, Bernard M. The key of *e*. *M.T.* 65:5–8; Jan. 1972.
Rice, D. History of pi. *Mathematics Newsletter* 2:6–8; Mar. 1928.
Schaumberger, Norman. Some comments on *e*. *M.T.* 66:236–38; Mar. 1973.
Trigg, Charles W. Rational approximations of *e*. *M.Mag.* 35:38, 54; Jan. 1962.
Uhler, Horace S. The value of i^i. *A.M.M.* 28:115; Mar. 1921.
The value of i^i computed to more than 50 decimal places.

7.3 Pi and Probability

Fey, James T. Probability, integers, and pi. *M.T.* 64:329–32; Apr. 1971.
Klamkin, Murray. On Barbier's solution of the Buffon needle problem. *M.Mag.* 28:135–38; 1955.
———. On the uniqueness of the distribution function for the Buffon needle problem. *A.M.M.* 60:677–80; 1953.
Mantel, L. An extension of the Buffon needle problem. *Annals of Mathematical Statistics* 22:314–15; 1951. Also, 24:674–77; 1953.
Neuts, M. F., and P. Purdue. Buffon in the round. *M.Mag.* 44:81–89; Mar. 1971. Comprehensive and technical analysis of a modification of Buffon's needle problem; bibliography, 10 references.
Ramaley, J. F. Buffon's noodle problem. *A.M.M.* 76:916–18; Oct. 1969.
Sylvester, J. J. On Buffon's problem of the needle. *Acta Mathematica* 14:185–205; 1891.

7.4 Trisection of an Angle

Angle Trisection. *Oklahoma University Mathematics Letter*, vol. 4, no. 4, p. 2; Apr. 1955.
Angle Trisection. [Note.] *Pentagon* 28:51–52, 55; Fall 1968.
Budin, Michael A. A good approximation to the trisection of an angle. *J.R.M.* 4:153–54; Apr. 1971.
Byrkit, Donald, and William Waters. A note concerning a common angle "trisection." *M.T.* 65:523–24; Oct. 1972.
Carnahan, W. H. A new trisection solution. *M.S.J.* vol. 2, no. 3, p. 1; Oct. 1955.
Daniells, Marian E. The trisector of Amadori. *M.T.* 33:80–81; Feb. 1940.
Davis, Elwyn H. Trisection revisited. *Pentagon*, vol. 30, no. 2, pp. 69–75; Spring 1971.
Proof of the impossibility of trisecting a general angle based on field theory.
Glaze, Janet W. Angle multisection by parallel straightedges. *Fib.Q.* 8:393–96; Oct. 1970.

Gould, Henry W., et al. [Problem 825.] *M.Mag.* 45:100–101; Mar. 1972. Also, 46:45–46; Jan. 1973.

On trisecting an angle.

Kazarinoff, Nicholas. *Ruler and the Round, or Angle Trisection and Circle Division.* Vol. 15. Boston: Prindle, Weber & Schmidt, 1970. 138 pp.

Peterson, Catherine. Trisection of an angle. *Pentagon,* vol. 30, no. 2, pp. 63–68; Spring 1971.

Sanders, S. T. The angle-trisection chimera once more. *Mathematics Newsletter* 7:1–6; Nov.–Dec. 1931.

Wernick, William. Geometric construction: the double straightedge. *M.T.* 64:697–704; Dec. 1971.

Yates, Robert C. *The Trisection Problem.* Reprint. Washington, D.C.: NCTM, 1971. 68 pp.

Photo-offset reprint of the original edition; impossibility of ruler and straightedge solution, mathematical solutions using other instruments, and some remarkable approximations.

Chapter 8

Combinatorial Recreations

8.1 Permutations, Combinations, and Partitions; Factorials

Abramson, H. D. On selecting separated objects from a row. *A.M.M.* 76:1130–31; Dec. 1969.

Abramson, Morton. Certain distributions of unlike objects into cells. *M.Mag.* 43:214–18; Sept. 1970.

Alfred, Brother, Charles W. Trigg, and John Wagner. Interlocking committees. [Problem 2890.] *S.S.M.* 63:688–90; Nov. 1963.

Atkins, Mark. Antifactorials. *Pentagon*, vol. 31, no. 1, pp. 12–16; Fall 1972.

Bartlow, T. L. An historical note on the parity of permutations. *A.M.M.* 79:766–69; Aug.–Sept. 1972.
Bibliography.

Bedingfield, Laurinda. Group theory—an application. *M.S.J.*, vol. 18, no. 4, pp. 5–6; May 1971.

Brenner, J. L. A new proof that no permutation is both even and odd. *A.M.M.* 64:499–500; 1957.

Carteblanche, F. de. The princess and the roses. *J.R.M.* 3:238–39; Oct. 1970.
An unusual problem involving partitions, parity, and so on.

Collins, K. S. Algebra from a cube. *M.Tchg.*, no. 46, pp. 58–62; Spring 1969.

Crowe, D. W., and T. A. McKee. Sylvester's problem on collinear points. *M.Mag.* 41:30–34; 1968.

Cunningham, F., Jr. Choreographic proof of a theorem on permutations. *M.Mag.* 43:154–55; May 1970.

Dessart, Donald J. To tip a waiter—a problem in unordered selections with repetitions. *M.T.* 64:307–10; Apr. 1971.

Doe, T. Two investigations. *M.Tchg.*, no. 47, pp. 34–36; Summer 1969.

Dunkum, William. Another use for binary numerals. *A.T.* 17:225–26; Mar. 1970.
Relation of binary notation to permutations and combinations.

Eisen, Martin. *Elementary Combinatorial Analysis*. New York: Gordon & Breach, 1969. 240 pp.
Undergraduate college level.

Feser, Victor G. Sums of factorials. *J.R.M.* 5:174–76; July 1972.

Flanders, Harley. A democratic proof of a combinatorial identity. *M.Mag.* 44:11; Jan. 1971.

Ford, Lester R., Jr., and Selmer E. Johnson. A tournament problem. *A.M.M.* 66:387–89; 1959.

Gardner, Martin. Combinatorial problems involving "tree" graphs and forests of trees. *Sci.Am.* 218:118–21; Feb. 1968.

———. "Combinatorial Theory." In *Martin Gardner's Sixth Book of Mathematical Games from Scientific American*, pp. 19–28. San Francisco: W. H. Freeman & Co., 1971.
The magic hexagon and other topics.

———. A handful of combinatorial problems based on dominoes. *Sci.Am.* 221:122–27; Dec. 1969. Also, 222:126–27; Jan. 1970.

Glaymann. Maurice. An aspect of combinatorial theory. *M.Tchg.*, no. 57, pp. 24–27; Winter 1971.
Sophisticated discussion involving Boolean matrices, partitions, and Stirling numbers; bibliography.

Goodman, A. W. On sets of acquaintances and strangers at any party. *A.M.M.* 66:778–83; 1959.

Göbel, F., and R. P. Nederpelt. The number of numerical outcomes of iterated powers. *A.M.M.* 78:1097–103; Dec. 1971.

Goldberg, Michael. Maximizing the smallest triangle made by *N* points in a square. *M.Mag.* 45:135–44; May 1972.

Golomb, S. W. New proof of a classic combinatorial theorem. *A.M.M.* 75:530–31; 1968.

Hall, Marshall, Jr., and D. E. Knuth. Combinatorial analysis and computers. *A.M.M.*, vol. 72, no. 2, p. 2, pp. 21–28; Feb. 1965.
Bibliography.

Halperin, I. Odd and even permutations. *Canadian Mathematics Bulletin* 3:185–86; 1960.

Harary, Frank. The two-triangle case of the acquaintance graph. *M.Mag.* 45:130–35; May 1972.

———. Unsolved problems in the enumeration of graphs. *Publications, Mathematics Institute, Hungarian Academy of Sciences*, vol. 5, pp. 63–95; 1960.

Harary, Frank, and E. Palmer. The enumeration methods of Redfield. *American Journal of Mathematics*, vol. 89, pp. 373–84; 1967.

Jordan, C. On Stirling's numbers. *Tohoku Mathematics Journal*, ser. 1, June 1933.

Kaye, R. M. Another triangle? *M.Tchg.*, no. 60, p. 43; Sept. 1972.
The question "How many different addition calculations make a particular whole number?" hinges on the meaning of "different."

Kelly, L. M., and W. O. J. Moser. On the number of ordinary lines determined by *n* points. *Canadian Journal of Mathematics* 10:210–19; 1958.

Lagrange, René. Deux problèmes de répartition mixte. *Bull. Sci. Math.* (2) 86:81–88; 1962.

———. Sur les combinaisons d'objets numérotés. *Bull. Sci. Math.* (2) 87:29–42; 1963.

Liu, C. L. *Introduction to Combinatorial Mathematics.* New York: McGraw-Hill Book Co., 1968.

Long, C. T. Proof of Tepper's factorial conjecture. *M.Mag.* 38:304–5; 1965.

Maxfield, J. M. A note on *N*! *M.Mag.* 43:64–67; 1970.

Moser, W. O. J., and Morton Abramson. Enumeration of combinations with restricted differences and cospan. *Journal of Combinatorial Theory*, vol. 7, pp.162–70; 1969.

Advanced discussion; bibliography.

Murty, U. S. R. How many magic configurations are there? *A.M.M.* 78:1000–1002; Nov. 1971.

Papp, F. J. Another proof of Tepper's identity. *M.Mag.* 45:119–21; May 1972.

Parker, Russell. Stirling and Stirling's numbers. *M.Tchg.*, no. 59, pp. 21–23; Summer 1972.

Pastides, Nicolas. A study of partitions. *M.Tchg.*, no. 53, pp. 26–27; Winter 1970.

The complete set of partitions of a rod using smaller rods, including the given rod; highly technical.

Ranucci, Ernest R. Permultation patterns. *M.T.* 65:333–38; Apr. 1972.

———. Teaching permutations. *Grade Teacher* 89:54–55+; Nov. 1971.

Rasof, Elvin. Fundamental principle of counting, tree diagrams, and the number of divisors of a number (the nu-function). *A.T.* 16:308–10; Apr. 1969.

Read, R. C. The use of *S*-functions in combinatorial analysis. *Canadian Journal of Mathematics*, vol. 20, pp. 808–41; 1968.

Rodseth, Oystein, et al. Telescoping Vandermonde convolutions. *A.M.M.* 79:88–89; Jan. 1972.

Deals with combinatorial identities; technical.

Roger, Jerry L. A factorial curiosity. *M.T.* 64:695; Dec. 1971.

Rota, G. C. The number of partitions of a set. *A.M.M.* 71:499–504; 1964.

Roth, Emile. Permutations arranged around a circle. *A.M.M.* 78:990–92; Nov. 1971.

Scott. *Programming a Combinatorial Problem*. Vol. 10. Princeton, N.J.: Princeton University, Dept. of Electrical Engineering, 1958.

Scott, D. Investigation of a "Maths Today" problem; an exercise in pattern-spotting. *M.Tchg.*, no. 56, pp. 38–45; Autumn 1971.

Shafer, Dale M., and Charles W. Trigg. [Problem 3412.] *S.S.M.* 72:357–58; Apr. 1972.

A puzzle game called "Drive Ya Nuts"; involves cyclic permutations.

Shipman, David C. A new proof of a combinatorial identity. *M.Mag.* 43:162–63; May 1970.

Silverman, David. "Rate Your Wits!" (Factorials!). *J.R.M.* 3:174–75; July 1970.

Stein, Robert G. A combinatorial proof that $\Sigma k^3 = (\Sigma k)^2$. *M.Mag.* 44:161–62; May 1971.

Tepper, M. A factorial conjecture. *M.Mag.* 38:303–4; 1965.

Trigg, Charles W. Interlocking committees. *A.M.M.* 69: Nov. 1962.

———. Triangles with balanced perimeters. *J.R.M.* 3:255–56; Oct. 1970.

Varga, Tamas. Boxes, marbles and tables. *M.Tchg.*, no. 50, pp. 36–37; Spring 1970.

The twelve possible situations for distributing four marbles in two boxes, no marble being left out.

Vaughn, Ruth. Investigation of line crossing in a circle. *A.T.* 18:157–60; Mar. 1971.

Wheeler, David. Partitions. *M.Tchg.*, no. 57, p. 29; Winter 1971.

Wiggins, Alvin D. An occupancy problem involving placement of pairs of balls. *M.Mag.* 45:82–85; Mar. 1972.

8.2 Pascal's Triangle

Barlow, Richard Lee, ed. On Pascal's triangle. *Pentagon* 29:114–16; Spring 1970.

Pascal's triangle written in terms of a prime modulus.

Doe, T. Two investigations. *M.Tchg.*, no. 47, pp. 34–36; Summer 1969.

Duncan, David R., and Bonnie H. Littwiller. Games, patterns, and Pascal's triangle. *S.S.M.* 73:187–93; Mar. 1973.

Esch, Gerald. Note on Pascal's triangle. *Pentagon* 28:89–90; Spring 1969.

The nth diagonal gives the coefficients in the Maclaurin series.

Ewen, Bruce. Pascal's triangle is upside down. *M.T.* 63:127; Feb. 1970.

Geldzahler, Barry. Powers of eleven by Pascal's triangle. *J.R.M.* 3:188–89; July 1970.

Gibbs, Richard A. Euler, Pascal, and the missing region. *M.T.* 66:27–28; Jan. 1973.

Glenn, John. The quest for the lost region. *M.Tchg.*, no. 43, pp. 23–25; 1968.

Horner, Walter W. New angles of an old triangle. *R.M.M.*, no. 14, pp. 52–54; Jan.–Feb. 1964.

Huntley, H. E. *The Divine Proportion: A Study in Mathematical Beauty.* New York: Dover Publications, 1970.

Chapter 10: "Pascal's Triangle and Fibonacci."

Jansson, Lars C. Spaces, functions, polygons, and Pascal's triangle. *M.T.* 66:71–77; Jan. 1973.

Keeney, R. L. On the trinomial coefficients. *M.Mag.* 42:210–12; Sept. 1969.

Scott, D. Investigation of a "Maths Today" problem: an exercise in pattern-spotting. *M.Tchg.*, no. 56, pp. 38–45; Autumn 1971.

Singmaster, David. How often does an integar occur as a binomial coefficient? *A.M.M.* 78:385–86; Apr. 1971.

Tracy, Rev. Melvin R. A triangle from trigonometry. *M.T.* 64:635–40; Nov. 1971.

Triangles of coefficients derived from trigonometric functions resemble Pascal's triangle.

Truran, T. P. A generalization of Pascal's triangle. *M.Tchg.*, no. 60, pp. 16–18; Sept. 1972.

8.3 Probability: Problems and Theory

Alter, Ronald, and Lawrence Ringenberg. Five full houses! *M.Mag.* 45:289–90; Nov. 1972.

Brown, Richard. Predicting the outcome of the world series. *M.T.* 63:494–500; Oct. 1970.

Buxton, R. Probability and its measurement. *M.Tchg.*, no. 49, pp. 4–12, Winter 1969; no. 50, pp. 56–61, Spring 1970.

Clarke, R. H. Let's form a queue. *M.Tchg.*, no. 56, pp. 28–33; Autumn 1971.

Fey, James T. Probability, integers, and pi. *M.T.* 64:329–32; Apr. 1971.
Shows that if two numbers are picked at random from the set of positive integers, the probability that they will have no common divisor is $6/\pi^2$.

Flory, David W. What are the chances? *A.T.* 16:581–82; Nov. 1969.
Activities used to introduce elementary school pupils to the concept of probability.

Gardner, Martin. The paradox of the nontransitive dice. *Sci.Am.* 223:110–13; Dec. 1970.
Philosophical aspect of probability and the principle of indifference.

———. St. Petersburg paradox. *Sci.Am.*, p. 168; Apr. 1957.

———. Why the long arm of coincidence is usually not as long as it seems. *Sci.Am.* 227:110–112B; Oct. 1972.

Gritsevicz, Cynthia. The different logics of chance. *Exponent*, pp. 4–5; June 1966.

Higgins, James E. Probability with marbles and a juice container. *A.T.* 20:165–66; Mar. 1973.

Holmes, Allen H. Statistical inference: some classroom activities. *S.S.M.* 71:75–78; Jan. 1971.

Howard, W. J. *A Simple Manual on Queues: The Long and Short of Waiting Lines*. Canoga Park, Calif.: Xyzyx Information Corp., 1971. 54 pp.

International Business Machine Corp. *Reference Manual on Random Number Generation and Testing*. 1959.

Klamkin, Murray S. A probability of more heads. *M.Mag.* 44:146–49; May 1971.

Lawler, Gregory, and Dale M. Shafer. [Problem 3410.] *S.S.M.* 72:356; Apr. 1972.
A probability problem about dice.

May, Lola J. Probability; chance for a change. *Grade Teacher* 86:31–32+; Jan. 1969.

Meyer, D. L. Methods of generating random normal numbers. *Education and Psychology Magazine*. 29:193–98; Spring 1969.

Mold, Josephine, and David S. Fielker. *Towards Probability*. Cambridge: at the University Press, 1971. 32 pp. (Paper)
For young children; informal introduction to the probability concept by means of simple experiments with coins, dice, dominoes, and so on.

Nelson, R. D. Undistributed middle—a question of probability. *M.Tchg.*, no. 46, pp. 34–35; Spring 1969.

Newell, G. F. *Applications of Queueing Theory*. Chapman Hall, 1971. 148 pp.
Emphasis more on practice than on theory.

Niman, John, and Robert Postman. Probability on the geoboard. *A.T.* 20:167–70; Mar. 1973.

Ohriner, M. Finding the area under a curve by the Monte Carlo method. *Physics Teacher* 9:449–50; Nov. 1971.

Ore, Oystein. Pascal and the invention of probability theory. *Colorado College Studies*, no. 3, pp. 11–24; 1959.

Phillips, T. C. Teacher or taught? *M.Tchg.*, no. 56, pp. 20–23; Autumn 1971.
Breaking a stick into three pieces that will form a triangle.

Prielipp, Robert W. The Euler ϕ-function and a problem of chance. *M.T.* 66:283–86; Mar. 1973.

Raini, R. The peculiar distribution of first digits in numbers that appear in tables, etc. *Sci.Am.* 221:109–20; Dec. 1969.

Ramaley, J. F. Buffon's noodle problem. *A.M.M.* 76:916–18; Oct. 1969.

Ryan, Sister M. Kara. Probability and the Platonic solids. *M.T.* 64:621–24; Nov. 1971.

Servien, Pius. "Chance and Mathematics." In *Great Currents in Mathematics*, edited by F. Le Lionnais, pt. 1, bk. 2. New York: Dover Publications, 1962.

Shakun, R. L. Geometry and probability. *Mathematics Student* [Brooklyn Technical High School], vol. 21, no. 3, pp. 6–7; June 1953.
  Breaking a stick into three pieces to form a triangle.

Shaw, H. *Simple Probability through Experiments*. Bond Educational [England], 1971. 90 pp. (Paper)

Silverman, David L. The substitute duellist. *J.R.M.* 4:71–72; Jan. 1971.
  An unusual probability problem.

Silverman, David L., problem ed. The wit-man sampler. [Problem 74.] *J.R.M.* 3:109; Apr. 1970.
  An unusual probability problem.

Simon, Julian L., and Allen Holmes. A new way to teach probability statistics. *M.T.* 62:283–88; Apr. 1969.
  The Monte Carlo method.

Smith, J. Philip. Probability, geometry, and witches. *M.S.J.*, vol. 19, no. 4, pp. 1–3; May 1972.

Three of the Five. *Pythagoras*, vol. 2, no. 11, pp. 89–108; 1969–70.
  Informal discussion of probability and related topics.

Walsh, James. An introduction to probability over infinite sample spaces. *Pentagon* 29:19–23; Fall 1969.

Wells, Peter. Decaying pennies. *M.Tchg.*, no. 53, pp. 2–3; Winter 1970.
  Analysis of a simple problem in the probability of coin tossing.

8.4 Games of Chance; Gambling

Bloom, D. M. A gambler's ruin problem. [Problem E2276.] *A.M.M.* 79:90–91; Jan. 1972.

Conrad, S. R., et al. Rencontres mod 13. [Problem E2269.] *A.M.M.* 78:1141; Dec. 1971.
  A well-known problem in probability when dealing a deck of cards in the manner of the French gambling game of Treize.

Dubins, Lester, and Leonard Savage. Optimal gambling systems. *Proceedings of the National Academy of Sciences*, vol. 46; 1960.

Epstein, Richard A. *Theory of Gambling and Statistical Logic*. New York: Academic Press, 1967. 492 pp.
  Survey of "kubeiagensis," probability, statistics, game theory, and decision theory; also excellent material on the mathematical theory of dice, cards, contract bridge, poker, blackjack, horseracing, and the stock market. Fallacies and sophistries.

Flory, David W. What are the chances? *A.T.* 16:581–82; Nov. 1969.

Goren, Charles. *Go with the Odds.* New York: Macmillan Co., 1969. 308 pp.
Popular discussion of lotteries, bridge, casino, and other games.

Greenblatt, M. H. That fifth card! *J.R.M.* 5:39; Jan. 1972.

Jacoby, Oswald. *Oswald Jacoby on Gambling.* New York: Hart Publishing Co., 1970. 288 pp. (Paper)

Jacoby, Oswald, and John R. Crawford. *The Backgammon Book.* New York: Viking Press, 1970. 224 pp.
A serious treatment of probabilities, acey-deucy, chouette, and so on.

Kemeny, John, and Laurie Snell. Game-theoretic solution of baccarat. *A.M.M.* 64:465–69; Aug.–Sept. 1957.

MacDougall, Michael. *MacDougall on Dice and Cards.* New York: Coward-McCann, 1944. 90 pp.

Radner, Sidney H. *How to Win at Roulette and Other Casino Games.* New York: Wehman Bros., 1958. 96 pp.

Riddle, Major A., and Joe Hyams. *The Weekend Gambler's Handbook.* New York: Random House, 1963. 157 pp.

Scarne, John. *Scarne's Complete Guide to Gambling.* New York: Simon & Schuster, 1961. 714 pp.

Sheinwold, Alfred. It's in the cards: blackjack—counting the cards. *Argosy,* Aug. 1961.

Thorp, Edward. A favorable strategy for "Twenty-one." *Proceedings of the National Academy of Science,* vol. 47; 1961.

———. A prof beats the gamblers. *Atlantic Monthly,* June 1962.

Wilson, Allan N. *The Casino Gambler's Guide.* New York: Harper & Row, 1970. 320 pp.
A revised and enlarged edition of an earlier work by an experienced mathematician and computer programmer; excellent bibliography.

Winning at Casino Gaming. (Anonymous.) Glen Head, N.Y.: Rouge et Noire, 1966. 341 pp.

Chapter 9

Manipulative Recreations

9.1 Ticktacktoe

Cohen, Daniel I. A. The solution of a simple game. *M.Mag.* 45:213–16; Sept. 1972.
   The game of Lose Ticktacktoe.
Gardner, Martin. Ticktacktoe and its complications. *Sci.Am.* 225:102–5; Aug. 1971.
Mercer, Gene B., and John R. Kolb. Three-dimensional Ticktacktoe. *M.T.* 64:119–22; Feb. 1971.
Random Ticktacktoe. *J.R.M.* 1:107; Apr. 1968. Also, *J.R.M.* 5:149; Apr. 1972.
Timmons, Robert A. Tic-tac-toe—a mathematical game for grades 4 through 9. *A.T.* 14:506–8; Oct. 1967.

9.2 The Fifteen Puzzle

Barlow, Richard L. The mathematical scrapbook. *Pentagon* 31:105–12; Spring 1972.
   Good discussion of the Fifteen Puzzle.
The Fifteen Puzzle. *Pythagoras* (English ed.), vol. 2, no. 8, pp. 28–30; 1969–70.
Gardner, Martin. Boss puzzle. *Sci.Am.*, p. 124; Aug. 1957.
Liebeck, Hans. Some generalizations of the 14–15 puzzle. *M.Mag.* 44:185–89; Sept. 1971.
MacGregor, Hilda. A problem in moving. *M.S.J.*, vol. 17, no. 2, p. 4; Jan. 1970.
   Somewhat similar to the Fifteen Puzzle.
Schwartz, Benjamin L. A new sliding block puzzle. *M.T.* 66:277–80; Mar. 1973.
Spitznagel, E. E., Jr. A new look at the Fifteen Puzzle. *M.Mag.* 40:171–74; 1967.
Story, W. E. Note on the "15" puzzle. *American Journal of Mathematics* 2:399–404; 1879.

9.3 Binary Recreations; Nim; Wythoff's Game

Gardner, Martin. How to triumph at Nim by playing safe. *Sci.Am.* 226:104–7; Jan. 1972.

Heath, F. G. Origins of the binary code. *Sci.Am.* 227:76–83; Aug. 1972.
    Use of the binary code in textile weaving; Francis Bacon's cipher; Beaudot's
    telegraph.
Howells, D. F., and J. C. Pond. More on Fibonacci Nim. *Fib.Q.* 3:61–63; Feb.
    1965.
Litwiller, B. H., and D. R. Duncan. Nim: an application of base two. *S.S.M.*
    72:761–64; Dec. 1972.
McIntosh, A. J. Binary and the Towers of Hanoi. *M.Tchg.*, no. 59, p. 15; Summer
    1972.
Merriell, David. Nim and natural numbers. *M.T.* 64:342–44; Apr. 1971.
Moore, E. H. A generalization of the game called Nim. *Annals of Mathematics,*
    vol. 2, no. 11, pp. 90–94; 1910.
Niman, John. Game introduction to the binary numeration system. *A.T.* 18:600–
    601; Dec. 1971.
O'Donnell, J. R. They are *not* "magic" number cards. *A.T.* 12:647–48; Dec. 1965.
    A recreation based on binary notation.
Schaaf, William. Binary applications: game of Nim. *M.T.* 47:416; Oct. 1954.
    Bibliography, 14 references.
Schwartz, Benjamin L. Some extensions of Nim. *M.Mag.* 44: 252–57; Nov. 1971.

9.4   Board Games

Austwick, G. Hexadiangle. *M.Tchg.*, no. 59, p. 13; Summer 1972.
    A game played on a hexagonal board laid out in equilateral triangles.
Ayres, F. H. *A Handbook of Reversi.* Jacques & Son, 1888.
Brooke, Maxey. The haunted checkerboards. *R.M.M.*, pp. 28–30; June 1961.
Bruijn, N. G. de. A solitaire game and its relation to a finite field. *J.R.M.* 5:133–
    37; Apr. 1972.
Burks, Arthur W., ed. *Essays on Cellular Automata.* Urbana, Ill.: University of
    Illinois Press, 1970.
Cady, Alice H. *Reversi.* New York: American Sports Publishing Co., 1896. 44 pp.
Culin, Stewart. *Korean Games, with Notes on the Corresponding Games of China
    and Japan.* Philadelphia: University of Pennsylvania, 1895.
———. *Games of the Orient.* Rutland, Vt.: Chas. E. Tuttle Co., 1958.
    A reprint of Culin's earlier monograph on "Korean Games, . . . "
Fielker, David S. Mathematical games. *M.Tchg.*, no. 56, pp. 11–13; Autumn 1971.
    Chinese draughts, Lancaster checkers, pegboard, and other games.
Gardner, Martin. About mathematical games that are played on boards. *Sci-Am.*
    202:170–78; Apr. 1960.
———. "Four Unusual Board Games." In *Martin Gardner's Sixth Book of
    Mathematical Games from Scientific American,* pp. 39–47. San Francisco:
    W. H. Freeman & Co., 1971.
    Topological board games, including the games of Tablut, Focus, Black, and
    the French Military Game.
———. The game of "Life." *Sci.Am.,* pp. 120–23; Oct. 1970; p. 118, Nov. 1970;
    p. 114, Dec. 1970; pp. 112–17, Feb. 1971.
    Conway's solitaire game, similar to polyominoes but more sophisticated;
    cellular automata; in short, a simulation game.

————. New puzzles from the game of Halma, the noble ancestor of Chinese checkers. *Sci. Am.* 225:104–7; Oct. 1971.

————. On cellular automata, self-reproduction, the Garden of Eden and the game of "Life." *Sci.Am.* 224:112–17; Feb. 1971. Also, 224:108; Mar. 1971, and 224:116–17; Apr. 1971.

Lasker, Emanuel. *Brettspiele der Völker*. Berlin, 1931.

Leete, Charles. Ye Olde Gayme of Rithomachy. *Engineering and Science Review* [Case Institute], pp. 18–20; Jan. 1960.

Lewis, Angelo [Professor Hoffmann]. *The Book of Table Games*. London: George Routledge & Sons, 1894.
"Reversi": pp. 611–23.

Peel, W. H. [Berkeley]. *Reversi and Go-Bang*. New York: F. A. Stokes & Co., 1890. 72 pp.

Richards, John F. C. Boissière's Pythagorean game. *Scrip.M.* 12:177–217; Sept. 1946.

Sackson, Sidney. *A Gamut of Games*. New York: Random House, 1969. 224 pp. A collection of nearly 40 unfamiliar games; also brief reviews of 200 conventional games.

Smith, D. E., and C. C. Eaton. Number games and number rhymes: Rithomachia. *Teachers College Record* 13:385–95; 1912. Also, *A.M.M.*, Apr. 1911.

9.5   Pencil and Paper Games

DeLoach, A. P. Some investigations into the game of Sim. *J.R.M.* 4:36–41; Jan. 1971.
A game played on the six vertices of a regular hexagon.

Duncan, David R., and Bonnie H. Litwiller. Games, patterns and Pascal's triangle. *S.S.M.* 73:187–93; Mar. 1973.

Engel, Douglas. Dim: three-dimensional Sim. *J.R.M.* 5:274–75; Oct. 1972.

Funkenbusch, W. W. Sim as a game of chance. *J.R.M.* 4:297–98; Oct. 1971.

Gardner, Martin. "Games." In *Scientific American:*
Bridg-it: July 1961, p. 150.
Brussel Sprouts: July 1967; Aug. 1967, p. 108.
Bulo: Feb. 1958, p. 102.
Clock Solitaire: Mar. 1968, p. 124.
Connecto: Aug. 1969, p. 121.
Contack: Mar. 1961, p. 173.
Focus: Oct. 1963, p. 129.
Foxhole: Jan. 1968, p. 126.
Go-Moku: Aug. 1971, p. 103; Sept. 1971, p. 212; Oct. 1971, p. 107.
Guess-It: Dec. 1967, p. 129.
Halma: July 1961, p. 152; Oct. 1961, p. 164; Oct. 1971.
Hamstrung Squad Car: Feb. 1967, p. 118.
Hexapawn: Mar. 1962, p. 140.
Hip: Oct. 1960, p. 172; Nov. 1960, p. 194.

Hit-and-Run: July 1969, p. 118.

Hot: Feb. 1967, p. 116.

Jam: Feb. 1967, p. 116.

Kayles: Feb. 1967, p. 116.

Life: Jan. 1970, p. 108; Feb. 1971, p. 108; Mar. 1971, p. 109; Apr. 1971, p. 117.

Military: Oct. 1962, p. 108; Nov. 1962, p. 164.

Reversi: Apr. 1960, p. 174.

Roulette: Dec. 1961, p. 152.

Solitaire: June 1968, p. 114; July 1968, p. 121; Aug. 1968, p. 111; Sept. 1968, p. 231.

Sprouts: July 1967; Aug. 1967, p. 108.

Tablut: Oct. 1963, p. 126.

Taxtic: Feb. 1958, p. 108; Apr. 1958, p. 122; May 1958, p. 126.

―――. The game of Slither. *Sci.Am.* 226:117–18; June 1972. Also, 227:182; Sept. 1972.
A lattice game.

―――. John Horton Conway's game of "Hackenbush." *Sci.Am.* 226:104–7; Jan. 1972. Also, 226:102–4; Feb. 1972.

―――. A new pencil-and-paper game based on inductive reasoning. *Sci.Am.* 221:140–44; Nov. 1969.

―――. Sim, Chomp and Race Track: new games for the intellect (and not for Lady Luck). *Sci.Am.* 228:108–13; Jan. 1973.

Papy, Frédérique, and Georges Papy. *Graph Games.* New York: Thomas Y. Crowell Co., 1971. 33 pp.

Simmons, G. J. The game of Sim. *J.R.M.* 2:66; Apr. 1969.

9.6 Manipulative Puzzles and Recreations

Barclay, Tim. Pattern blocks. *M.Tchg.*, no. 49, pp. 51–53; Winter 1969.

Barwell, Brian R. Cutting string and arranging counters. *J.R.M.* 4:164–68; July 1971.

Bergerson, Howard. Nine-coin move. *J.R.M.* 3:47–48; 233–34; Jan.–Oct. 1970.

Bidwell, James. The ten-coin triangle. *M.Tchg.*, no. 54, pp. 21–22; Spring 1971.

Boys, C. V. *Soap Bubbles and the Forces Which Mold Them.* New York: Doubleday & Co., Anchor Books, 1959.

Creative Publications: 1973 Catalog. Available from Creative Publications, P. C. Box 10328, Palo Alto, Calif. 94303.
A 95-page illustrated catalog of mathematical puzzles, games, and recreations.

Davidson, Patricia S. An annotated bibliography of suggested manipulative devices. *A.T.* 15:509–24; Oct. 1968.

DeBono, Edward. *The Five Day Course in Thinking.* Baltimore: Penguin Books, 1969. 160 pp.
Recreations involving knives and bottles, match boxes, and a game similar to a pentomino game.

Eisenberg, Theodore, and John Van Beynen. Mathematics through visual problems. *A.T.* 20:85–90; Feb. 1973.
Hidden squares; painted cubes and rectangular solids; Tower of Hanoi.

Epps, P. R., and J. F. Deans. *Mathematical Games.* Macmillan Education, 1972.
A folder of 22 games.

Even, Shimon. "The price is right" game. *A.M.M.* 73:180–82; Feb. 1966.

Fielker, D. S. "Master Mind" (and other games). *M.Tchg.*, no. 60, pp. 24–25; Sept. 1972.

Gardner, Martin. Chinese ring puzzle. *Sci.Am.* 227:108–9; Aug. 1972.

———. Coin problems. *Sci.Am.* Feb. 1966, pp. 112–18; Mar. 1966, p. 116; May 1966, p. 127.

———. Cord and ring puzzle. *Sci.Am.*, Oct. 1958, p. 128; Nov. 1958, p. 142.

———. Further encounters with touching cubes, and the paradoxes of Zeno as "supertasks." *Sci.Am.* 225:96–99; Dec. 1971.

———. "Mathematical Magic Tricks." In *Martin Gardner's Sixth Book of Mathematical Games from Scientific American,* pp. 135–42. San Francisco: W. H. Freeman & Co., 1971.

———. Piet Hein's mechanical puzzles. *Sci.Am.* 228:109; Feb. 1973.

———. Pony puzzle. *Sci.Am.*, Nov. 1971, p. 115; Dec. 1971, p. 99.

———. Sliding block puzzles. *Sci.Am.*, Feb. 1964, p. 122; Mar. 1964, p. 128; May 1964, p. 124.

———. "Sliding-Block Puzzles." In *Martin Gardner's Sixth Book of Mathematical Games from Scientific American,* pp. 64–70. San Francisco: W. H. Freeman & Co., 1971.

———. Sliding-block puzzle invented by Edward B. Escott. *Sci.Am.* 222:113; Feb. 1970.

———. T-puzzle. *Sci.Am.*, Nov. 1971, p. 114; Dec. 1971, p. 99.

Gibson, Walter. *Fell's Guide to Papercraft Tricks, Games and Puzzles.* New York: Frederick Fell, 1963.
Chapters 5 and 7: manipulative puzzles and tricks.

Gombert, Jan M. Coin strings. *M.Mag.* 42:244–47; Nov. 1969.

Hadley, Judy. Functions occurring in puzzles and games. *M.Tchg.*, no. 49, p. 22; Winter 1969.

Hollands, Roy. Last. *M.Tchg.*, no. 48, pp. 31–32; Autumn 1969.
A game for two players requiring only a rectangular sheet of paper and a few pennies.

Kaczynski, T. J., et al. A match stick problem. [Problem 787.] *M.Mag.* 44:294–96; Nov. 1971. Also, 45:110–12; Mar. 1972.

Kadesch, Robert R. *Math Menagerie.* New York: Harper & Row, Publishers, 1970. 112 pp.
Some two dozen experiments: probability, binary numeration, mappings, soap films, math machines, and so on.

Kordemsky, Boris. *The Moscow Puzzles.* New York: Charles Scribner's Sons, 1972.
Chapter 3: "Geometry with Matches," pp. 50–58; Chapter 10: "Mathematical Games and Tricks," pp. 120–34.

Krulik, Stephen. *A Handbook of Aids for Teaching Junior-Senior High School Mathematics.* Philadelphia: W. B. Saunders Co., 1971. 120 pp.
Collection of 40 games and devices, including the Möbius strip, the Tower of Hanoi, Chinese tangrams, curve stitching, and the number-base calendar.

Li, H. Y., and S. S. Morrill. *I Ching Games*. San Francisco: Cadleon Press (P.O. Box 24), n.d. 134 pp.
Contains many games, especially variations of Tangram and the Fifteen Puzzle.
McIntosh, Alistair. A puzzle untangled. *M.Tchg.*, no. 46, pp. 16–18; Spring 1969.
A puzzle with moving counters.
McKerrell, A. Solitaire: an application of the four-group. *M.Tchg.*, no. 60, pp. 38–39; Sept. 1972.
Mathematical Games. *Encyclopedia International*, vol. 11, p. 442. New York: Grolier, 1965.
More Askew Than the Tower of Pisa. *Pythagoras* (English ed.), vol. 1, no. 4, pp. 66, 74–76; 1968.
A matchbox trick depending on principles of mechanics.
Nsimbi, M. B. *Omweso, a Game People Play in Uganda*. Occasional Paper no. 6, African Studies Center. Los Angeles: University of California at Los Angeles, 1968.
Ranucci, Ernest R. Isosceles point sets. *J.R.M.* 5:151; Apr. 1972.
Arranging seven points in space so that all the 35 triples form isosceles triangles.
Ricci, Mark A. Perfectly odd squares. *J.R.M.* 5:138–43; Apr. 1972.
Rohrbough, Lynn., ed. *Count and Capture*. Delaware, Ohio: Cooperative Recreation Service, 1955.
Sackson, Sidney. *A Gamut of Games*. New York: Random House, 1969. 224 pp.
Collection of 40 unfamiliar games; brief reviews of 200 conventional games.
Schwartz, Benjamin L. Double trouble. *J.R.M.* 4:245–51; Oct. 1971.
Shafer, D. M., and Charles W. Trigg. The puzzle game "Drive Ya Nuts." [Problem 3412.] *S.S.M.* 72:357–58; Apr. 1972.
Spielman, Bryan. Rigidity and framework models. *M.Tchg.*, no. 51, pp. 39–43; Summer 1970.
Stephens, Jo. Five counters. *M.Tchg.*, no. 46, p. 30; Spring 1969.
Trigg, Charles W. Inverting coin triangles. *J.R.M.* 2:150–52; July 1969.
――――. Triangular arrangements of numbered disks. *M.T.* 65:157–60; Feb. 1972.
Viggiano, Joseph. Dots and triangles. *J.R.M.* 4:157–63; July 1971.
Wahl, M. Stoessel. A permanent-soap-bubble geometry. *A.T.* 19:307–8; Apr. 1972.
Walter, Marion, and Stephen Brown. What if not? *M.Tchg.*, no. 46, pp. 38–45; Spring 1969.
Geoboards, lattice points, and so on.
Wells, Peter. Do we meet? A mathematical activity for secondary children. *M.Tchg.*, no. 60, pp. 19–21; Sept. 1972.

9.7 Card Games; Card Tricks

Abbott, Robert. *Abbott's New Card Games*. New York: Stein & Day Publishers, 1963.
Austin, A. K. Jeep trips and card stacks. *M.Tchg.*, no. 58, pp. 24–25; Spring 1972.

Gardner, Martin. Amazing mathematical card tricks that do not require presti-digitation. *Sci.Am.* 227:102–5; July 1972.

Kohler, Alfred, and Mannis Charosh. Card shuffling. [Problem 720.] *M.Mag.* 42:269–70; Nov. 1969.

Kohler, Alfred, and Charles W. Trigg. Card shuffling. [Problem 3196.] *S.S.M.* 69:468–69; May 1969.

Mendelsohn, N. S. Shuffling cards. [Problem E792.] *A.M.M.* 55:430–31; Sept. 1948.

Slater, M. The Monge shuffle. [Problem E2223; 1970, p. 307.] *A.M.M.* 78:198–99; Feb. 1971.

Trigg, Charles W. A card trick. *M.T.* 63:395–96; May 1970.

———. [Problem 3196.] *S.S.M.* 69:468–69; May 1969.

Wilde, Edwin F., and Daniel A. Tomandi. On shuffling cards. *M.Mag.* 42:139–42; May 1969.

Yoshigahara, Nobuyuki. Card-return numbers. *J.R.M.* 5:36–38; Jan. 1972.

9.8 Colored Squares; Tiles and Cubes

Duncan, Dewey C. Instant Insanity: that ubiquitous baffler. *M.T.* 65:131–35; Feb. 1972.

There is only one distinct solution, but 191 other equivalent solutions may be obtained from this one by suitable permutations and rotations.

Engle, Douglas. An *n*-dimensional binary coloring problem. *J.R.M.* 4:199–200; July 1971.

———. Cubo-Caibo. *J.R.M.* 5:211–15; July 1972.

A recreational activity with cubical blocks that involves cubic matrices.

Farrell, Margaret A. The Mayblox problem. *J.R.M.* 2:51–56; Jan. 1969.

Fielker, David. *Cubes.* New York: Cambridge University Press, 1969. 32 pp.

Assorted topics: nets, plaits, volumes, polycubes, cube-coloring, dissections, symmetries, supercubes, and so on.

Gardner, Martin. Instant Insanity. *Sci.Am.,* p. 124; Oct. 1968.

Grecos, A. P., and R. W. Gibberd. A diagrammatic solution to "Instant Insanity" problem. *M.Mag.* 44:119–24; May 1971.

Gridgeman, N. T. The 23 colored cubes. *M.Mag.* 44:243–52; Nov. 1971.

Harris, Joyce. The missing cube. [Problem M. T. no. 46.] *M.Tchg.,* no. 51, p 38; Summer 1970.

Instant Insanity. [Letter to the editor.] *American Statistician,* vol. 24, no. 5, pp. 37–38; 1970.

Kahan, Steven J. "Eight Blocks to Madness"—a logical solution. *M.Mag.* 45:57–65; Mar. 1972.

A colored-block puzzle similar to Instant Insanity and the Mayblox problem.

Levin, Robert E. Solving "Instant Insanity." *J.R.M.* 2:189–92; July 1969.

Litchfield, Kay P. A 2 × 2 × 1 solution to "Instant Insanity." *P.M.E.J.* 5:334–37; Fall 1972.

McPhee, G. J., and W. Skelding. Colouring polyhedra. *M.Tchg.,* no. 59, pp. 15–16; Summer 1972.

Macrae, M. The "Niger cubes" box. *M.Tchg.,* no. 51, pp. 44–47; Summer 1970.

Philpott, Wade E. A MacMahon triangle problem. *J.R.M.* 5:72–73; Jan. 1972.
Schwartz, B. L. An improved solution to "Instant Insanity." *M.Mag.* 43:20–23; Jan. 1970.
Shubrikov, A. V., and N. V. Belov. *Colored Symmetry.* New York: Pergamon Press, 1964.
Smillie, K. W. The four color cube problem as an instructive exercise in computing. *Information Processing Society of Canada, Quarterly Bulletin,* vol. 9, pp. 5–7; 1968–69.
Varga, T. Boxes, marbles and tables. *M.Tchg.*, no. 50, pp. 35–37; Spring 1970.
Wahl, Paul. Crazy cubes. *Popular Science* 193:132–33; Nov. 1968.
Instant Insanity.
Wegman, Edward J. A cure for Instant Insanity. *P.M.E.J.* 5:221–23; Fall 1971.
Yeh, Chiao. Instant Insanity. *American Statistician*, vol. 24, no. 3, p. 13; 1970.

9.9   Games and Game Strategy

Barlow, R. L., ed. The game of Hex. *Pentagon*, vol. 31, no. 1, pp. 53–54; Fall 1972.
Bernhart, Arthur. Two-by-two games. *Oklahoma University Mathematics Letter*, vol. 6, no. 1, Oct. 1956; vol. 6, no. 2, Dec. 1956; vol. 6, no. 3, Feb. 1957.
Bugs and Loops. *M.Tchg.*, no. 60, pp. 24–25; Sept. 1972. Also available from Creative Specialties, 83 Prospect St., West Newton, Mass. 02165.
Carteblanche, F. de The princess and the roses. *J.R.M.* 3:238–39; Oct. 1970.
Computer Games. *M.Tchg.*, no. 60, p. 25; Sept. 1972. Also available from Griffin Junior Studies, P. O. Box 13, Wembley, Middlesex, HAO 1LD, U.K.
Davis, Morton C. *Game Theory: A Nontechnical Introduction.* New York. Basic Books, 1970. 220 pp.
    Includes utility theory, nonzero sum games, *n*-person game, and Arrow's social welfare theorem.
Find the Needle. *J.R.M.* 5:69–70; Jan. 1972.
Games and Puzzles. P.O. Box 4, London N6 4DF, England.
    A monthly periodical; launched in 1972.
Gotkin, Lassar G. *Math Matrix Games.* New York: Appleton-Century-Crofts, 1971.
    Teacher's manual; 47 pp.
Hurwicz, Leonid. Game theory and decisions. *Sci.Am.* 192:78–83; Feb. 1955.
Lukács, C., and E. Tarjan. *Mathematical Games.* New York: Walker & Co., 1968. 200 pp.
Mathematics in Games. *Pythagoras* (English ed.), vol. 1, no. 6, pp. 110–30; 1968.
    Game strategy as applied to Nim, Go, and Black's game.
Raymont, P. J. Computer Tic-Tac-Toe. *M.Tchg.*, no. 60, p. 25; Sept. 1972.
    An extended version of Think-A-Dot.
Silverman, David L. *Your Move.* New York: McGraw-Hill Book Co., 1971. 221 pp.
    A collection of 100 puzzles and problems based on game strategy and decision making, drawn from playing cards, chess, geography, number games, and other fields.

Spencer, Donald D. *Game Playing with Computers.* New York: Spartan Books, 1968. 441 pp.

> Game-playing programs and games proposed for computer solution; both FORTRAN and BASIC languages.

Steiner, Hans-Georg. Operational systems and checker games. *M.Tchg.*, no. 48, pp. 4–7; Autumn 1969. Reprinted from *M.T.* 60; Dec. 1967.

Strategy and Tactics. 44 E. 23d St., New York, N.Y. 10010.

> A bimonthly journal devoted primarily to games that simulate political conflicts, etc., but also discusses all sorts of mathematical games.

Zuckerman, David, and Robert Horn. *The Guide to Simulation Games for Education and Training.* Available from Information Resources, 1675 Massachusetts Ave., Cambridge, Mass. 02138; 1970. 334 pp.

9.10 Domino Recreations

Dudeney, H. E. *536 Puzzles and Curious Problems.* New York: Charles Scribner's Sons, 1967.

> Dominoes: pp. 194–95, 397–98.

Gardner, Martin. The domino magic-square problem. *Sci.Am.* 221:122–27; Dec. 1969. Also, 222:126–27; Jan. 1970.

———. A handful of combinatorial games based on dominoes. *Sci.Am.* 221:122–27; Dec. 1969.

Kordemsky, Boris. *The Moscow Puzzles.* New York: Charles Scribner's Sons, 1972.

> Chapter 6: "Dominoes and Dice," pp. 82–90.

Kraitchik, Maurice. *Mathematical Recreations.* New York: Dover Publications, 1953.

> Dominoes, pp. 302–4.

Lucas, Edouard. *Récréations mathématiques.* Vol 2. Paris: A. Blanchard, 1960.

> Dominoes, pp. 52–63.

Madachy, Joseph S. *Mathematics on Vacation.* New York: Charles Scribner's Sons, 1966.

> Dominoes, pp. 209–19.

Massey, Tom E. Dominoes in the mathematics classroom. *A.T.* 18:53–54; Jan. 1971.

Ore, Oystein. *Graphs and Their Uses.* New York: L. W. Singer Co., 1963.

> Dominoes, pp. 5–20, 94–107.

Philpott, Wade E. Domino and superdomino recreations. (Five parts.) *J.R.M.* 4:2–18, 79–87, 229–43; Jan., Apr., Oct. 1971. Also, 5:102–22; Apr. 1972. Also, 5:177–96; July 1972.

> Bibliography.

———. A general quadrille solution. *M.Gaz.* 51:287–90; Dec. 1967.

———. MacMahon's three-color squares. *J.R.M.* 2:67–78; Apr. 1969.

———. Quadrilles. *R.M.M.*, no. 14, pp. 5–11; Jan.–Feb. 1964.

Sands, Bill. The gunport problem. *M.Mag.* 44:193–96; Sept. 1971.

Schuh, Fred. *The Master Book of Mathematical Recreations.* New York: Dover Publications, 1968.
Dominoes, pp. 38–68.

9.11   Chess Recreations

Ball, W. W. R. *Mathematical Recreations and Essays.* New York: Macmillan Co., 1962. (Paper)
Chapter 6, pp. 161–92; chessboard recreations.

Botvinnik, M. M. *Computers, Chess and Long-Range Planning.* Translated by Arthur Brown. New York: Springer-Verlag, 1970. 102 pp.
In addition to chess, the discussion includes concepts from cybernetics, automation, management science, and so on.

Boyer, Joseph. *Les jeux d'échecs non orthodoxes.* Paris: The Author, 1951.

———. *Nouveaux jeux d'échecs non orthodoxes.* Paris: The Author, 1954.

———. *Les jeux de dames non orthodoxes.* Paris: The Author, 1956.

Ceriani, L. *La genesi della posizioni.* Milan: The Author, 1961.

Charosh, Mannis. Detective at the chessboard. *J.R.M.* 5:94–101, 229–30; Apr.–July, 1972.
Bibliography.

Cheng, Henry, and Jordi Dou. Crooked paths. [Problem E2278; 1971, p. 196.] *A.M.M.* 79:92; Jan. 1972.
What is the number of shortest paths from one corner of a chessboard to the diagonally opposite corner which can be traversed by a rook in seven moves, but no fewer?

Cretaine, A. C. *Etudes sur le problème de la marche du cavalier aux jeux des échecs et solution du problème des huit dames.* Paris: The Author, 1865.

Cross, Donald. The road to Geba Oasis. *J.R.M.* 5:281–83, 305–6; Oct. 1972.
A puzzle involving knight moves.

Dawson, T. R., and W. Hunsdorfer. *Retrograde Analysis.* Leeds: Whitehead & Miller, 1915.

Dickins, Anthony S. M. *A Guide to Fairy Chess.* New York: Dover Publications, 1971. 66 pp.
Includes over 90 positions in which various conditions involving maxima and minima are satisfied.

Dickins, Anthony S. M., and W. Cross. *Records in One-Mover Chess Construction Tasks.* The Q Press, 6a Royal Parade, Station Approach, Kew Gardens, Surrey, England, 1970. 8 pp.
Pamphlet listing more than 100 records.

Engel, Douglas A. Quantum chess. *Pentagon* 27:99–103; Spring 1968.

Fabel, K. *Rund um das Schachbrett.* Berlin: Walter de Gruyter, 1955.

Gardner, Martin. Challenging chess tasks for puzzle buffs. *Sci.Am.* 226:112–16; May 1972. Also, 226:117; June 1972.

———. Chess knight's move. *Sci.Am.* 217:128–32; Oct. 1967.

———. Chessplayers. *Sci.Am.,* p. 116; Aug. 1963.

———. Lessons from Dr. Matrix in chess and numerology. *Sci.Am.* 224:104–8; Jan. 1971.

Gibbins, N. M. Chess in three and four dimensions. *M.Gaz.* 28:46–50; May 1944.

Goppelt, John W. Mathematics and the game of checkers. *J.R.M.* 4:262–64; Oct. 1971.

Kraitchik, Maurice. *Mathematical Recreations.* New York: Dover Publications, 1953.

    Chess, checkers, and positional games, pp. 267–323; Fairy chess, pp. 276–79.

Littlewood, J. E. *A Mathematician's Miscellany.* London: Methuen, 1963.

    Number of games of chess, p. 109.

Madachy, Joseph. *Mathematics on Vacation.* New York: Charles Scribner's Sons, 1966.

    Chapter 2, pp. 34–54; chessboard placement problems.

Moser, L. King paths on a chessboard. *M.Gaz.* 39:54; 1955.

Newman, Irving, et al. Nonattacking knights on a chessboard. *A.M.M.* 71:210–11; 1964.

O'hara, E. *Japanese Chess, the Game of Shogi.* Charles E. Tuttle Co., Bridgeway Press, 1958.

Okunev, L. Y. *Combinatorial Problems on the Chessboard,* n.p., 1935.

Parton, V. R. Variations on chess. *New Scientist* [England], 27 May 1965; p. 607.

Rice, John M. *An ABC of Chess Problems.* New York: Dover Publications, 1970. 349 pp.

    Excellent survey, with ample problems and solutions; bibliography.

Rowe, R. Robinson. Roundtripping a chessboard. *J.R.M.* 4:265–67; Oct. 1971.

Scheid, F. Some packing problem. *A.M.M.* 67:231–35; 1960.

Silverman, David L. Rate your wits. *J.R.M.* 3:229–30; Oct. 1970.

    Retrograde analysis problems; including cyclic knight's tours, dummy pawns, quadraphage, and so on.

———. *Your Move.* New York: McGraw-Hill Book Co., 1971. 221 pp.

Stewart, Ian. The number of possible games of chess. *J.R.M.* 4:50; Jan. 1971.

Stover, Mel. Wager problems—old and new. *R.M.M.,* no. 1, pp. 9–18; Feb. 1961.

    Chess and bridge strategies.

Verney, Maj. George H. *Chess Eccentricities.* London: Longmans, Green & Co., 1885.

    Excellent reference work.

White, Alan C. *Sam Loyd and His Chess Problems.* New York: Dover Publications, 1913.

Wilkes, Charles F. *A Manual of Chinese Chess.* San Francisco: Yamato Press, 1952.

Yaglom, A. M., and I. M. Yaglom. *Challenging Mathematical Problems.* Vol. 1. San Francisco: Holden-Day, 1964.

    Chapter 3: Chess problems.

Znosko-Borovsky, Eugene A. *How to Play the Chess Openings.* New York: Dover Publications, 1935, 1971. 147 pp. (Paper)

Chapter 10

Miscellaneous Recreations

10.1 Logic; Inferential Problems; Logical Paradoxes; Infinity

Bartley, W. W., III. Lewis Carroll's lost book on logic. *Sci.Am.* 227:39–46; July 1972.
> Includes comments on the "Liar Paradox."

Buchhalter, Barbara. The logic of nonsense. *M.T.* 55:330–33; May 1962.

Davis, Martin, and Reuben Hersh. Nonstandard analysis. *Sci.Am.* 226:78–86; June 1972.
> The relation between "infinitesimals" and conventional calculus, and their relation to formal logic and computation.

De Long, Howard. Unsolved problems in arithmetic. *Sci.Am.* 224:50–60; Mar. 1971.
> Comments on logic, paradoxes, axiomatics, Gödel's theorem, and so on.

DeVries, Peter Hugh. A note on the nature of the infinite. *J.R.M.* 4:260–61; Oct. 1971.

Gardner, Martin. Further encounter with touching cubes, and the paradoxes of Zeno as "supertasks." *Sci.Am.* 225:96–99; Dec. 1971.

——. Hempel's paradox. *Sci.Am.* Apr. 1957, p. 170.

——. "Infinite Regress." In *Martin Gardner's Sixth Book of Mathematical Games from Scientific American*, pp. 220–29. San Francisco: W. H. Freeman & Co., 1971.

——. Infinite series. *Sci.Am.*, May 1961, p. 164; June 1961, p. 176.

——. "Limits of Infinite Series." In *Martin Gardner's Sixth Book of Mathematical Games from Scientific American*, pp. 163–72. San Francisco: W. H. Freeman & Co., 1971.

——. The orders of infinity, the topological nature of dimension and "supertasks." *Sci.Am.* 224:106–9; Mar. 1971.
> Paradoxes of the infinite.

——. Paradox of the unexpected egg. *Sci.Am.*, Mar. 1963, p. 146; May 1963, p. 112.

——. Zeno's paradox. *Sci.Am.*, Dec. 1971, pp. 96–99.

Goodrich, Ruth. An analysis of some of the syllogisms found in Alice in Wonderland. *Pentagon* 21:30–38; Fall 1961.

Greenblatt, M. H. Pons Asinorum. *J.R.M.* 3:205–6; Oct. 1970.
> Note on logic problems like the "three smudges problem."

Hann, George. Language, logic and the conditional. *M.Tchg.*, no. 59, pp. 18–20; Summer 1972.

Hollis, Martin. *Tantalizers: A Book of Original Logical Puzzles.* London: Allen & Unwin, 1970.

Martin, Robert L., ed. *The Paradoxes of the Liar.* New Haven, Conn.: Yale University Press, 1970. 149 pp.
Comprehensive discussion of Epimenides' Cretan paradox; bibliography, 250 references.

Marvin, Les. At least two Welshmen have the same number of Welsh friends. *J.R.M.* 3:107, 112, 259–60; Apr.–Oct. 1970.
Problem 2 under "Rate Your Wits."

Passmore, John. "The Infinite Regress." In *Philosophical Reasoning.* New York: Charles Scribner's Sons, 1961.

Quine, W. V. Paradox. *Sci.Am.* 206:84–96; Apr. 1962.
Russell's paradox, Greeling's paradox, and the paradoxes of Zeno and Epimenides.

Rapoport, Anatol. Escape from paradox. *Sci.Am.* 217:50–56; July 1967.
The "Prisoner's Dilemma" and other logical paradoxes.

Rosen, Robert. Consequences of Russell's paradox. *M.S.J.* 17:1–3, 5; May 1970.

Silverman, David L. A problem of relations. *J.R.M.* 4:147; Apr. 1971.
A riddle about the brother-in-law relationship.

Starr, Norton. A paradox in probability theory. *M.T.* 66:166–68; Feb. 1973.
Problem of the prisoner's dilemma.

Summers, George J. *Test Your Logic.* New York: Dover Publications, 1972. 100 pp. (Paper)

Teensma, E. *The Paradoxes.* Van Gorcum, 1969. 44 pp.
Logical paradoxes such as the liar, Richard's, and Greeling's paradoxes.

Thomson, James. "Infinity in Mathematics and Logic." In *The Encyclopedia of Philosophy*, vol. 4, pp. 183–90. New York: Crowell Collier, 1967.

Wang, Hao. Games, logic and computers. *Sci.Am.* 213:98–106; Nov. 1965.
Using the domino problem to facilitate the solution of infinite decision problems.

10.2 Cryptography; Cryptanalysis; Codes and Ciphers

Biermann, Kurt-R. Zum Gauss'chen Kryptogramm von 1812. *Monatsberichte der Deutschen Akademie der Wissenschaften zu Berlin*, vol. 13, no. 2, pp. 152–57; 1971.
Bibliography.

Binary Codes. *Pythagoras* (English ed.), vol. 1, no. 4, pp. 70–74; 1968.

Gardner, Martin. On the practical uses and bizarre abuses of Sir Francis Bacon's biliteral cipher. *Sci.Am.* 227:114–18; Nov. 1972.

Sinkov, Abraham. *Elementary Cryptanalysis—a Mathematical Approach.* New Mathematical Library no. 22; monograph project of the School Mathematics Study Group. New York: Random House/Singer, 1968. 198 pp. (Paper)
Makes use of probability, statistics, matrix theory, modular arithmetic, and combinatorics.

Vaughan, Michael. Deciphering a telex tape—a project. *M.Tchg.*, no. 51, pp. 55–59; Summer 1970.

Willerding, Margaret. Codes for boys and girls. *A.T.* 2:23–24; Feb. 1955.
A very simple elementary cipher.
Wolfe, James R. *Secret Writing: The Craft of the Cryptographer.* New York:
McGraw-Hill Book Co., 1970. 192 pp.

10.3   Humor and Mathematics

Analog: Science Fiction—Science Fact. *Engineering Procedure,* Nov. 1967. Re-
printed in *Florida Council of Teachers of Mathematics Newsletter,* vol. 14, no.
1; Fall 1971.
Humorous skit on expressing $1 + 1 = 2$ in a "clearer and more easily
understood" fashion.
Babcock, Donald C. Of these the infinite. (Poem.) *Scrip.M.* 14:264–65; Sept.
1948.
Bankoff, Leon, and Charles W. Trigg. Mathematical ideography: rebuses.
[Problem 222.] *M.Mag.* 29:172–73; Jan. 1956.
———. Mathematical rebuses. [Problem E1095.] *A.M.M.* 60:712; Dec. 1953.
Also, 61:426–27; June 1954.
Becker, H. W. How to capitalize on schizophrenia. (Poem.) *M.Mag.* 22:108;
Nov. 1948.
———. Unfinished symbol. (Poem.) *M.Mag.* 22:108; Nov. 1948.
Block, Daniel. A humorous proof of Euclid's postulate *Scrip.M.* 16:292; Dec.
1950.
Boyle, Patrick J. Sinusoidal snooper. *S.S.M.* 71:231–32; Apr. 1971.
Humorous graph based on trigonometric equations.
Coffee, M. M. H., and J. J. Zeltmacher, Jr. [A Moebius band limerick.] *A.M.M.*
72:758; Sept. 1965.
Cordes, Rich, and Dick Nungester. Pascal's triangle. *S.S.M.* 72:718–20; Nov.
1972.
Humorous verse.
Court, Nathan A. Perplexities of a potato-pusher. *Scrip.M.* 14:151–56; June 1948.
Debelak, R. J., and Charles W. Trigg. The chicken rancher. [Problem 2823.]
S.S.M. 62:463; June 1962.
Descartes, Blanche. Bourbaki in reverse. *J.R.M.* 2:206–11; Oct. 1969.
A Fable. *Scrip.M.* 21:137; June 1955. Also, *M.Gaz.* 38:208; 1954.
Fedep, Ya I. M. The schnitzelbank school of mathematical pedagogy. *M.Mag.*
34:340–43; Sept. 1961.
Hagis, Peter, Jr. An analyst's bookshelf. *A.M.M.* 69:980–81; Dec. 1962. Also,
71:283; Mar. 1964.
Karapetoff, V. The way logarithms might have been discovered even though
they weren't. *Scrip.M.* 12:153–59; 1946.
Kochański, S. J. The Columbus quadratic. *J.R.M.* 5:10; Jan. 1972.
McLaughlin, Billie. A mythical history of the jargon of mathematics. *P.M.E.J.,*
Spring 1966, pp. 156–58. Also, *M.T.* 60:880; Dec. 1967.
Matthews, G. Confusion rings. *M.Mag.* 33:282; May 1960.
Mientka, W. E. Professor Leo Moser—reflections of a visit. *A.M.M.* 79:609–14;
June 1972.
Includes selections from Moser's collection of humorous mathematical verse.

Mode, Elmer B. Hidden mathematicians. *M.Mag.* 21:236; Mar. 1948.

———. Trigonometric scrambles. *M.Mag.* 21:287; May 1948.

Nev. R. Mind [N. Altshiller-Court]. Too many? *Scrip.M.* 21:296–98; Dec. 1955.

Nicholson, Fred F., and Charles W. Trigg. Hiawatha and the arrow. *N.M.M.* 14:169–70; Dec. 1939.

A parody of Longfellow's poem.

Onymous. Aristotle Nicholas. *A.M.M.* 73:157; Feb. 1966.

A limerick.

Pance, Fred. Mathematical show me's. *J.R.M.* 5:176, 210, 217, 228; July 1972.

Petard, H. A brief dictionary of phrases used in mathematical writing. *A.M.M.* 73:196–97; Feb. 1966.

Portune, Robert G. A review of arithmetrickery. *M.S.J.*, vol. 19, no. 1, pp. 3–5; Nov. 1971.

A humorous piece about numeration systems.

Prouse, Howard, and Charles W. Trigg. Relation of name change to area of mathematical interest. [Problem 3072.] *S.S.M.* 67:206; Feb. 1967.

Sad Ballad of the Jealous Cones. *M.Mag.* 21:164–65; Jan. 1948.

Smythe, R. T. Mathematical swifties. *A.M.M.* 71:71, 641, 754, 1103; 1964. Also, 72:138, 980; 1965. Also, 73:603, 1061; 1966.

Trigg, Charles W. Dig the ten digits. *M.T.* 62:291; Apr. 1969.

———. Discussion of Maria Agnesi. [Problem 2991.] *S.S.M.* 65:653; Oct. 1965.

———. Facetious integrals. *M.T.* 63:645; Dec. 1970.

———. An invariant determinant. [Problem E1016.] *A.M.M.* 60:115; Feb. 1953.

———. [Letter to the editor.] *M.T.* 63:645; Dec. 1970.

Humorous toying with integral signs.

———. Mathematical show me's. *J.R.M.* 4:35, 44, 49, 77; Jan. 1971. Also, 5:9, 26, 35, 38, 54, 64, 137; 1972.

———. Mathematical terms represented by story paragraphs. [Problem 250.] *P.M.E.J.* 5:299; Spring 1972.

———. Mathematical terms represented by unorthodox expressions. [Problem 3215.] *S.S.M.* 69:747; Nov. 1969.

———. TRIGGonometry exam. [Problem 1191.] *A.M.M.* 63:422; June 1956.

———. Unorthodox definitions. [Problem 376.] *M.Mag.* 33:166; Jan. 1960.

Trigg, Charles W., and Leon Bankoff. Mathematical ideography. *M.Mag.* 29:172; Jan. 1956.

———. Rebuses. *A.M.M.* 61:426; June 1954.

Uhler, Horace S. A story for the nursery. *Scrip.M.* 16:267; Dec. 1950.

Various Short Paragraphs. *A.M.M.* 71:264, Mar. 1964; 72:846, Oct. 1965; 73:486, May 1966.

A Vesgueary. *A.M.M.* 69:811; Oct. 1962.

A limerick vagary.

Widner, Frank. Living by the numbers. *Life*, 18 Feb. 1966, pp. 76A–80.

Are we becoming an impersonalized society of numbers?

———. Today everything is by the numbers. *Indianapolis Star*, 14 Aug. 1966.

Williams, Leland H. The story of (BGG); ($i = 1, 2, 3$). *M.Mag.* 35:228; Sept. 1962.

Williamson, R. S. Genius in disguise. *Scrip.M.* 16:185; Sept. 1950.

10.4   Sports and Mathematics

Austin, A. K. A football problem. *M.Tchg.*, no. 53, p. 35; Winter 1970.
Bedford, Crayton W. Ski judge bias. *M.T.* 65:397–400; May 1972.
   A statistical analysis that reveals a genuine bias.
Brearley, M. N. The long jump miracle of Mexico City. *M.Mag.* 45:241–46; Nov. 1972.
   Mathematical analysis of the broad-jump record of R. Beamon in the 1968 Olympic Games at Mexico City.
Brown, Richard. Predicting the outcome of the World Series. *M.T.* 63:494–500; Oct. 1970.
Cook, E., and W. R. Garner. *Percentage Baseball.* Cambridge, Mass.: M.I.T. Press, 1966. 330 pp.
   A statistical, probabilistic study.
Crispin, Mary. Mathematics and billiards. *M.S.J.*, vol. 20, no. 3, pp. 1–4; Feb. 1973.
Duncan, David, and Bonnie Litwiller. Mathematics in sports: examples for general mathematics. *M.T.* 66:201–6; Mar. 1973.
Gale, David. Optimal strategy for serving tennis. *M.Mag.* 44:197–99; Sept. 1971.
Grant, Nicholas. Mathematics on a pool table. *M.T.* 64:255–57; Mar. 1971.
Mosteller, Frederick. The World Series competition. *Journal of the American Statistical Association* 47:335–80; Sept. 1952.
Munvez, Ronald. Geometry in football. *M.S.J.*, vol. 19, no. 3, pp. 3–4; Mar. 1972.
Ormerod, F. The circular billiard table. *J.R.M.* 3:104–5; Apr. 1970.

10.5   Philately and Mathematics

Corbett, William. The one and six-tenths cent stamp. *A.T.* 17:623; Nov. 1970.
Dodd, Arthur. More mathematics on stamps. *Mathematics in School* [England] 1:21; Sept. 1972.
Lint, J. H. van. Computer stamps from the Netherlands. *J.R.M.* 4:20–23; Jan. 1971.
Makowski, Andrzej. Philately. *J.R.M.* 3:262; Oct. 1970.
   Illustration of a Polish postcard with printed stamp portraying Stefan Banach.
Mathematical Browsing—Philately. *J.R.M.* 2:50; Jan. 1969.
Niman, John. Mathematical concepts and the postage stamp. *A.T.* 19:452–55; Oct. 1972.
Schaaf, William L. Mathematicians and mathematics on postage stamps. *J.R.M.* 1:195–216; Oct. 1968.
———. More mathematics on stamps. *J.R.M.* 5:1–9; Jan. 1972.

10.6   Assorted Diversions and Amusements

Bailey, William T. The "shape" of suitcases. *S.S.M.* 71:659; Oct. 1971.
   Simple solution to the problem of what shape will hold the most luggage.

Bronowski, J. The clock paradox. *Sci.Am.* 208:134–44; Feb. 1963.
The Pythagorean theorem in relation to the clock paradox and the basis of the special theory of relativity.

Casey, Richard, and George Nagy. Advances in pattern recognition. *Sci.Am.* 224:56–64; Apr. 1971.
Automatic machine methods of interpreting various kinds of patterns and clusters.

Corballis, Michael, and Ivan Beale. On telling left from right. *Sci.Am.* 224:96–104; Mar. 1971.
Bilateral symmetry, mirror image reversal, and so on.

Daykin, D. E. The bicycle problem. *M.Mag.* 45:1; Jan. 1972.
An interesting paradox, but perfectly sound mechanics.

Deakin, Michael A. B. Walking in the rain. *M.Mag.* 45:246–53; Nov. 1972.
Analysis of a mathematical model to determine the optimum speed of running in the rain to minimize the extent of wetness.

Engel, Douglas. Some interesting properties of spherical motion. *J.R.M.* 5:275–76; Oct. 1972.

Frederickson, Greg N. Geometric arrangements of flashing lights. *J.R.M.* 5:269–73; Oct. 1972.

Gardner, Martin. The abacus: primitive but effective digital computer. *Sci.Am.* 222:124–26; Jan. 1970.

———. Advertising premiums to beguile the mind; classics by Sam Loyd, master puzzle-poser. *Sci.Am.* 225:114–21; Nov. 1971.
Includes the classic T-puzzle, the Pythagorean-square puzzle, and Loyd's Pony Puzzle.

———. Can time go backwards? *Sci.Am.* 216:98–108; Jan. 1967.
Implications for nuclear physics and for philosophy.

———. Cooked puzzles. *Sci.Am.*, May 1966, pp. 122–27.

———. Elevator problems. *Sci.Am.* 228:106–9; Feb. 1973.

———. Mathematical games. *Sci.Am.* 222:112–14; Feb. 1970.
Nine new puzzles, including a chess problem, an alphametic, and a sliding-block puzzle created by E. B. Escott.

———. A miscellany of transcendental problems: simple to state but not at all easy to solve. *Sci.Am.* 226:114–18; June 1972.
Discussion of π and e; map-coloring problems, "looping" problems, the game of Slither.

———. A new collection of short problems. *Sci.Am.* 223:120–23; Oct. 1970.

———. Quickie problems: not hard, but look out for the curves. *Sci.Am.* 225:106–9; July 1971.
A card trick, a cryptarithm, and some topological questions; 36 problems in all.

———. Some mathematical curiosities embedded in the solar system. *Sci.Am.* 222:108–12; Apr. 1970.

———. Tricks, games and puzzles that employ matches as counters and line segments. *Sci.Am.* 221:116–19; July 1969.

———. The Turing machine and the question it presents: can a computer think? *Sci.Am.* 224:120–23; June 1971.

Gibson, Walter. *Fell's Guide to Papercraft Tricks, Games and Puzzles.* New York: Frederick Fell, 1963.
    Mysterious tricks and stunts, chapters 8, 9, and 10.
Jacobs, Harold. *Mathematics: A Human Endeavor.* San Francisco: W. H. Freeman & Co., 1970. 634 pp.
    Primarily a textbook, but contains several hundred illustrations of a recreational nature.
Moiré Patterns. *Amateur Scientist,* Nov. 1964.
O'Brien, Katherine. *Excavation and Other Verse.* Portland, Maine: Anthoensen Press, 1967. 67 pp.
    Collection containing 14 poems on mathematics.
Orter, G., and Y. Nishijima. Moiré patterns. *Sci.Am.* 208:54–63; May 1963.
    Patterns formed by overlapping figures having periodic rulings.
Peas and Particles. Teacher's guide. Manchester, Mo.: McGraw-Hill Book Co., Webster Division, n.d.
    Booklet suggesting clever ways of guessing how many beans will fill a jar, etc.
Roberts, Charles D. The infinite stamp problem. *American Statistician,* Apr. 1969, pp. 9–10.
Schaek, R. J. Mathematics and the language of literary criticism. *Varsity Graduate: University of Toronto,* Summer 1966, pp. 49–64.
Silverman, David L. Show me's (Rate Your Wits). *J.R.M.* 5:288; Oct. 1972.

Chapter 11

Mathematics in Related Fields

11.1 Ornament and Design; Art and Architecture

Baravalle, Hermann von. Conic sections in relation to physics and astronomy. *M.T.* 63:101–9; Feb. 1970.
  Interesting designs based on parabolas, ellipses, and hyperbolas.
Billings, Robert William. *The Power of Form Applied to Geometric Tracery.* Edinburgh, 1851.
  One hundred designs.
Canaday, John. Less art, more computer, please. *New York Times*, 30 August 1970, p. D19.
Diaz-Bolio, José. *La geometria de los Mayas.* Documental Arqueológico, Area Maya, No. 2 T. 1, Oct.–Nov. 1967. (P.O. Box 155, Mérida, Yucatán, Mexico.)
Forseth, Sonia, and Patricia Adams. Symmetry. *A.T.* 17:119–21; Feb. 1970.
  Repeating patterns and reflections.
Fyfe, R. M. Is it maths? *M.Tchg.*, no. 56, pp. 36–37; Autumn 1971.
  Designs based on combinations of polygons.
Gardner, Martin. "Op Art." In *Martin Gardner's Sixth Book of Mathematical Games from Scientific American,* pp. 239–52. San Francisco: W. H. Freeman & Co., 1971.
Gridgeman, N. T. Latin-square tiling. *M.T.* 64:358–60; Apr. 1971.
———. Quadrarcs, St. Peter's, and the Colosseum. *M.T.* 63:209–15; Mar. 1970.
  Rather technical.
Helwig, Paul Iwan. *Eine Theorie des Schönen; Mathematisch-Psychologische Studie.* Amsterdam, 1897.
Huntley, H. E. *The Divine Proportion: A Study in Mathematical Beauty.* New York: Dover Publications, 1970.
  Art, beauty, and mathematics: chapters 1, 3, 5, 6, and 7.
Ibe, Milagros D. Mathematics and art from one shape. *A.T.* 18:183–84; Mar. 1971.
Le Corbusier. "Architecture and the Mathematical Spirit." In *Great Currents of Mathematical Thought,* pt. 3, bk. 4, edited by F. Le Lionnais. New York: Dover Publications, 1962.
Lehnert, Reinhard. Layered surface design, its pictures and games. *M.Tchg.*, no. 55, pp. 36–43; Summer 1971.
  An original and stimulating discussion of design based on geometric grids and involving the concepts of rational and irrational numbers; bibliography.

Le Lionnais, François. "Beauty in Mathematics." In *Great Currents in Mathematical Thought*, pt. 3, bk. 4, edited by François Le Lionnais. New York: Dover Publications, 1962.

Leonardo's Last Notebook. *Life*, 3 March 1967, pp. 24–32.

Locke, Phil. Residue designs. *M.T.* 65:260–63; Mar. 1972.
 Relation of congruence theory of modular arithmetic to the creation of designs.

March, L., and P. Steadman. *The Geometry of Environment*. London: RIBA Publications, 1971. 360 pp.
 Addressed to students of architecture; replete with significant applications to design including transformations, modules, networks, mosaics, and so on.

Mark, Robert. The structural analysis of Gothic cathedrals. *Sci.Am.* 227:90–98; Nov. 1972.
 Study of the mechanics of flying buttresses, arches, and so on.

Mott-Smith, John. Computers and art. *A.T.* 16:169–72; Mar. 1969.

O'Connor, Susan M. Equilateral triangles and the parallelogram. *Pentagon* 29:73–83; Spring 1970.

Ogletree, Earl. Geometry: an artistic approach. *A.T.* 16:457–61; Oct. 1969.

Reichardt, Jasia, ed. *Cybernetic Serendipity: The Computer and the Arts*. New York: Praeger Publishers, 1969. 101 pp.

Sitomer, Mindel, and Harry Sitomer. *What Is Symmetry?* New York: Thomas Y. Crowell Co., 1970.

Speiser, Andreas. "The Notion of Group and the Arts." In *Great Currents in Mathematical Thought*, pt. 3, bk. 4, edited by F. Le Lionnais. New York: Dover Publications, 1962.

Sperry, A. B., and J. S. Madachy. Calculator art contest. *J.R.M.* 4:201–7; July 1971.
 Exhibits designs made by controlled electronic calculators.

11.2 Dynamic Symmetry; Golden Section

Bicknell, Marjorie, and James Leissner. A near-golden rectangle and related recursive series. *Fib.Q.*, Oct. 1965, pp. 227–31.

Edwards, Edward B. *Pattern and Design with Dynamic Symmetry*. New York: Dover Publications, 1967. 142 pp.
 Reprint of the original book, based on the work of Jay Hambidge, published in 1932 under the title *Dynamarythmic Design*.

Hambidge, Jay. *The Elements of Dynamic Symmetry*. New York: Dover Publications, 1967. 150 pp.
 Reprint of an original work first published in 1926, based on papers originally appearing in 1919.

Holt, Marvin. The golden section. *Pentagon*, Spring 1964; pp. 80–104.

———. Mystery puzzler and phi. *Fib.Q.*, Apr. 1965, pp. 135–38.

Huntley, H. E. *The Divine Proportion: A Study in Mathematical Beauty*. New York: Dover Publications, 1970. 186 pp.
 Golden rectangle, dynamic symmetry, Fibonacci numbers, phyllotaxis and shells, analysis of art and beauty.

―――. Fibonacci geometry. *Fib.Q.* 2:104; Apr. 1964.

Triangle inscribed in a golden rectangle.

Kaiser, Ludwig. *Über die Verhältniszahl des goldenen Schnitts.* Leipzig: Teubner, 1929. 123 pp.

Ledin, George. Log of the golden mean. *Fib.Q.* 2:305; Dec. 1964.

Read, R. C. An introduction to chromatic polynomials. *Journal of Combinatorial Theory* 4:52–71; 1968.

Runion, Garth E. *The Golden Section and Related Curiosa.* Glenville, Ill.: Scott Foresman & Co., 1972. 150 pp.

Tutte, W. T. The golden ratio in the theory of chromatic polynomials. *Annals, New York Academy of Sciences* 175:391–402; 1970.

―――. On chromatic polynomials and the golden ratio. *Journal of Combinatorial Theory* 9:289–96; Oct. 1970.

Viertel, William K., et al. [Problem 3395.] *S.S.M.* 72:94; Jan. 1972.

Proof that in a regular pentagon the ratio of any diagonal to a side is equal to the golden ratio $(1 + \sqrt{5})/2$.

11.3 Music and Mathematics

Adler, Irving, and William McWorter. Twelve-tone intervals. [Problem E-2283.] *A.M.M.* 79:182–83; Feb. 1972.

Partitioning the twelve-tone scale into two six-tone sets.

Barati, G. Mathematics and music. *Music Journal* 24:25+ Nov. and 22+ Dec., 1966.

Dartmouth's Congregation. *Saturday Review,* 31 July 1965, pp. 35, 44–45.

Account of a chamber program of Fibonacci music.

Delman, Morton. Counterpoint as an equivalence relation. *M.T.* 60:137–38; Feb. 1967.

―――. A reply to "More about Counterpoint and Equivalence." *M.T.* 64:94; Jan. 1971.

Donaldson, B. Science: the father of music. *Music Journal* 27:42+; Sept. 1969.

Halsey, G. D., and Edwin Hewitt. More on the superparticular ratios in music. *A.M.M.* 79:1096–100; Dec. 1972.

Excellent analysis; bibliography.

Helm, E. Eugene. The vibrating string of the Pythagoreans. *Sci.Am.* 217:92–103; Dec. 1967.

Excellent insight into the structure of music.

Link, J. Meantone revived: phoenix on record. *Music Journal* 25:58; Sept. 1967.

Macey, J. E. A mathematical method of finding the number of sharps or flats in any musical key. *M.Tchg.,* no. 52, pp. 28–30; Autumn 1970.

McClain, Ernest G. Pythagorean paper folding: a study in tuning and temperament. *M.T.* 63:233–37; Mar. 1970.

Malcom, Paul S. Mathematics of musical scales. *M.T.* 65:611–15; Nov. 1972.

Martin, Henri. "Mathematics and Music." In *Great Currents of Mathematical Thought,* pt. 3, bk. 4, edited by F. Le Lionnais. New York: Dover Publications, 1962.

Mason, R. M. Formula, nomogram, and tables for determining musical interval relationships. *Journal of Research in Musical Education* 15:110–19; Summer 1967.

O'Keeffe, Vincent. Mathematical-musical relationships: a bibliography. *M.T.* 65:315–24; Apr. 1972.
   A unique and extensive list of 300 references to (1) historical aspects; (2) music and computers; (3)·mathematical approaches to musical composition and analysis; and (4) musico-acoustical phenomena.

Silver, A. L. Leigh. Equal beating chromatic scale. *Journal of the Acoustical Society of America.* 29:476–81; 1957.

——. Musimatics or the Nun's Fiddle. *A.M.M.* 78:351–57; Apr. 1971.
   An unusually perceptive analysis of the mathematics of musical tones, etc. Bibliography.

——. *Notes on the Duodecimal Division of the Octave.* London: Institute of Musical Instrument Technology, 1964.

——. Some musico-mathematical curiosities. *M.Gaz.* 48:1–17; 1964.

Taylor, C. A. *The Physics of Musical Sounds.* New York: American Elsevier Publishing Co., 1965.

Wood, A. *The Physics of Music.* 6th ed. Edited by J. M. Bowker. London: Methuen, 1962. Reprint. New York: Barnes & Noble, 1964. 255 pp.

Xenakis, Iannis. *Formalized Music: Thought and Mathematics in Composition.* Bloomington, Ind.: Indiana University Press, 1971. 273 pp.
   Stimulating discussion of avant-garde musical composition; makes use of game theory, stochastic processes, and modern algebra.

Yearout, Paul. More about counterpoint and equivalence. *M.T.* 64:91, 94; Jan. 1971.

11.4   Music and Computers

Appleton, J. New role for the composer. *Music Journal* 27:28+; Mar. 1969.

Fowler, C. Interview with Milton Babbitt. *Music Educators Journal* 55:56–61+; Nov. 1968.

Games, Music and Artificial Intelligence in Computers and Computations. Edited by R. J. Fenichel and J. Weizenbaum. Readings from *Scientific American.* San Francisco: W. H. Freeman & Co., 1971. 283 pp.

Hagemann, V., and A. Modugno. Electronic composition. *Music Educators Journal* 55:86–90; Nov. 1968.

Mason, R. F. Encoding algorithm and tables for the digital analysis of harmony. *Journal of Research in Music Education* 17:286–300, 369–87; Fall–Winter 1969.

Mathews, Max V., et al. *The Technology of Computer Music.* Cambridge, Mass.: M.I.T. Press, 1969. 188 pp.

Peyser, Joan. The evolution of twentieth-century music. *Columbia Forum,* vol. 13, no. 1, pp. 12–17; Spring 1970.

Reich, N. B. Subject is computers. *Music Educators Journal* 55:47–49+; Feb. 1969.

11.5 Mathematics in Nature

Ainsworth, Nathan. An introduction to sequence: elementary school mathematics and science enrichment. *A.T.* 17:143–45; Feb. 1970.

Discussion of spiral arrangements in nature; cones, twigs, shells; Fibonacci sequence and phyllotaxis.

Airy, H. On leaf arrangement. *Proceedings of the Royal Society of London* 21: 176–79; 1873.

Bleicher, M. N., and L. Fejes-Tóth. Two-dimensional honeycombs. *A.M.M.* 72:969–73; Nov. 1965.

Cells analagous to those of the bee.

Gardner, Martin. A discussion of helical structures, from corkscrews to DNA molecules. *Sci-Am.*, June 1963; pp. 152 ff.

———. "The Helix." In *Martin Gardner's Sixth Book of Mathematical Games from Scientific American*, pp. 1–8. San Francisco: W. H. Freeman & Co., 1971.

Discussion of asymmetric space curves.

Goldberg, Michael. Viruses and a mathematical problem. *Journal of Molecular Biology* 24:337–38; 1967.

Huntley, H. E. *The Divine Proportion: A Study in Mathematical Beauty.* New York: Dover Publications, 1970.

Phyllotaxis; the spirals in the sunflower and in seashells.

Kalmus, H. Animals as mathematicians. *Nature* 202:1156–60; 1964.

Karchmar, E. J. Phyllotaxis. *Fib.Q.* 3:64–66; Feb. 1965.

Knight, Charles, and Nancy Knight. Snow crystals. *Sci.Am.* 228:100–107; Jan. 1973.

Mason, B. J. The growth of snow crystals. *Sci.Am.* 204:120–34; Jan. 1961.

Geometric forms of various ice crystals and minerals.

Mind, Nev. R. Running around in circles. *Scrip.M.* 20:92–95; 1954.

Interesting analysis of why men and animals—when they cannot see—tend to move in circles rather than in a straight line as they want to.

Onderdonk, Philip B. Pineapples and Fibonacci numbers. *Fib.Q.* 8:507–8; Dec. 1970.

Oxnard, Charles E. Mathematics, shape and function: a study in primate anatomy. *American Scientist*, Spring 1969, pp. 75–96.

Peirce, B. Mathematical investigation of the fractions which occur in phyllotaxis. *Proceedings of the American Association for the Advancement of Science* 2:444–47; 1849.

Quander, D. D. Snowflakes: an introduction to symmetry. *Science & Child* 8:22–24; Dec. 1970.

Szymkiewicz, D. Role of Fibonacci numbers in botany. *Acta Soc. Botanicorum Poloniae* 5:380–91; 1928.

Watson, James D. *The Double Helix.* New York: Atheneum Publishers, 1968.

Asymmetry in nature.

Chapter 12

Recreations in the Classroom

12.1 Elementary School Activities

Adkins, Bryce. Adapting magic squares to classroom use. *A.T.* 10:498–500; Dec. 1963.
   Methods for constructing fourth-order magic squares and for odd-cell magic squares.

Aichele, Douglas B. "Pica-Centro"—a game of logic. *A.T.* 19:359–61; May 1972.

Allen, Ernest E. Bang, buzz, buzz-bang, and prime. *A.T.* 16:494–95; Oct. 1969.
   A counting game.

Armstrong, Charles. "Fradécent"—a game using equivalent fractions, decimals, and percents. *A.T.* 19:222–23; Mar. 1972.

Arnsdorf, Edward E. A game for reviewing basic facts of arithmetic. *A.T.* 19:589–90; Nov. 1972.

Ashlock, R. B. Floor-tile math. *Instructor* 78:43; Oct. 1968.

Beard, V. E. Math games. *Instructor* 78:43; May 1969.

Bishop, David C. A mathematical diversion. *A.T.* 12:430; Oct. 1965. Also, *M.T.* 58:527; Oct. 1965.
   A word-guessing puzzle involving mathematical words.

Bohan, Harry. Paper folding and equivalent fractions—bridging a gap. *A.T.* 18:245–49; Apr. 1970.

Bradfield, Donald L. Sparking interest in the mathematics classroom. *A.T.* 17:239–42; Mar. 1970.

Brewster, Paul G. Children's games as a means of memory training in primitive and near-primitive societies. *J.R.M.* 4:208–11; July 1971.
   Bibliography.

Broadbent, Frank W. "Contig": a game to practice and sharpen skills and facts in the four fundamental operations. *A.T.* 19:388–90; May 1972.
   For intermediate grades.

Brong, Tedi. Fun with pegs and pegboards. *A.T.* 18:234–35; Apr. 1971.

Brown, Gerald W. Applying "Madam I'm Adam" to mathematics: a discovery project. *A.T.* 19:549–51; Nov. 1972.

Caldwell, J. D. Just for fun. *A.T.* 15:464; May 1968.

Calvo, Robert C. Placo—a number-place game. *A.T.* 15:465–66; May 1968.

Cantlon, Merle M., Doris Homan, and Barbara Stone. A student-constructed game for drill with integers. *A.T.* 19:587–89; Nov. 1972.

Cappon, John. Easy construction of magic squares for classroom use. *A.T.* 12:100–105; Feb. 1965.
   Construction of both odd- and even-cell magic squares to give any magic sum.

100

Chilcote, Blaine, and Nason Chilcote. *Happy Math*. Palo Alto, Calif.: Creative Publications, 1973. 200 pp.
Games and activities in a looseleaf format; primary grades.

Condron, Bernadine F. Game to review basic properties and vocabulary. *A.T.* 12:227–28; Mar. 1965.
Teaches commutative, associative, and distributive properties by means of a matrix arrangement.

Cook, Nancy. Fraction bingo. *A.T.* 17:237–39; Mar. 1970.

Crescimbeni, Joseph. *Treasury of Classroom Arithmetic Activities*. New York: Parker Publishing Co., 1969.

Deans, Edwina. Games for the early grades. *A.T.* 13:140–41, 238–40; Feb.–Mar. 1966.
For grades 1 and 2, to develop number sense.

Dilley, Clyde A., and Walter E. Rucker. Arithmetical games. *A.T.* 19:157–58; Feb. 1972.

Dohler, Dora. The role of games, puzzles, and riddles in elementary mathematics. *A.T.* 10:450–52; Nov. 1963.
Miscellaneous recreations to strengthen number facts, simple equalities, and recognition of geometric figures.

Fennel, Francis M. Multiplication football. *A.T.* 17:236–37; Mar. 1970.

Froelich, Effie. Now what? *A.T.* 14:225–27; Mar. 1967.
Using magic squares.

Gessel, Robert C., Carolyn Johnson, Marty Boren, and Charles Smith. Rainy-day games. *A.T.* 19:303–5; Apr. 1972.

Gifune, C. S. Teen facts drill; game to help children master addition and subtraction. *Grade Teacher* 89:34; May 1972.

Glatz, R. ℞ for Friday, take a number. *Grade Teacher* 74:67; Oct. 1956.
Number tricks.

Gogan, Daisy. A game with shapes. *A.T.* 16:283–84; Apr. 1969.
Illustrates rotations, symmetry, and congruence.

Golden, Sarah R. Fostering enthusiasm through child-created games. *A.T.* 17:111–15; Feb. 1970.

Gorts, Jeannie. Magic square patterns. *A.T.* 16:314–16; Apr. 1969.
A simple, interesting method of constructing 3 × 3 squares.

Gurau, Peter K. A deck of cards, a bunch of kids, and thou. *A.T.* 16:115–17; Feb. 1969.

Haggerty, John B. Kalah—an ancient game of mathematical skill. *A.T.* 11:326–30; May 1964.
Well-known game involving all four fundamental processes as well as pure reasoning; also known as Oware.

Hall, Gary D. A Pythagorean puzzle. *A.T.* 19:67–70; Jan. 1972.

Hammond, Robert C. A device for practice with common denominators and addition of unlike fractions. *A.T.* 8:373; Nov. 1961.
Makes use of magic squares.

Hampton, Homer F. The concentration game. *A.T.* 19:65–67; Jan. 1972.
Provides drill in fundamental operations of arithmetic, especially multiplication; grades 2–6.

Heard, Lola M. Number games with young children. *Young Children* 24:146–50; Jan. 1969.

Henderson, George L., Adeline Walter, Lynn Oberlin, and Lowell D. Glunn. *Let's Play Games in Mathematics.* Vol. K–6. Skokie, Ill.: National Textbook Co., 1970. 70 pp. each (average).
Games and other activities of interest to teachers and parents as well as pupils.

Hestwood, Orf, and Huseby Hestwood. *Crossnumber Puzzles: Books 1 and 2.* Palo Alto, Calif.: Creative Publications, 1973.
Furnishes practice with whole numbers, fractions, decimals, and percents; cartoon format.

Hewitt, Frances. 4 × 4 magic squares. *A.T.* 9:392–95; Nov. 1962.
An analysis of the construction of 4 × 4 squares; relation to modular arithmetic hinted at.

Hickerson, Jay A. Mathematical puzzles and games. *A.T.* 16:85, 114; Feb. 1969.

Holtkamp, Larry. The match game. *A.T.* 19:221–22; Mar. 1972.

Humphrey, James H., and Dorothy D. Sullivan. *Teaching Slow Learners through Active Games.* Springfield, Ill.: Charles C. Thomas, 1970. 184 pp.
The book consists of three chapters respectively devoted to reading, science, and mathematics; the chapter on mathematics describes over 100 games, pointing out both the concepts and their applications.

Hunt, Martin H. Arithmetic card games. *A.T.* 15:736–38; Dec. 1968.
Practice with number facts.

Johnson, Donovan. Enjoy the mathematics you teach. *A.T.* 15:328–32; Apr. 1968.
A brief overview of possibilities such as number patterns, puzzles, paradoxes, and so on.

Jordan, Diana. Tick-tack-four. *A.T.* 15:454–55; May 1968.
Drill in basic number facts and fundamental operations.

Keller, C. Modern education meets Chinese puzzle result: tangrams! *Pennsylvania School Journal* 117:312–13; Jan. 1969.

Kennedy, Joseph, and Violet Blume. Multiplication tables and dominoes. *A.T.* 10:283; May 1963.
Dominoes used as a device to give practice in the addition and multiplication facts.

Kopp, Audrey, and Robert Hamada. Fun can be mathematics. *A.T.* 16:575–77; Nov. 1969.

Lazerick, Beth Ellen. The conversion game. *A.T.* 18:54–55; Jan. 1971.

Martin, Marylou, and Justina Davis. *M cubed.* Palo Alto, Calif.: Creative Publications, 1970. 127 pp.
Description of inexpensive devices for use in supplementing mathematical instruction, chiefly in the primary grades.

Massey, Tom E. Dominoes in the mathematics classroom. *A.T.* 18:53–54; Jan. 1971.

Mathison, Sally. Mathematicalosterms. *A.T.* 16:64–65; Jan. 1969. Also, 16:495–96, 650–51; Oct.–Dec. 1969.

Matthews, W. Try magic squares. *Instructor* 77:98; Jan. 1968.

Mauthe, Albert H. Climb the ladder. *A.T.* 16:354–56; May 1969.

May, Lola J. Arrowmath. *Grade Teacher* 89:38+; Mar. 1972.

———. Educational games in math. *Audiovisual Instruction* 14:27–29; Feb. 1969.

———. Enrichment games get pupils to think. *Grade Teacher* 83:53–54; May 1966.
Using magic squares.

———. Math games. *Grade Teacher* 88:70–73; Sept. 1970.

———. Strategies; games for problem-solving practice. *Grade Teacher* 89:66+; May 1972.

———. Variations on mathematical themes. *Grade Teacher* 86:127–30; Feb. 1969.

Milne, Esther. Disguised practice for multiplication and addition of directed numbers. *A.T.* 16:397–98; May 1969.

Muth, C. About magic squares. *Baltimore Bulletin of Education* 34:17–19; June 1957.

Nies, Ruth. Classroom experiences with recreational arithmetic. *A.T.* 3:90–93; Apr. 1956.
Number tricks and curiosities; alphametics, cross-number puzzles, and magic squares are suggested to enliven classwork.

Niman, John. A game introduction to the binary numeration system. *A.T.* 18:600–601; Dec. 1971.

O'Donnell, J. R. They are *not* "magic" number cards. *A.T.* 12:647–48; Dec. 1965.
A recreation based on the use of the binary system.

Overholser, Jean S. Hide-a-region—$N \geq 2$ can play. *A.T.* 16:496–97; Oct. 1969.

Parker, Helen. See-saw game. *A.T.* 10:449–50; Nov. 1963.
For practicing addition, subtraction, multiplication, and division facts.

Phillips, J. M. April fool math. *Instructor* 77:90+; Apr. 1968.

———. Games for the new math. *Instructor* 77:89+; Dec. 1967.

Prielipp, Robert. Calendar arithmetic. *A.T.* 16:69; Jan. 1969.

Primary Math Games. *Instructor* 78:34; June 1969.

Ranucci, Ernest R. Four-color game, a mathematical mystery. *Grade Teacher* 86:109–10; Oct. 1968.

Rode, Joann. Making a whole—a game using simple fractions. *A.T.* 18:116–18; Feb. 1971.

Rowland, Rowena. "Fraction Rummy"—a game. *A.T.* 19:387–88; May 1972.
A card game for two to six players; practice in addition of fractions.

Ruderman, Harry. Nu-tic tac toe. *A.T.* 12:571–72; Nov. 1965.
An unusually interesting modification of a familiar game; involves "strategy thinking."

Sawyer, W. W. "Tricks and Why They Work." In *Enrichment Mathematics for the Grades*, pp. 173–79. Twenty-seventh Yearbook of the NCTM. Washington, D.C.: NCTM, 1963.
Good discussion of "think-of-a-number" tricks.

Schadler, Reuben A., and Dale G. Seymour. *Pic-a-Puzzle: A Book of Geometric Puzzle Patterns*. Palo Alto, Calif.: Creative Publications, 1970. 127 pp.

Schreiner, Nikki. *Games and Aids for Teaching Math*. Palo Alto, Calif: Creative Publications, 1973. 117 pp.
Grades K–8.

Schulz, Charles E. Pattern analysis in magic squares. *A.T.* 10:214–15; Apr. 1963.
Limited to the 3 × 3 magic square.
Scott, Joseph. With sticks and rubber bands. *A.T.* 17:147–50; Feb. 1970.
Shurlow, Harold J. The game of five. *A.T.* 10:290–91; May 1963.
Helps to understand numeration systems, particularly base five.
Spitzer, Herbert. *Enrichment of Arithmetic.* New York: McGraw-Hill Book Co.,
1964. 576 pp.
An indispensable handbook containing much scattered material on games,
puzzles, tricks, and other number activities.
Stephens, Carol H. Yahoo—a game for fun and skill. *A.T.* 14:284, 288; Apr.
1967.
Drill on multiplication facts.
Stephens, Lois. An adventure in division. *A.T.* 15:427–29; May 1968.
Stone, A. C. Could Amanda be a turtle and other mathematical mysteries. *Grade
Teacher* 87:61–62; Feb. 1970.
Swart, William L. Secret number sentence. *A.T.* 16:113–14; Feb. 1969.
Timmons, Robert A. Tick-tac-toe—a mathematical game for grades 4 through
9. *A.T.* 14:506–8; Oct. 1967.
Trotter, Terrell, Jr. Five "nontrivial" number games. *A.T.* 19:558–60; Nov. 1972.
Tucker, Benny F. "Parallelograms"; a simple answer to drill motivation and
individualized instruction. *A.T.* 18:489–93; Nov. 1971.
University of Maryland Mathematics Project. Games and algorithms—a new
view in elementary school mathematics for teachers. *A.T.* 17:342–46; Apr. 1970.
Wagner, Guy W., et al. *Arithmetic Games and Activities.* Darien, Conn.: Teachers
Publishing Corp., 1965.
Weston, F. Bowling game. *Instructor* 80:30; Dec. 1970.
Willerding, Margaret. Codes for boys and girls. *A.T.* 2:23–24; Feb. 1955.
A simple elementary cipher used to arouse interest in cryptography.
Williams, Russel. Bingtac. *A.T.* 16:310–11; Apr. 1969. Also, 16:579–80; Nov.
1969.
A game similar to the game of Yahoo.
Wills, Herbert. Diffy. *A.T.* 18:402–5; Oct. 1971.
A game that provides drill in subtraction.
Winick, David F. "Arithmecode" puzzle. *A.T.* 15:178–79; Feb. 1968.
Zuckerman, David W., and Robert E. Horn. *The Guide to Simulation Games
for Education and Training.* Cambridge, Mass.: Information Resources, 1970.
334 pp.
Contains a section devoted to mathematical skill-development games.
Zytkowski, Richard T. A game with fraction numbers. *A.T.* 17:82–83; Jan. 1970.

12.2   Secondary School Activities

Abeles, Francine, and Edward Zoll. Networks, maps and Betti numbers: an
eight-year-old's thinking. *S.S.M.* 71:369–72; May 1971.
Ackerman, Judy. Computers teach math. *A.T.* 15:467–68; May 1968.
A game called hexapawn; construction of a game-learning computer of the
ticktacktoe type.

Aichele, Douglas B. "Pica-Centro"—a game of logic. *A.T.* 19:359–62; May 1972.

Albaugh, A. Henry. The game of Euclid. *M.T.* 54:436–39; Oct. 1961.
A card game, similar to gin rummy.

Allen, Chuck. *Daily Chores in Mathematics.* Palo Alto, Calif.: Creative Publications, 1970. 123 pp.
Among other things, contains directions for games and activities for slow learners at the junior high school level.

Allen, Layman E. Toward autotelic learning of mathematics. *M.T.* 56:8–21; Jan. 1963.
Games involving logical inference; a report on WFF'N PROOF games.

Anderson, Robert. *Mathematical Bingo.* Portland, Maine: J. Weston Walch, 1963. 75 + 21 pp.
Entertaining practice exercises, similar to conventional bingo.

Banwell, Saunders, and Tahta. *Starting Points.* Palo Alto, Calif.: Creative Publications, 1973. 246 pp.
Activities designed to stimulate discovery.

Bezuszka, Stanley, et al. *Contemporary Motivated Mathematics—Books 1, 2 and 3.* Boston College Mathematics Institute. Chestnut Hill, Mass.: The Author, 1971.
Contains material on magic squares, number pleasantries, figurate numbers, Pythagorean triples, golden section, and so on; suitable for grades 5–10.

Brandes, Louis G. Math can be fun; tricks, puzzles, wrinkles raise grades. *Clearing House* 25:75–79; Oct. 1950.
Bibliography.

———. Recreational mathematics as it may be used with secondary school pupils. *S.S.M.* 54:383–94; May 1954.

———. Recreational mathematics for the mathematics classrooms of our secondary schools. *S.S.M.* 54:617–27; Nov. 1954.

———. Recreational mathematics materials in the classroom. *California Journal of Secondary Education* 28:51–55; Jan. 1953.
Bibliography.

———. Using recreational mathematics materials in the classroom. *M.T.* 46:326–29, 336; May 1953.
Bibliography.

———. Why use recreational mathematics in our secondary school mathematics classes? *S.S.M.* 54:289–93; Apr. 1954.
Bibliography.

Brumfiel, Charles F. "Numbers and Games." In *Enrichment Mathematics for the Grades*, pp. 245–60. Twenty-seventh Yearbook of the NCTM. Washington, D.C.: NCTM, 1963.
Repeating decimals, continued fractions, irrational numbers, number line games, ticktacktoe.

Bruyr, Donald. *Geometrical Models and Demonstrations.* Portland, Maine: J. Weston Walch, 1954. 173 pp.
Over 150 diagrams depicting curves, surfaces, solids, mathematical instruments, and so on.

Burkhill, J. C., and H. M. Cundy. *Mathematical Scholarship Problems.* New York: Cambridge University Press, 1961. 118 pp.
Of interest to the more capable students.

Cameron, A. J. *Mathematical Enterprises for Schools.* New York: Pergamon Press, 1966. 188 pp.
Suggestions for making models of polyhedrons, etc.; topics for "investigation" include Pascal's triangle and heredity, the Fibonacci series, and the golden section.

Charosh, Mannis. *Mathematical Challenges.* Washington, D.C.: NCTM, 1965. 135 pp. (Paper)
A collection of 140 problems selected from the *Mathematics Student Journal;* solutions.

Cundy, H. Martyn. A demonstration binary adder. *M.Gaz.* 42:272–74; Dec. 1958.
A simple electrical-circuit device.

Cundy, H. M., and A. P. Rollett. *Mathematical Models.* London: Oxford University Press, 1952. 240 pp.
Directions for making models in plane geometry, models of polyhedra, ruled surfaces, Möbius strips, and so forth.

DeJong, L. Mathematics crossword. *S.S.M.* 62:45–46; Jan. 1962.

Duncan, Donald C. Happy integers. *M.T.* 65:627–29; Nov. 1972.

———. Ten mathematical refreshments. *M.T.* 58:102–8; Feb. 1965.
Patterns of polygonal numbers.

Esmond, Robert V. Magic letters—TV—and magic squares. *M.T.* 48:26–29; Jan. 1955.
How a magic-squares program was broadcast over a television network.

Field, P. B. Description of a math field day. *S.S.M.* 64:12–14; Jan. 1964.
Describes four contests and four games. The games: Five-in-a-Row, Nim, Hex, and Three-dimensional Tic Tac Toe.

Frank, Charlotte. Play shuffleboard with negative numbers. *A.T.* 16:395–97; May 1969.

Giles, G. Trays and coloured rods. *M.Tchg.,* no. 56, p. 19; Autumn 1971.

Glenn, William, and Donovan Johnson. *Fun with Mathematics.* Exploring Mathematics on Your Own. St. Louis: Webster Publishing Co., 1960. 43 pp. (Paper)
Number tricks; calendar problems; tricks with cards, dice, and dominoes.

Godsave, Bruce E. Three games. *A.T.* 18:327–29; May 1971.
These games are designed to give practice in using Cartesian coordinates.

Hall, Arthur J. Using mathematical recreations in the junior high school. *M.T.* 48:484–87; Nov. 1955.

Hall, Gary D. A Pythagorean puzzle. *A.T.* 19:67–70; Jan. 1972.

Harris, Patricia A. Mathematical bingo. *M.T.* 54:577–78; Nov. 1961.
Similar to conventional bingo, in which solution sets of given equations must be identified.

Hess, Adrian. *Mathematics Projects Handbook.* Boston: D. C. Heath & Co., 1962. 60 pp. (Paper)

Homan, Doris. Television games adapted for use in junior high school mathematics classes. *A.T.* 20:219–22; Mar. 1973.

Janicki, George. Number cartoons. *M.T.* 48:372; May 1955.

Jeffryes, James. Let's play Wff'n Proof. *M.T.* 62:113–17; Feb. 1969.

Johnson, Donovan. *Games for Learning Mathematics.* Portland, Maine: J. Weston Walch, 1963. 176 pp.

Directions for 70 games involving arithmetic, algebra, and geometry.

Jones, L. E. Merry Christmas, happy new year. *S.S.M.* 67:766–71; Dec. 1967.

Jones, Thomas. Effect of modified programmed lectures and mathematical games upon achievement and attitudes of ninth-grade low achievers in mathematics. *M.T.* 61:603–7; Oct. 1968.

Kenna, L. A. *Understanding Mathematics, with Visual Aids.* Paterson, N.J.: Littlefield Adams & Co., 1962. 174 pp. (Paper)

Curve stitching, string models, wooden models, paper folding, and the abacus.

Let's Play Games in General Mathematics. Skokie, Ill.: National Textbook Co., 1973.

Games and activities suggested for secondary level.

Liedtke, Werner. What can you do with a geoboard? *A.T.* 16:491–93; Oct. 1969.

Manheimer, Wallace. Club project in a modern use of mathematics. *M.T.* 50:350–55; May 1957.

Recreations based on the binary system; Nim; computers; and so on.

Moskowitz, Sheila. The crossnumber puzzle solves a teaching problem. *M.T.* 62:200–204; Mar. 1969.

Mosteller, Frederick. Optimal length of play for a binomial game. *M.T.* 54:411–12; Oct. 1961.

Moyer, Haverly O. Testing with a tangram. *M.T.* 48:525–27; Dec. 1955.

National Council of Teachers of Mathematics. *Enrichment Mathematics for the Grades.* Twenty-seventh Yearbook. Washington, D.C.: The Council, 1963. 368 pp.

"Probability" (Chap. 8); "Topology" (Chap. 10); "Tricks and Why They Work" (Chap. 12); "Puzzles for Thinkers" (Chap. 14); "Numbers and Games" (Chap. 18).

———. *Enrichment Mathematics for High School.* Twenty-eighth Yearbook. Washington, D.C.: The Council, 1963. 388 pp.

"Farey Sequences" (Chap. 1); "Nets" (Chap. 7); "Geometry, Right or Left" (Chap. 8); "Random Walks" (Chap. 21); "The Geometry of Color" (Chap. 22); "Knots and Wheels" (Chap. 25).

———. *Multi-sensory Aids in the Teaching of Mathematics.* Eighteenth Yearbook. New York: Teachers College, Columbia University, 1945. 455 pp.

Contains a wealth of recreational material: curve stitching, linkages, paper folding, model construction, homemade instruments, and so on.

Nygaard, P. H. Odd and even—a game. *M.T.* 49:397; May 1956.

Parker, Jean. The use of puzzles in teaching mathematics. *M.T.* 48:218–27; Apr. 1955.

Bibliography.

Perisho, C. R. Conics for Thanksgiving. *S.S.M.* 57:640–41; Nov. 1957.

Ransom, William R. *Thirty Projects for Mathematical Clubs and Exhibitions.* Portland, Maine: J. Weston Walch, 1961. Student manual, 84 pp.; teacher's manual, 50 pp.

Gives a list of possible topics, some of which are unusual.

Ranucci, Ernest R. *Four by Four*. Boston: Houghton Mifflin Co., 1968. 60 pp.
An assortment of recreations using a 4 × 4 network of squares.

———. *Seeing Shapes*. Palo Alto, Calif.: Creative Publications, 1973.
Paper folding, tangrams, and so on; grades 1–12.

———. Tantalizing ternary. *A.T.* 15:718–22; Dec. 1968.
Puzzles based on numbers in base three.

Reeve, J. E., and J. A. Tyrrell. Maestro puzzles. *M.Gaz.* 45:97–99; May 1961.
Puzzles concerned with packing a given set of figures to form a certain figure.

Ruderman, Harry. The greatest—a game. *A.T.* 17:80–81; Jan. 1970.

Saidan, A. S. Recreational problems in a medieval arithmetic. *M.T.* 59:666–67; Nov. 1966.

Schicker, Joseph. *P-T Aids to Mathematics*. New York: Vantage Press, 1965. 91 pp.

Scorer, R. S., P. M. Grundy, and C. A. B. Smith. Some binary games. *M.Gaz.* 30:96–103; July 1944.

Seymour, Dale. *Finite Differences*. Palo Alto, Calif.: Creative Publications, 1973.
Problem-solving activities; grades 7–12.

Sinkhorn, Richard, and Cecil B. Read. Mathematical bingo. *S.S.M.* 55:650–52; Nov. 1955.

Smith, Eugene P. "Some Puzzlers for Thinkers." In *Enrichment Mathematics for the Grades*, pp. 211–20. Twenty-seventh Yearbook. Washington, D.C.: NCTM, 1963.
For the junior high school level; about two dozen assorted problems, including magic squares.

Steiger, Sister Anne Agnes von. Christmas puzzle. *M.T.* 60:848–49; Dec. 1967.

Steinen, Ramon F. More about 1965 and 1966. *M.T.* 59:737–38; Dec. 1966.

Stokes, William T. *Notable Numbers*. Palo Alto, Calif.: Creative Publications, 1973.
Number relations, patterns, curiosities, and so on; grades 5–12.

Trigg, Charles W. Holiday greetings from thirty scrambled mathematicians. *S.S.M.* 54:679; Dec. 1954.

———. Triangular arrangements of numbered disks. *M.T.* 65:157–60; Feb. 1972.

Wessel, G. Base minus-ten numeration system. *S.S.M.* 68:701–6; Nov. 1968.

Winick, David F. "Arithmecode" puzzle. *A.T.* 15:178–79; Feb. 1968.
Similar to a cross-number puzzle.

12.3   Mathematics Clubs, Plays, Programs, Projects

Bleustein, Robert. The King and *i*; a play in three scenes. *M.S.J.* vol. 17, no. 4, pp. 3–4; May 1970.

Bruyr, Donald. *Geometrical Models and Demonstrations*. Portland, Maine: J. Weston Walch, 1964. 173 pp.
Curves, surfaces, solids, instruments, and so on; over 150 diagrams.

Cordell, Christobal. *Dramatizing Mathematics.* Portland, Maine: J. Weston Walch, 1963. 170 pp.

>A collection of 17 skits, contests, and so on, appropriate for mathematics club programs and school assemblies.

Dienes, Z. P., and E. W. Golding. *Sets, Numbers and Powers.* New York: Herder & Herder, 1966. 122 pp. (Paper)

>Practical suggestions for lessons and games to help develop the ideas embodied in the title; companion volume to a handbook.

Granito, Dolores. What to do in a mathematics club. *M.T.* 57:35–40; Jan. 1964.

Humphrey, J. H., and Dorothy Sullivan. *Teaching Slow Learners through Active Games.* Springfield, Ill.: Charles C. Thomas (301 E. Lawrence Ave.), 1970. 184 pp.

>Describes over 100 games related to reading, science, and mathematics.

Johnson, Donovan, C. H. Lund, and W. D. Hamerston. *Bulletin Board Displays for Mathematics.* Belmont, Calif.: Dickenson Publishing Co., 1967. 99 pp.

Kapur, J. N. *Suggested Experiments in School Mathematics.* 2 vols. Karol Bagh, New Delhi: Arya Book Depot, 1969. 144 + 232 pp.

>Experiments, grouped by topics, to facilitate the understanding of modern mathematical concepts.

Schaaf, William L. Mathematical plays and programs. *M.T.* 44:526–28; Nov. 1951.

>Contains an annotated list of 50 plays, pageants, and skits and a list of 20 references on programs for assemblies and mathematics clubs.

Todd, Audrey. *The Maths Club.* London: H. Hamilton, 1968.

Willerding, Margaret. Dramatizing mathematics. *S.S.M.* 60:99–104; Feb. 1960.

>An annotated list of 77 plays, pageants, and skits and a bibliography of 7 references on quiz shows and assembly programs.

12.4 Mathematics Contests, Competitions, Leagues

Altendorf, J. J., and M. A. McCormick. Stimulating enthusiasm about math.; Missouri Southern College math league. *School and Community* [Missouri State Teachers Association] 55:26; Apr. 1969.

Burkhill, J. C., and H. M. Cundy. *Mathematical Scholarship Problems.* New York: Cambridge University Press, 1961. 118 pp.

Cash Prizes to be Awarded to Florida Students in the High School Mathematics Contest. *Florida Council of Teachers of Mathematics Newsletter,* vol. 14, no. 2, pp. 11–13; Winter 1972.

Charosh, Mannis, ed. *Mathematical Challenges.* Washington, D.C.: NCTM, 1965. 135 pp. (Paper)

>Collection of problems appropriate for grades 7 through 12.

Cromack, Norman E. An assessment of a mathematics league as judged by its participants. *M.T.* 63:432–38; May 1970.

———. Mathematics leagues in New Jersey. *New Jersey Mathematics Teacher* 24:21–23; May 1967.

Hlavaty, Julius H. The Czechoslovak national mathematical olympiads. *M.T.* 61:80–85; Jan. 1968.

McCormick, Martha. Students become math-minded through league influence. *M.T.* 64:245–46; Mar. 1971.

Maths Olympiad a True Test. *Times* (London) *Education Supplement* 2739:1136; 17 November 1967.

Paarlberg, Teunis. The mathematics league. *M.T.* 60:38–40; Jan. 1967.

Turner, Nura D. The U.S.A. mathematical olympiad. *A.M.M.* 79:301–2; Mar. 1972.

———. Why can't we have a U.S.A. mathematical olympiad? *A.M.M.* 78:192–95; 1971.

Contemporary Works on Mathematical Recreations

Books and monographs devoted exclusively to a specific topic (e.g., *Dissections* or *Magic Squares* or *Tangrams*) are listed under the appropriate chapter and subtopic headings.

Barr, George. *Entertaining with Number Tricks*. New York: McGraw-Hill Book Co., 1971. 143 pp.

Basile, Joseph. *100 (Cent) problèmes de mathématiques amusantes*. Paris: L'Inter, 1967.

Beard, Robert S. *Patterns in Space*. San Jose, Calif.: Fibonacci Association, 1971. 200 pp. (approx.)
　An unusual collection of geometric drawings, patterns, curves, solids, and so on.

Beck, Anatole, Michael Bleicher, and Donald Crowe. *Excursions into Mathematics*. New York: Worth Publishers, 1969. 489 pp.
　Chapters on polyhedra, perfect numbers, area concept, a variety of geometries, mathematical games, and numeration systems.

Beer, Fritz [Von Complexus]. *Fröhliches Kopfzerbrechen; 100 Aufgaben für scharfe Denker, mit einem Anhang: Lösungen und Erläuterungen*. Vienna and Leipzig: M. Perles, 1934.

Bold, Benjamin. *Famous Problems of Mathematics*. New York: Van Nostrand Reinhold, 1969. 112 pp.

British Broadcasting Corporation (BBC), School Broadcasting Department. *Mathematics Miscellany: A Source Book for Teachers, By Members of the School Broadcasting Dept., BBC Television*. London: BBC, 1966.

Charosh, Mannis. *Mathematical Games for One or Two*. New York: Thomas Y. Crowell Co., 1972. 33 pp.

Conference for the Development of Mathematical Puzzles, Problems and Games: A Report. Stanford, Calif.: Stanford University, 1965.

Dobrovolný, Bohumil. *Matematické rekreace; zajímavé problémy s 90 obrázky a s řešením*. Prague: Práce, 1961.

Emmet, E. R. *Puzzles for Pleasure*. New York: Emerson Books, 1972. 310 pp.

Férez, Antonio H. *Maravillas recreativas del calculo aritmético;* . . . *con nuevas curiosidades.* Madrid: Editorial E. C. M., 1952.

Friedland, Aaron J. *Puzzles in Math and Logic.* New York: Dover Publications, 1970. 72 pp. (Paper)
  One hundred original problems; not a reprint book.

Gardner, Martin. *Martin Gardner's Sixth Book of Mathematical Games from Scientific American.* San Francisco: W. H. Freeman & Co., 1971. 262 pp.
  Two dozen recreations never before published in book form.

Gibson, Walter B. *Fell's Guide to Papercraft, Tricks, Games and Puzzles.* New York: Frederick Fells, 1963. 125 pp.

Haber, Heinz. *Das mathematische Kabinett.* Stuttgart: Deutsche Verlagsanstalt, 1967.

Hochkeppel, W. *Denken als Spiel.* Ebenhausen, 1970. 224 pp.
  Psychological, logical, and physical problems; linguistic puzzles.

Hollis, Martin. *Tantalizers: A Book of Original Logical Puzzles.* London: George Allen & Unwin, 1970. 153 pp.

Hunter, J. A. H. *Figures Are Fun: Books 1–5.* With teacher's manual. Toronto: Copp Clark Publishing Co., 1959.
  Designed for use in grades 4–9.

———. *Figures for Fun.* London: J. M. Dent & Sons, 1957.
  Mathematical puzzles couched in little stories; for young readers.

Hurley, James F., ed. *Litton's Problematical Recreations.* New York: Van Nostrand Reinhold, 1971. 337 pp.
  Over 250 puzzles, many of which have appeared previously in *Mathematical Bafflers*, by Angela Dunn (McGraw-Hill Book Co., 1964).

Kabinett, D. *Mathematische Auslese mathematischer und Denksport-Aufgaben.* 2 vols. Stuttgart, 1967. 128 + 110 pp.

Kordemsky, Boris A. *Matematicheskaya smekalka.* Moscow, 1957. French translation: *Sur le sentier des mathématiques.* 2 vols. Paris: Dunod, 1963.

———. *The Moscow Puzzles; 359 Mathematical Recreations.* New York: Charles Scribner's Sons, 1972. 309 pp.
  A very popular puzzle book in the USSR; in English.

Krbek, F. v. U. *Zahlen und Überzahlen.* Leipzig, 1964. 146 pp.

Krulik, Stephen. *A Handbook of Aids for Teaching Junior-Senior High School Mathematics.* Philadelphia: W. B. Saunders Co., 1971. 120 pp.
  A collection of some 40 interesting games and devices, including the Möbius strip, the Tower of Hanoi, Chinese tangrams, curve stitching, and the number-base calendar.

Lamb, Sydney H. *The Magic of Numbers.* New York: Arco Publishing Co., 1965. 71 pp.
  General introductory material for very young readers.

Linn, Charles F. *Odd Angles: Thirty-three Mathematical Entertainments.* Garden City, N.Y.: Doubleday & Co., 1971. 127 pp.

Litton's Problematical Recreations. Edited by J. F. Hurley. New York: Van Nostrand Reinhold, 1971. 337 pp.

Longley-Cook, L. H. *New Math Puzzle Book.* New York: Van Nostrand Reinhold, 1970. 176 pp.
  Recreations combined with ideas from "new math."

Lukács, Clara, and Emma Tarján. *Mathematical Games.* Translated by John Dobai. New York: Walker & Co., 1969. 200 pp.
———. *Spiele mit Zahlen* (Mathematische Spiele, wie Karten—und Rechentricks, Denksportaufgaben, u.s.w.). Benziger-Tabu, 1968. 168 pp.
Mira, Julio A. *Mathematical Teasers.* New York: Barnes & Noble, 1970. 279 pp. (Paper)
    Problems, puzzles, and tricks; with explanations.
Morris, Ivan. *The Riverside Puzzles.* New York: Walker & Co., 1969. 127 pp.
    A collection of 50 or more word puzzles, stick games, logic problems, and mathematical puzzles.
Muller, Fritz. *Warum? Fröhliche Fragen zum Nachdenken.* Leipzig: Staackmann, 1926.
Papin, Maurice. *Colles et astuces mathématiques.* Paris: Blanchard, 1972. 163 pp.
    A collection of problems and puzzles, appropriate for secondary school level; some well known, some new.
Perleman, Ya. I. *Zanimatelnye zadachi i opiti.* Moscow, 1959.
Phillips, Hubert. *Something to Think About.* London: M. Parrish, 1958.
Ranucci, Ernest R. *Puzzles, Problems, Posers, and Pastimes.* Boston: Houghton Mifflin Co., 1972.
    A series of three booklets, each containing problems at a different level of difficulty; 75 problems in all.
Rosenberg, Nancy. *How to Enjoy Mathematics with Your Child.* New York: Stein & Day, 1970. 186 pp.
    Figurate numbers, magic squares, intuitive topology, flexagons, paper folding, and so on.
Sackson, Sidney. *A Gamut of Games.* New York: Random House, 1969. 224 pp.
    Comprehensive and authoritative.
Scripture, Nicholas E. *Puzzles and Teasers.* New York: Van Nostrand Reinhold Co., 1970. 74 pp.
    A brief collection of simple puzzles involving elementary mathematics.
Silverman, David L. *Your Move.* New York: McGraw-Hill Book Co., 1971. 221 pp.
    Puzzles dealing with cards, chess, number games, and so on, with emphasis on game strategy and decision making.
Souza, Júlio. *Matemática divertida e fabulosa; problemas curiosos anedotas, recreaçõs geométricas, etc.* São Paulo: Edicão Saraiva, 1962.
Sperling, Walter. *Die Grübelkiste; ein Buch zum Kopfzerbrechen.* Zurich: A. Müller, 1953.
Taylor, Judith M. *Fun with Mathematics.* Oxford: Basil Blackwood, 1972. 32 pp.
    Simple recreations for the elementary school level.
Ulam, Stanislaw. *Problems in Modern Mathematics.* New York: John Wiley & Sons, 1960, 1964. (Paper)
Webster, David. *Brain Boosters.* London: J. M. Dent & Sons, 1969. 94 pp.
    Mostly science riddles; some puzzles concerning shapes and knots; junior high school level.
Yaglom, A. M., and I. M. Yaglom. *Challenging Mathematical Problems.* Vol. 1. San Francisco: Holden-Day, 1964.

Chronological Synopsis of Martin Gardner's Column in Scientific American

The well-known monthly column "Mathematical Games" by Martin Gardner in *Scientific American* does not always lend itself neatly to bibliographic listing. Much of this material has appeared subsequently in book form, and many of the items are listed in volumes 1 and 2 of the present *Bibliography of Recreational Mathematics*. Most of the more recent articles are given here in volume 3 under appropriate subheadings. Nevertheless, for the reader's convenience we append a complete list of titles, in essential form, dating from December 1956 (the column's inception) to February 1973, inclusive.

NOTE. Based in large part on a list compiled by James A. Dunn in *Mathematics Teaching*, no. 52, pp. 59–60; Autumn 1970. By courtesy of the author and editor.

Dec	56	Flexagons
Jan	57	Magic matrices
Feb	57	Nine problems
Mar	57	The game "Ticktacktoe"
Apr	57	Paradoxes
May	57	Games: Icosian; Tower of Hanoi; polyominoes
June	57	The Möbius band
July	57	The game of HEX
Aug	57	Sam Loyd
Sept	57	Card tricks
Oct	57	Mnemonic devices
Nov	57	Nine puzzles
Dec	57	Polyominoes
Jan	58	Fallacies
Feb	58	The game of Nim
Mar	58	Left and right handedness

May   62 Symmetry and asymmetry
June 62 The game of solitaire
July 62 Abbot's "Flatland" and two-dimensional geometry
Aug   62 Tricks collected at a fictitious magicians' convention.
Sept 62 Tests of division
Oct   62 A collection of nine puzzles involving numbers, logic and probability
Nov   62 Checker-board puzzles: dissections, etc.
Dec   62 Manipulations with strings
Jan   63 Numerology (Dr. Matrix)
Feb   63 Curves of constant width
Mar   63 Paradoxes
Apr   63 Foolishness for April Fools' Day
May   63 Reptiles
June 63 Helical structures: spirals and corkscrews
July 63 Topological diversions
Aug   63 Perms and paradoxes in combinatorial mathematics
Sept 63 How to solve puzzles by graphing the rebounds of a bouncing ball
Oct   63 Four board games
Nov   63 Nine problems
Dec   63 Parity tests: odd and even
Jan   64 Numerology (Dr. Matrix)
Feb   64 Sliding puzzles: the 15 puzzle
Mar   64 Prime numbers
Apr   64 Planar graphs: sets of vertices connected by edges
May   64 Number bases: the false coin problem
June 64 Nine short problems and more about primes
July 64 Curious properties of a cycloid curve
Aug   64 Magic tricks based on mathematical principles
Sept 64 Word games: puns, palindromes, etc.
Oct   64 Simple proofs of Pythagoras
Nov   64 Infinite series and the concept of limit
Dec   64 Polyiamonds
Jan   65 Numerology (Dr. Matrix)
Feb   65 Tetrahedrons
Mar   65 Nine short problems
Apr   65 The infinite regress: snowflake curves, etc.
May   65 The lattice of integers considered as an orchard or a billiard table
June 65 Postman problems: routing problems
July 65 "Op Art" patterns: tessellations
Aug   65 Communication with intelligent organisms in other worlds
Sept 65 The "Superellipse": a curve between the ellipse and the rectangle
Oct   65 Pentominoes and polyominoes
Nov   65 Nine elementary word and number problems
Dec   65 Magic stars, graphs and polyhedrons
Jan   66 Numerology (Dr. Matrix)
Feb   66 Coin puzzles
Mar   66 The hierarchy of infinities
Apr   66 The eerie mathematical art of Maurits C. Escher
May   66 How to "cook" a puzzle, or mathematical one-uppery

June 70   Elegant triangle theorems
July 70   Diophantine analysis and Fermat's "last theorem"
Aug 70   Backward run numbers, letters, words and sentences
Sept 70   On the cyclical curves generated by rolling wheels
Oct 70   Solitaire game of "Life"
Nov 70   New collection of short problems
Dec 70   The paradox of the nontransitive dice
Jan 71   Lessons from Dr. Matrix in chess and numerology
Feb 71   On cellular automata, self-reproduction, the Garden of Eden and the
          game of "Life"
Mar 71   The orders of infinity, the topological nature of dimension and "super-
          tasks"
Apr 71   Geometric fallacies: hidden errors pave the road to absurd conclusions
May 71   The combinatorial richness of folding a piece of paper
June 71   The Turing game and the question it presents: can a computer think?
July 71   Quickie problems: not hard, but look out for the curves!
Aug 71   Ticktacktoe and its complications
Sept 71   The plaiting of Plato's polyhedrons and the asymmetrical Yin-Yang-Lee
Oct 71   New puzzles from the game of Halma, the noble ancestor of Chinese
          checkers
Nov 71   Advertising premiums to beguile the mind: classics by Sam Loyd,
          master puzzle-poser
Dec 71   Further encounters with touching cubes, and the paradoxes of Zeno
          as "supertasks"
Jan 72   How to triumph at Nim; the Hackenbush game
Feb 72   Dr. Matrix proposes some heteroliteral puzzles
Mar 72   The graceful graphs of Solomon Golomb
Apr 72   A topological problem, and eight other puzzles
May 72   Challenging chess tasks for puzzle buffs
June 72   A miscellany of transcendental problems
July 72   Amazing mathematical card tricks
Aug 72   The binary Gray code and puzzle solving
Sept 72   Pleasurable problems with polycubes
Oct 72   The long arm of coincidence
Nov 72   Sir Francis Bacon's biliteral cipher
Dec 72   Knotty problems with a two-hole torus
Jan 73   New games: Sim, Chomp, and Race Track
Feb. 73   Up and Down Elevator games; Piet Hein's mechanical puzzles
Mar 73   The calculating rods of John Napier

Glossary

The following selected list of 500 entries contains many, if not most, of the terms commonly encountered in the literature of recreational mathematics. Some of the terms are doubtless familiar to the reader, but others may not be so widely known. For some of the more technical terms, a simple basic explanation is offered rather than a precise mathematical definition.

The number of mathematical "games" with identifiable names (for example, Nim, Oware, Reversi) has been judiciously held to a minimum, for new ones seem to sprout every day.

In some instances a brief annotation indicates the presumed originator of the term or the place where the term probably first appeared in print. Much as it might have been desirable, it became unfeasible to do this systematically throughout.

Insofar as the writer is aware, no such extensive glossary has ever been compiled. As a "first approximation," may it serve the reader well.

Abacus. A mechanical device used to facilitate arithmetical computation. In Roman times it took the form of a dust board with counters or a grooved table with beads. In more modern times it was commonly fashioned in the form of a rectangular frame with parallel wires on which an appropriate number of beads might slide, the wires serving as positional-value markers. In China the abacus is known as the *suanpan;* in Japan, the *soroban;* in Russia, the *s'choty.*

Abundant number. Any integer the sum of whose divisors, excluding the given integer, exceeds the number itself. Thus 18 is an abundant number, since $1 + 2 + 3 + 6 + 9 > 18$. Every multiple of a perfect number (excluding the first multiple) or of an abundant number is an abundant number.

Abundant numbers are also known as *excessive* or *redundant* numbers (q.v.).

119

Acrostic. A series of printed lines or verses in which the first, last, or other particular letters from a meaningful word, phrase, sentence, or name.

Afghan bands. Another name for Möbius bands; sometimes used by professional magicians when suitably adapted. See *Möbius band.*

Algebraic magic square. Any even magic square in which the sum of the numbers in every quadrant of the square equals the magic constant.

Algorism. An earlier term, now replaced by the term *algorithm.* In medieval times, *algorism* pertained specifically to positional notation used with Arabic numerals and a decimal-numeration system.

Algorithm. Any particular procedure for solving a given type of problem; or, any specific method used to carry out a computation.

Aliquot divisors. The aliquot divisors of an integer comprise all its integral divisors, including unity, but excluding the integer itself; synonymous with *proper divisors.*

Allomorph. As sometimes used in crystallography or geometry, an allomorph is a polyhedron having the same Eulerian description (V_n, F_n, E_n) as another polyhedron but differing from it in the types of polygons that make up its faces.

Alphametic. Any cryptarithm that employs letters in place of digits, with these letters forming related words or meaningful phrases. [J. A. H. Hunter, 1955.]

Amicable numbers. Any two numbers N_1 and N_2 such that the sum of the proper divisors of N_1 equals N_2 and the sum of the proper divisors of N_2 equals N_1. Thus 220 and 284 constitute a pair of amicable numbers, since $S(220) = 284$ and $S(284) = 220$, where $S(N)$ represents the sum of the divisors of N, exclusive of N itself.

An alternative definition is that two numbers are amicable if their sum is the sum of *all* the divisors of either of the numbers.

A "chain" of numbers is said to be amicable if each is the sum of the proper divisors of the preceding number, the last being considered as preceding the first of the chain. Amicable number triples, quadruples, quintuples, and k-tuples have also been defined. [*A.M.M.* 20:84; 1913.]

Anabasis. An old board game similar to Chinese checkers.

Anaglyph. A composite picture or diagram printed in two colors, usually blue and red, such that a three-dimensional image is seen when viewed through spectacles having lenses of corresponding colors.

Anagram. The transposition of the letters of a word or sentence to form a new word or sentence. Also, a word-building game.

Anallagmatic pavement. A variety of pavement made with square tiles of two colors so arranged that when any two rows or any two columns are placed together side by side, half the cells next to one another are of the same color and half are of different colors. [J. J. Sylvester, 1868.]

Anchor ring. See *Torus*.

Annulus. The area included between two concentric circles. The area of an annulus is given by $A = \pi (R^2 - r^2)$, where R and r are the radii of the larger and smaller circles, respectively.

Antimagic squares. An $n \times n$ square array of integers from 1 to n such that each row, column, and principal diagonal produces a different sum and these sums form a scrambled sequence of consecutive integers. [*R.M.M.*, no. 7, p. 16; Feb. 1962.]

Antipalindromic number. An integer in which each digit differs from the corresponding digit of its reverse, as in 17683492; it must have an even number of digits. Its coincidence ratio is zero.

Antisnowflake curve. Formed in the same way as in the snowflake curve, only the equilateral triangles are turned inwards instead of outwards.

Antinomy. A logical contradiction, such as between two statements or laws both of which are assumed to be true; or, the contradiction arising between the conclusions correctly derived from two such statements. In common practice, *antinomy* and *paradox* are regarded as synonymous, although strictly speaking, the term *paradox* is also correctly used in a broader sense.

Antiprism. A prismatic polyhedron whose two bases, although parallel, are not similarly situated, but each vertex of either corresponds to a side of the other so that the lateral edges form a zig-zag; also known as a *prismoid*.

Apeirogon. A degenerate polygon, that is, the limiting form of a *p*-gon, as *p* approaches infinity, and hence an infinite line broken into segments.

Apollonian problem. A classic problem of antiquity that required the construction of a circle or circles tangent (internally or externally) to three given circles. Depending on the original given configuration, there may be as many as eight required circles or there may be none.

Arbelos. A geometric configuration attributed to Archimedes: also known as the *cobbler's knife* or the *sickle of Archimedes.* It is bounded by three semicircles tangent to each other at their extremities. The arbelos in the figure shown has the same area as the circle having $\overline{CD}$ as a diameter. The segment $\overline{CD}$ divides the arbelos into two parts, whose inscribed circles are equal.

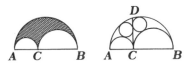

Arc. A route in a graph that passes through no vertex more than once.

Archimedean solids. These are semiregular polyhedra, that is, "facially" regular, which means that every face is a regular polygon, although the faces are not all of the same kind; however, the faces are arranged in the same order around each vertex. There are exactly thirteen Archimedean solids, two of which occur in two (enantiomorphic) forms. See also *Uniform polyhedrons.*

The term *semiregular* may appropriately be applied to both facially and vertically regular polyhedra, but it is often used exclusively of the former. [L. Lines, *Solid Geometry,* 1935.]

These semiregular polyhedra may also be extended to include stellated forms of Archimedean solids with star faces or star vertices, or both.

Asymmetric. The condition of being identical on both sides of the central line of symmetry but in "reverse" order; a mirror image kind of relation.

Automorph. Any integer expressible in only one way in the form $x^2 + Dy^2$ or $x^2 - Dy^2$ is called a *monomorph;* if it is so expressible in more than one way, it is called a *polymorph.* Both forms are known as *automorphs.*

More technically, an integral transformation of determinant unity that leaves q unaltered is called an automorph of q, where by q is meant a form such as $x^2 + y^2$, and so on. [L. E. Dickson, *Introduction to the Theory of Numbers,* p. 72.]

Automorphic numbers. The class of those integers with the property that the squares of the last n digits are the same as those of the number itself; for example, $25^2 = 625$; $76^2 = 5,776$. Again, the square of any number ending in 625 also ends in 625; for example, $(625)^2 = 390,625$; $(2,625)^2 = 6,890,625$.

Ball-piling. Refers to the possible ways of arranging a number of small equal spheres in horizontal layers to fill a rectangular box.

Betti number. The Betti number of a surface is a topological invariant that gives the maximum number of cuts that can be made without dividing the surface into two separate pieces.

Bicimals. A term sometimes used to designate binary decimals.

Bifactorials. Bifactorial n, written as $n!!$, is defined as follows:

$$n!! = 1! \cdot 2! \cdot 3! \cdot \ldots \cdot (n-1)! \ n!$$

For example, $4!! = 1! \ 2! \ 3! \ 4! = (1) \ (2) \ (6) \ (24) = 288$.

Bigrade. A multigrade that holds only for $n = 1,2$.

Bimagic square. A magic square is bimagic if the square formed by replacing each of its numbers by its second power is also a magic square.

Binary games. Recreational puzzles or games (such as Nim) that involve the binary scale of notation in their solution.

Binary numeration. A numeration system having base two, or on the scale of two, and so requiring only two digits, viz., 0 and 1. Thus:

Base 10	Base 2
0	0
1	1
2	10
3	11
4	100
5	101
6	110
7	111
8	1000
9	1001
10	1010
11	1011
12	1100
.	.
.	.
.	.

Binary numeration is used in solving certain weight problems, in explaining peasant multiplication, and in playing the game of Nim.

Bishop's re-entrant path. Similar to a knight's re-entrant tour, referring of course to the bishop. See *Knight's tour*.

Black. A topological pencil-and-paper game played on a checkered field, usually 8 × 8. [William Black, 1960.]

Bordered magic square. A magic square that contains within itself one or more other magic squares, revealed by successively stripping off each border of cells.

Borromean rings. A unique interlacing of three rings such that no two of the rings are linked, and yet the arrangement cannot be separated; however, if any single ring is broken and removed, the two remaining rings will be found to be unconnected.

Boss puzzle. See *Fifteen puzzle*.

Bracelet. One period of a simple periodic series considered as a closed sequence with terms equally spaced around a circle. Hence a bracelet may be regenerated by starting at any arbitrary point and applying the generating law. [*A.M.M.* 74:769; June 1967.]

Brachistochrone. The curve between two points that is traced in the shortest time by a body moving under an external force without friction; the curve of quickest descent.

Bridg-it. A topological game using a board of thirty black and thirty red spots placed in alternate rows. Two players, using black and red pencils, connect pairs of black and red spots, respectively, without crossing lines. [David Gale, 1958.]

A winning strategy has been determined, thus making it useless as a fair game. [Martin Gardner, *New Mathematical Diversions from Scientific American*, pp. 212–13.]

Brussels sprouts. A modification of the game of Sprouts (q.v.).

Buffon's needle problem. In its original form (1733), the problem was, Given a needle of length a and an infinite grid of parallel lines with a common distance d between them, what is the probability $P(E)$ that the needle, when tossed at the grid randomly, will cross one of the parallel lines? A modern generalization asks, How many lines might we expect the needle to cross? The answer in the first case is $P(E) = \dfrac{a}{\pi d}$, where $a \gtreqless d$; in the second case, $e(N) = \dfrac{2a}{\pi d}$.

Bulo. The name applied in Denmark to the game of *Tac Tix*.

Cabala. A system of occult interpretation of the Scriptures among Jewish rabbis and some medieval Christians; hence a Cabalist was a person engaged in mystic arts, including numerology, gematria, and so on.

Calculating prodigies. Individuals manifesting extraordinary powers of mental calculation. Their performances, although remarkable, in all probability reflect no "different kind" of mental abilities than those of others. Documented instances of calculating prodigies for the most part are those of young, illiterate, or uneducated persons with exceptionally good memory facilities who nearly always lost these powers in later life.

Calendar problems. Any problems or puzzles related to the calendar; commonly concerned with the determination of the date of Easter, the construction of a perpetual calendar, the probability of coincident birthdays, the occurrence of leap years or of Friday the 13th, and so on.

Cantometrics. A new field (ca. 1965) of activities that musicologists suggest deals with the relation of any culture's music with its social characteristics. Interest in this field was presumably stimulated by computerized music.

Cattle problem of Archimedes. A fantastic problem in which it is required to determine the number of white, black, spotted, and yellow bulls and the number of cows of the corresponding colors, given nine numerical conditions to be satisfied with regard to these eight variables. Analysis of the problem leads to the Pellian equation

$$y^2 - 410{,}286{,}423{,}278{,}424t^2 = 1,$$

an equation that has yet to be solved completely.

Charm. A side chain of a bracelet. [*A.M.M.* 74:769; June 1967.]

Cheery sequence. A sequence of integers, starting with any arbitrary integer, where each succeeding term is the sum of the squares of the digits of the previous terms. For example:

(A) 4, 16, 37, 58, 89, 145, 42, 20, 4, . . .

(B) 12, 5, 25, 29, 85, 89, 145, 42, 20, 4, 16, 37, 58, 89, . . .

[Donald C. Duncan, *M.T.* 65:627–29; Nov. 1972.]

Chess task. Refers to a specific objective to be reached; not to be confounded with a "task problem" in chess (q.v.).

Chinese checkers. A game played on a hexagonal-cell board that is generally shaped like a six-pointed star.

Chinese rings. A recreational toy consisting of several rings hung on a bar in such a way that the ring (or first two rings) at one end can be taken off or put on the bar at pleasure; but any other ring can be taken off or put on only when the one next to it (towards the end ring) is on and all the rest are off. Only one ring can be taken off or put on at a time, and the order of the rings cannot be changed.

Chromatic graph. A complete graph (in a plane or in 3-space) whose edges are colored either red or blue; then a monochromatic triangle is one whose three sides are of the same color.

Chromatic number. A topological invariant for a given surface, the chromatic number is the maximum number of regions that can be drawn on the surface in such a way that each region has a border in common with every other region. Thus if each region is assigned a different color, each color will border on every other color. Hence the term *chromatic number* is also used to designate the minimum number of colors sufficient to color any finite map on a given surface.

Cipher. See *Cryptogram.*

Circuit. An arc that returns to its starting point, that is, a route that revisits only the beginning vertex.

Circuit rank. The circuit rank of a particular graph G is the number of edges of G minus the number of vertices of G plus one.

Circulating decimal. See *Repeating decimal.*

Clock solitaire. A solitaire type of card game in which the fifty-two cards of a deck are dealt into thirteen face-down piles of four cards each, arranged like the numerals of a clock, with one pile in the center.

Close packing. The arranging of equal circles (or equal spheres) so that they are inscribed in regular tessellations. Such packings vary in density, depending on the tessellation used.

Code. The system or key used in preparing a cryptogram.

Coincidence ratio. The ratio of the number of coincidences (agreements) between the digits of an integer and the digits of its reverse to the number of digits in the integer. Thus the coincidence ratio of 1437245 is 3/7.

Collapsible compasses. See *Euclidean compasses.*

Colored cubes (and squares). A variety of recreations with colored squares and cubes, ranging from Major MacMahon's tiles and cubes to puzzles such as Instant Insanity.

Combination. Any particular selection of one, several, or all of the elements of a finite set of entities, irrespective of the order of selection.

Compasses. Modern compasses, that is, those that do not collapse when opened and may thus be used as a divider to transfer a distance as well as to draw a circle. It can be shown that any geometric construction that can be effected with the straightedge and modern compasses can also be performed with the straightedge and Euclidean compasses; however, the converse is not true. See also *Euclidean compasses.*

Complete graph. A graph of n vertices with edges connecting all pairs of vertices, that is, with $\frac{1}{2}n(n-1)$ edges.

Composite number. Any integer that is composed of two or more proper factors or divisors, not necessarily different. Examples: $8 = 2 \cdot 2 \cdot 2$; $14 = 2 \cdot 7$; $18 = 2 \cdot 3 \cdot 3$; $100 = 10 \cdot 10$. The number 1 is regarded as neither composite nor prime.

Any composite number can be expressed as the product of prime numbers in one and only one way, disregarding the order in which the factors are stated. For example: $105 = 3 \cdot 5 \cdot 7$; $360 = 2 \cdot 2 \cdot 2 \cdot 3 \cdot 3 \cdot 5 = 2^3 \cdot 3^2 \cdot 5$.

Concentric magic squares. See *Bordered magic squares.*

Congruent numbers. A number k is called congruent if integers x and y exist such that both $x^2 + ky^2$ and $x^2 - ky^2$ are perfect squares. An example of a possible solution for the smallest congruent number 5 is the following: $(41)^2 + 5(12)^2 = (49)^2$ and $(41)^2 - 5(12)^2 = (31)^2$.

Connected graph. A graph in which every vertex is connected to every other vertex by some arc.

Conservative number. A number that has the property of dividing evenly into its reverse; for example, $9801/1089 = 9$. Or, a number in which the digits are "conserved" after some operational change or transformation. The term is not as yet universally recognized.

Constant-width curves. If a closed convex curve is placed between two parallel lines and the lines are moved together until they are tangent to the curve, the distance between the parallels is called the width of the curve. If a curve (e.g., the circle) has the same width in all directions, it is a curve of constant width. There are infinitely many such curves.

Contack. A game played with equilateral-triangle tiles. [Martin Gardner, *Sci.Am.* 204:173; Mar. 1961.]

Cosmograph. A visual pattern produced by interfering sound waves, somewhat similar to Lissajous's figures. These infinitely varied optical pictures of sound waves are easily related to modern-art forms.

Cross-number puzzle. Similar to crossword puzzles, with numbers instead of words to be identified.

Crossed ladders. A perennial geometric problem involving two ladders of known but unequal lengths crossing so that their feet are respectively at the bases of two walls encompassing an alley. The usual question is, If the height above the pavement of the point at which the ladders cross is known, find the width of the alley.

Crossings, problems of. Problems of difficult crossings, such as the dilemma of the boatman with the wolf, the cabbage, and the goat, or the problem of the jealous husbands and their wives trying to cross a river in a boat that can hold only two persons.

Cryptanalysis. The art or science of solving a cryptogram, that is, discovering the true meaning of a "secret" or coded message without the knowledge of the code or key used in preparing the cryptogram; not to be confounded with the practice of deciphering a cryptogram, which refers to "translating" it with the aid of an appropriate code.

Cryptarithm. An indicated arithmetical operation in which some or all of the digits have been replaced by letters or symbols and where the restoration of the original digits is required. Embraces *alphametics*, *faded documents*, and *skeleton divisions* (q.v.). [*Sphinx* 1:50; 1931.]

Cryptogram. A "secret" or concealed message consisting of specific letters, numerals, or other symbols used in connection with some prearranged system (key or code) that permits of conveying a meaning other than the apparent message. Cryptograms are also called *ciphers*.

Cryptography. The art of composing secret messages that are intelligible to those who are in possession of the key, or code, and unintelligible to all others. The act of writing such a secret message is called *encoding* it; the act of interpreting it with the aid of a key is called *decoding*, or deciphering.

Curve of error. See *Probability curve.*

Curve stitching. The art of creating designs consisting of straight-line envelopes made with colored threads stitched on cards in accordance with some preassigned pattern of punched holes. [Edith Somervell, London, 1906.]

Cyclic decimal. See *Repeating decimal.*

Cyclic number. An integer of n digits with the unusual property that when multiplied by any number from 1 through n the product contains the same n digits as the original number in the same cyclic order. The smallest cyclic number is 142,857.

Cyclic path. A path that returns to its starting point.

Cyclomatic number. Another name for the circuit rank of a graph, that is, the number of edges of the graph minus the number of vertices of the graph plus one.

Cyclotomic equation. The equation $x^{p-1} + x^{p-2} + x^{p-3} + \cdots + 1 = 0$, obtained by dividing $x^p - 1 = 0$ by $x - 1$, where p is prime. The cyclotomic equation is irreducible, and its roots are on a circle.

Decanting problems. Also known as pouring problems, jug problems, and Tartaglia's measuring problems. The problem is how to transfer a given quantity of liquid from one container to another, using only a definite number of specific measuring vessels for the purpose.

Dee-dee consecutives. If one number divides another, and the dividend D suggests a consecutive extension of the divisor d, then we have a $d|D$ consecutive, that is, d divides D. For example: $1|2$; $2|3456$; $3|456789$; $5|43210$; $34|3536$; $7|800009$.

Defective number. *See Deficient number.*

Deficient number. Any integer the sum of whose integral divisors, excluding the given integer, is less than the integer itself. Thus 10 is a deficient number, since $1 + 2 + 5 < 10$. Or, alternatively, a deficient number is one that is greater than the sum of its proper divisors; same as *Defective number*. Every proper divisor of a perfect number is deficient.

Delian problem. See *Duplication of the cube.*

Denary numeration. A numeration system using base ten, or on the scale of ten, and requiring the ten digits 0, 1, 2, 3, 4, 5, 6, 7, 8, and 9. Also called *decimal notation*.

Deployment. A pencil and paper game for two players, played on a 5 × 5 array of 25 squares; similar to ticktacktoe but considerably more sophisticated. [William H. McGrail, Worcester, Mass.]

Derangement. If $(a_1, a_2, a_3, \cdots, a_n)$ is a permutation of n elements labeled 1, 2, 3, $\cdots$, n, then the permutation $(a_1, a_2, a_3, \cdots, a_n)$ is a derangement if $a_i \neq i$ $(i = 1, 2, 3, \cdots, n)$. Thus a derangement has no element in its natural position. [H. J. Ryser, *Combinatorial Mathematics* (Carus Monograph no. 14), 1963.]

Diablotin. See *Fifteen puzzle*.

Diabolic doughnut. A panmagic square, first rolled into a cylinder, then bent into a torus; all the rows, columns, and diagonals are closed loops, but the diabolic properties still hold.

Diabolic hypercube. The two-dimensional projection of the hypercube (or tesseract) lends itself to magic-square arrangements.

Diabolic magic square. Same as a panmagic square; also called *pandiagonal* and *Nasik* squares.

Diamond. A polyiamond consisting of two triangles.

Dido's problem. To find the curve, with a given perimeter, that encloses the maximum area; in general, it is a circle. If a portion of the boundary is to be an arbitrary straight-line segment, then the required curve is a semicircle.

Difficult crossings. See *Crossings*.

Digit. In the base-ten system, any one of the ten Hindu-Arabic numerals 0, 1, 2, 3, 4, 5, 6, 7, 8, and 9. In general, the individual symbols used in any cipherized system of numeration.

Digital diversions. The manipulation of numbers in such a way as to use their digits once only in order to arrive at a certain result, usually an identity. In general, the customary arithmetical operations and symbols are allowed, although in some instances the use of radicals, exponents, and factorials may also be admitted.

Digital invariant. An integer that is equal to the sum of the nth powers of its digits, or an integer for which the sum of the nth power of its digits is equal to some particular number. An example of the former is $153 = 1^3 + 5^3 + 3^3$.

Digital root (of an integer). The smallest positive integer to which the given integer is congruent modulo 9. It may be obtained by casting out 9s (replacing a final 0 with 9) or more laboriously by summing the digits of the integer, summing the digits of that sum, and continuing the process until a single digit is obtained. In any base b, use $b - 1$ in place of 9. [H. E. Dudeney, *Amusements in Mathematics*, p. 157; 1917.]

Digital sum. The digital sum of a number is the sum of the digits of its numerals. For example, the digital sum of 124 is $1 + 2 + 4 = 7$; or, the "first" digital sum of 79 is $7 + 9 = 16$, whereupon these digits are again added, giving a final digital sum of $1 + 6 = 7$.

Dim. A three-dimensional version of the game of Sim. [Douglas Engel, *J.R.M.* 5:274; Oct. 1972.]

Diophantine equation. An indeterminate polynomial equation in two or more variables for which the desired solution values are to be either rational or integral numbers, usually the latter; for example, $x + 2y = 13$, or $a^2 + b^2 = c^2$.

Dissection problems. Geometric dissections involve the cutting up of a geometric figure in accordance with some specified goal. More specifically, such problems call for the conversion of one figure to another by directly cutting it into a finite number of pieces and then rearranging them to form the other figure.

Divine proportion. See *Golden section*.

Dodecahedron. A convex dodecahedron is a convex solid bounded by twelve congruent pentagons; it has 12 faces, 20 vertices, and 30 edges.

Domino. A two-square polyomino. Also, familiar rectangular pieces divided into congruent squares bearing up to as many as six (or nine) pips in all possible combinations.

Doubly true addition. A cryptarithm or alphametic in which the addition of both the words and the numerals is true. [*A.M.M.* 68:1006; Dec. 1961.]

Dual solids. The dual of a polytope is another whose planes correspond to the vertices of the original figure and vice versa.

Duodecimal system. A system of numeration using base twelve and twelve digits: 0, 1, 2, 3, 4, 5, 6, 7, 8, 9, T, E. Thus:

$$130_{(twelve)} = 1(12)^2 + 3(12)^1 + 0(12)^0 =$$
$$144 \quad + 36 \quad + 0 \quad = 180_{(ten)}$$
$$2ET_{(twelve)} = 2(12)^2 + 11(12)^1 + 10(12)^0 =$$
$$288 \quad + 132 \quad + 10 \quad = 430_{(ten)}$$
$$19E_{(twelve)} = 1(12)^2 + 9(12)^1 + 11(12)^0 =$$
$$144 \quad + 108 \quad + 11 \quad = 263_{(ten)}$$

Duplication of a cube. One of the three famous problems of antiquity—to construct a cube having twice the volume of a given cube, using only the straightedge and compasses. Known also as the *Delian* problem, it is impossible to solve under the given conditions, since it is impossible to construct with Euclidean tools a segment whose length is a root of a cubic equation with rational coefficients but with no rational root.

Dynamic symmetry. Refers to the classic art periods of Egypt and Greece, in which designs commonly involved ratios of $1:\sqrt{2}$, $1:\sqrt{3}$, and $1:\sqrt{5}$. These dynamic designs, so designated by Jay Hambidge, evolved by the use of areas rather than by line measurements.

Edge. A piece of a curve connecting two vertices of a graph and containing no other vertex.

Eleusis. A card game for three or more players, invented by Robert Abbott. It is played with a standard deck of playing cards and is characterized by its dependence on inductive thinking.

Ellipsograph. Known also as the *trammel of Archimedes;* a mechanical device used in drafting rooms for constructing an ellipse.

Elliptipool. Pool played on an elliptically shaped pool table; originally only a theoretical concept, but reportedly such a table has been built.

Enantiomorphic. A figure that is not reflexible is said to be enantiomorphic to its mirror image; for example, a pair of gloves.

Epimenides' paradox. A Cretan by birth, Epimenides said that all Cretans are liars, a statement that, if true, makes the speaker a liar for telling the truth.

Equidecomposable. Two figures are said to be equidecomposable if it is possible to decompose one of them into a finite number of parts that can be rearranged to form the second figure.

Euclidean algorithm. To find the highest common factor of two integers, divide the smaller into the larger, then divide the remainder into the preceding divisor; repeat this process until the remainder is zero. The last divisor used is the highest common factor.

Euclidean compasses. A pair of compasses such that if either leg is lifted from the plane, the instrument will automatically collapse. Thus the Euclidean compasses cannot be used for transferring a distance. Such an instrument, along with an unmarked straightedge, was indicated by the ancients when they spoke of "geometric construction," that is, using Euclidean tools. See also *Compasses*.

Euler circles. Similar to Venn diagrams; used not only to exhibit relations between sets but also to illustrate syllogistic reasoning.

Euler circuit. A cyclic path that covers each edge of a graph exactly once and returns to the starting point. See also *Unicursal curve*.

Euler line. A cyclic path that covers every edge of a graph.

Euler-Poincaré characteristic. A constant X, which defines a property of a surface:

$$X = V - E + F,$$

where $V =$ the number of vertices, $E =$ the number of edges, and F = the number of faces.

In a simply connected polyhedron (or connected map in a plane), the characteristic constant X $= 2$, yielding the familiar Euler formula $V - E + F = 2$.

Euler squares. An Euler square of order n is a square in which the cells are filled with n elements of one kind, $a_1, a_2, a_3, \cdot \cdot \cdot, a_n$, and n elements of another kind, $b_1, b_2, b_3, \cdot \cdot \cdot, b_n$, in such a way that—
1. each cell contains one element of each kind;
2. each element of the first kind is paired with each element of the second kind exactly once;
3. each row and each column contains all the elements of both kinds.
An Euler square may be regarded as a combination of two Latin squares. Euler squares are also known as *Graeco-Latin* squares.

Euler's theorem. This states that, topologically, for any map on a sphere, $V - E + F = 2$. The theorem also applies to convex polyhedrons; for example, a hexahedron, for which $V = 8$, $E = 12$, and $F = 6$.

Excessive number. An excessive number is any number that is less than the sum of its proper divisors; synonymous with *abundant* number and *redundant* number. For example, 12 is an abundant number, since $12 < 1 + 2 + 3 + 4 + 6$.

Factor. Any one of two or more numbers that are multiplied to form a product.

Factorials. If n is a natural number, then *factorial n* designates the product. $1 \cdot 2 \cdot 3 \cdot 4 \cdot \ldots \cdot (n - 1)(n)$. This product is written as $\lfloor n$ or $n!$, and is read "factorial n" or "n factorial." Factorial zero, $0!$, is arbitrarily defined to be unity.

Faded document. An indicated arithmetical operation in which some of the numerals have been rendered illegible, thus producing a cryptarithm.

Fairy chess. Any unconventional set of rules or nontraditional pieces used with some kind of a chessboard, as, for example, cooperative chess, four-handed chess, retrograde analysis, no checkmate, move-and-a-half, vertical-cylinder board, maximummer game, no capture chess, three- and four- dimensional chess, transportation chess, Möbius-strip chess, no-pawn chess, and so on.

Fallacies. A mathematical fallacy is an instance of reasoning that leads to a false or absurd conclusion. It may be due to a violation of a principle of logic, to a misleading diagram, to the denial of a previous assumption, or to the violation of a previously established definition, theorem, or principle.

Farey sequence. If all the proper fractions (written in lowest terms) having denominators not greater than a given integer are arranged in order of magnitude, the sequence is called a *Farey sequence*. In such a sequence, each fraction is equal to the fraction whose numerator is the sum of the two numerators on either side of it and whose denominator is the sum of the corresponding denominators. For example, for $N = 4$:

$$\frac{0}{1}, \frac{1}{4}, \frac{1}{3}, \frac{1}{2}, \frac{2}{3}, \frac{3}{4}, \frac{1}{1}.$$

Fault-free rectangles. Any rectangular arrangement of interlocking dominoes such that there is no straight line, vertical or horizontal, that joins the opposite sides of the rectangular arrangement; for example, in the figure shown, $\overline{AB}$ is a fault line.

Feminine numbers. This term was used by the ancient Greeks to denote *even* numbers, which were regarded as ephemeral. Odd numbers were masculine; even numbers, which always contained other numbers, were femimine. Thus odd numbers were divine and heavenly, but even numbers were regarded as human and earthly. The number 2 was the first feminine number; the number 3 was the first masculine number. (The number 1 was the source of all numbers.)

Fermat numbers. Fermat numbers are numbers of the form

$$2^{2^n} + 1.$$

The first five Fermat numbers ($n = 0, 1, 2, 3, 4$) are 3, 5, 17, 257, and 65,537. Some Fermat numbers are prime; others are composite.

Fermat's last theorem. Fermat's statement was that $x^n + y^n = z^n$ has no solution in integers or rational numbers for $n > 2$. The "theorem" has not yet been proved.

Ferrying problems. See *Crossings*.

Fibonacci Nim. A modified form of Nim, for two players. Starting with a pile of n counters, the first player may not take the entire pile; thereafter either player may remove all remaining counters provided (1) that at least one counter is taken at each play, and (2) that neither player ever takes more than twice as many counters as his opponent took on his last play. [Robert E. Gaskell, ca. 1965; Martin Gardner, *Sci.Am.*, Mar. 1969, p. 119.]

Fibonacci numbers. The Fibonacci sequence $\{F_n\}$ is defined by $F_0 = 0$, $F_1 = 1$, $F_n = F_{n-1} + F_{n-2}$ for $n \geq 2$. Thus $\{F_n\} = \{0, 1, 1, 2, 3, 5, 8, 13, \cdots \}$.

Fifteen puzzle. This consists of a shallow square tray that holds exactly fifteen small square counters numbered from 1 to 15, with provision for a blank-square place. Initially placed in random order, the puzzle is to rearrange the fifteen squares in numerical order by sliding only, with the blank space finally remaining in the lower right-hand corner.

1	2	3	4
5	6	7	8
9	10	11	12
13	14	15	

Figurate numbers. Figurate numbers are defined as the terms of certain arithmetic series and the terms of "sum-series" formed from these series. For example:

(A) 1, 2, 3, 4, 5, $\cdots r$
(B) 1, 3, 5, 7, 9, $\cdots (2r - 1)$
(A′) 1, 3, 6, 10, 15, $\cdots r(r + 1)/2$
(B′) 1, 4, 9, 16, 25, $\cdots r^2$

The terms of series such as (A′) and (B′) are called *plane figurate numbers*.

Finite geometry. Sometimes called a "miniature geometry"; any system of geometry based on the postulation of a finite number of points and a finite number of lines, where "points" and "lines" are not only undefined terms but admit of unconventional interpretations.

Flexagons. These are paper polygons specially folded from a strip of paper and having the unique property of changing exposed faces when they are "flexed." The original models were hexagonal in form with exposed triangular faces; other models, developed later, are made from square forms and expose square faces. Many varieties of both forms (hexaflexagons and tetraflexagons) have been developed, some of which are available on the market as toys under various trade names. [A. H. Stone, 1939.]

Flexahedron. Three-dimensional structures comprised of connected solids in such a way that they can be rotated or flexed in various ways.

Focus. A board game played with thirty-six counters, half of one color and half of another, on an 8×8 board from which three cells at each corner have been removed. [Sidney Sackson, in *Martin Gardner's Sixth Book of Mathematical Games from Scientific American*, p. 44; 1971.]

Four-color problem. The original map-coloring problem, which asked, Are four colors *sufficient* to color every possible map in the plane (or on the surface of a sphere) so that no two adjoining countries are of the same color? See also *Map coloring*.

Four-digits problem. To express with the digits 1, 2, 3, 4 the consecutive numbers from 1 upwards as far as possible, using each of the four digits once and once only in conjunction with arbitrarily chosen mathematical operations.

Four-fours problem. To express, using "ordinary" arithmetic and algebraic notation, the consecutive numbers from 1 upwards as far as possible in terms of four 4s.

Fourth dimension. A term referring alternatively to the "popular" aspects and to the mathematical considerations of n-dimensional space, where $n = 4$.

Franklin squares. An ingenious 8×8 magic square and another 16×16 square, both of which have unusual properties not possessed by other even-numbered magic squares. Both were created by Benjamin Franklin.

Freak cancellations. See *Illegal operations.*

Gale. A pencil and paper game that involves connecting black dots and colored dots, respectively; one set of dots is embedded in a similar rectangular array of the other set of dots. [Martin Gardner, *Second Scientific American Book of Mathematical Puzzles and Diversions*, p. 84; 1961.]

Galileo sequence. A sequence of the form

$$\frac{1}{3} = \frac{1 + 3}{5 + 7} = \frac{1 + 3 + 5}{7 + 9 + 11} = \cdots .$$

Galton probability board. A physical model illustrating the normal binomial distribution curve by allowing many small steel balls to drop over a series of rows of staggered pins, as shown in the figure. The probabilities of each ball falling to the left or to the right of two adjacent pins, or between them, are in the ratio 1:2:1; hence the probabilities for the entire board are proportional to the numbers of Pascal's triangle. (q.v.)

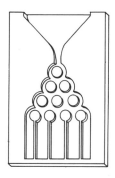

Galton quincunx. Same as the *Galton probability board.*

Gaussian curve. See *Probability curve.*

Gematria. A mystic pseudoscience based on the fact that the letters of various ancient alphabets (e.g., Greek, Hebrew) had numerical values and hence were used in computation.

Geoboard. A flat board into which nails or pins have been driven in a regular pattern. By slipping rubber bands around the pins, geometric figures and relations may be discovered. The pattern may be a square grid, a circular grid, or an isometric grid.

Geodesic. The shortest distance between two points on a surface. On a sphere, a geodesic is an arc of a great circle. Sometimes there are many equally short paths, as, for example, between two poles of a sphere.

Geometric magic square. An $n \times n$ array of n^2 distinct integers with the property that the product of the n integers in any row, column, or main diagonal is equal to the same magic constant.

Glissette. The curve generated by a fixed point on a curve as the curve slides between given curves.

Gnomic magic square (third order). A 3×3 array in which the elements in each 2×2 corner have the same sum. [*M.Mag.* 43:70; Mar. 1970.]

Gnomic numbers. The successive numbers that, when added to triangles, squares, pentagons, and so on, produce an additional triangle, square, pentagon, and so on.
For triangles, the gnomic numbers are 1, 2, 3, 4, · · · .

For squares, the gnomic numbers are 1, 3, 5, 7, · · ·.

For pentagons, the gnomic numbers are 1, 4, 7, 10, · · ·.

Gnomon (1). In ancient Babylonia and Greece a gnomon was an astronomical instrument consisting of a vertical column or shaft for determining the altitude of the sun or the latitude of a position by measuring the length of the shaft's shadow cast at noon. By extension, it also refers to the raised part of a modern sundial that casts the shadow.

Gnomon (2). In connection with the theory of polygonal numbers, there is always a gnomon that can be added to a square number to create the next greater square number; for example, 5 is the gnomon of 4, 7 is the gnomon of 9, and so on. Or, conversely, the figure that remains of a square when a smaller square is cut off one corner.

 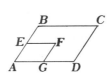

Gnomon (3). In geometry, a gnomon is a portion of a geometric figure that has been added to (or taken away from) a figure so that the new figure (or remaining figure) is similar to the original figure. For example, in the figure shown $\triangle\,BCD$ is a gnomon to $\triangle\,ABD$ if $\angle\,y = \angle\,x$; or, $EFGDCB$ is the gnomon of $\square ABCD$.

 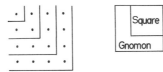

Go. The national game of Japan; exceedingly complicated and difficult. The board consists of two sets of 19 parallel lines, mutually at right angles, forming 361 points of intersection. The game is played with 361 pieces called *stones* placed on these points of intersection; once a stone is placed on an intersection it remains there unless captured. The object of the game is to capture territory and pieces by surrounding them in certain ways.

Goldbach's conjecture. An unproved (by 1972) conjecture to the effect that every even integer (except 2) is the sum of two primes; for example, $28 = 11 + 17$, or $62 = 19 + 43$.

Golden rectangle. A rectangle whose sides are in the ratio of $\Phi:1$; that is, approximately 8:5. Such a rectangle is said to be aesthetically the most pleasing rectangular shape; an ordinary postal card is very nearly this shape. See also *Phi*.

Golden section. A given line segment is said to be divided in extreme and mean ratio, or in the golden section, when the two parts a and b, are such that $a/b = b/(a + b)$, where $a < b$. See also *Phi*.

Go-moku. An Oriental board game played on a 19×19 Go-board. The number of stones is the same as in Go, although not all need to be used. The object of the game is to form a straight line of exactly five (not more) adjacent stones of one color.

Googol. A term coined by the late Edward Kasner; it represents the number 10^{100}. When written in full, it is seen as 1 followed by one hundred zeros.

Googolplex. Also coined by Kasner, a googolplex is 1 followed by a googol of zeros; that is, a googolplex is 10 raised to the googolth power, or $10^{(10^{100})}$.

Graeco-Latin square. Also known as Graeco-Roman square; another name for the Euler square (q.v.).

Graph. A figure consisting of points (vertices) and segments (edges) connecting some or all of these vertices. The edges may be straight or curved segments.

Graph theory. The term *graph* used in the context of graph theory, or network theory, refers to "linear graphs," that is, simple geometric figures consisting of points and lines connecting some of these points.

Halma. A game somewhat like Chinese checkers; played by two or four persons on a checkerboard with sixteen cells on each side. [Martin Gardner, *Sci.Am.*, Oct. 1971.]

Hamilton circuit. A circuit that covers all vertices of a graph.

Hamiltonian game. Determining along the edges of a regular dodecahedron the route that will pass once and only once through every vertex.

Happy integers. An integer is happy if and only if its cheery sequence has a period of 1. For example: 7 : 7 , 49, 97, 130, 10, 1, 1, 1, $\cdot$ $\cdot$ $\cdot$. [Donald C. Duncan, *M.T.* 65:627–29; Nov. 1972.] See *Cheery sequence*.

Harmonograph. An arrangement of swinging pendulums, frequently used to demonstrate simple harmonic motion. Suitably adjusted, it yields a variety of attractive patterns known as Lissajous's figures.

Hempel's paradox. A logical paradox according to which it can be shown that apparently no crows are black.

Heronian triangle. Any triangle whose sides are rational and whose area is also rational; also called a Heronian triple. There are infinitely many Heronian triangles; for example, (125, 136, 99) is a Heronian triple. Any Pythagorean triple is necessarily Heronian.

Heterosquare. An n by n array in which the $4n$ sums of the elements in the rows, columns, and diagonals (broken and unbroken) are all different. [*M.Mag.* 24:166; Jan. 1951.]

Hex. A game played on a board consisting of an array of congruent, interlocking hexagons, eleven on a side. [Invented independently by Piet Hein in 1942 and John F. Nash in 1948.]

Hexacube. The 166 pieces formed by joining six-unit cubes in all possible ways. [David Klarner.]

Hexadiangle. A board game played on a hexagonal board marked out in equilateral triangles. [G. Austwick, *M.Tchg.*, no. 59, p. 13; Summer 1972.]

Hexaflexagon. Six-sided paper structures that can be "flexed" so as to successively bring various surfaces to view; they are constructed by suitably folding a narrow strip of paper and can also be made effectively from strips of thin metal foil.

Hexagonal numbers. A class of polygonal numbers that may be defined by the geometric figure they represent; thus for a hexagon:

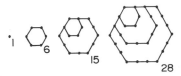

They may also be defined as sums of a special arithmetic sequence; thus
$$1 + 5 + 9 + 13 + 17 + \cdots + (4n - 3) = n(2n - 1).$$

Hexagram. The six-pointed starlike figure formed by two congruent equilateral triangles superposed so that their six vertices become the vertices of a regular hexagon.

Hexahedron. A convex hexahedron is a solid figure bounded by six plane polygons. There are only seven varieties of convex hexahedrons; one of these varieties is the regular hexahedron, or cube, which is bounded by six congruent squares, with 8 vertices, 6 faces, and 12 edges.

Hexatetraflexagon. A special species of tetraflexagon that can be flexed along both horizontal and vertical axes to expose all six of its square faces.

Hexiamond. A polyiamond consisting of six triangles.

Homeomorphic. If a geometric figure can be transformed into another by a topological transformation, the two figures are topologically equivalent, or homeomorphic. A topological transformation is a one-to-one correspondence between the points of two figures A and B such that open (or closed) sets in A correspond to open (or closed) sets in B. Any transformation that shrinks, expands, twists, and so forth, in any way without tearing, that is, a continuous transformation, is also a topological transformation.

Honeycomb. A three-dimensional honeycomb, or solid tessellation, is an infinite set of polyhedra fitting together in such a way as to fill all space exactly once, and such that every face of each polyhedron belongs to one other polyhedron. A honeycomb is regular if its cells are regular and equal.

Hopscotch. A modification of ticktacktoe played on a square array of nine lattice points, each player using three pieces; not to be confounded with the children's hopping game of the same name.

Howler. An amusing illegal (mathematical) operation; also known as a "lucky boner" or "making the right mistake."

Hypercube. A four-dimensional cube; also known as a tesseract. More generally, the term *hypercube* refers to any n-dimensional cube.

Icosahedron. A convex icosahedron is a convex solid bounded by twenty plane polygons. The regular icosahedron is bounded by twenty congruent equilateral triangles; it has 20 faces, 12 vertices, and 30 edges.

Icosian game. Same as the *Hamiltonian game.*

Illegal operation. An incorrect mathematical operation or algorithm innocently introduced into a calculation or proof but which nevertheless leads to a correct result. For example:

1. $\dfrac{16}{64} = \dfrac{1\cancel{6}}{\cancel{6}4} = \dfrac{1}{4}$

2. $1^3 + 2^3 = 1 \times 3 + 2 \times 3 = 3 + 6 = 9$

Imbedded numerals. A two-digit numeral is said to be imbedded, for example, in a four-digit numeral if the digits of the former occur in any order in the latter. Thus in 2559 are imbedded 25, 29, 55, 59, 95, 92, and 52. [Mannis Charosh, *Mathematics Student Journal*, Problem 261; Jan. 1967.]

Indifference, principle of. Formerly known as the principle of insufficient reason, it states that if there are no grounds whatever for believing that any one of n mutually exclusive events is more likely to occur than any other, a probability of $1/n$ is assigned to each.

Inferential problems. Problems or puzzles of a logical nature rather than those involving computation or geometric configurations. For example: problems of difficult crossings; pouring problems; Smith-Jones-Robinson type of problems; the "unexpected egg" or the "unexpected hanging"; the colored hats or the smudges; truth and lying situations; and so on.

Infinite regress. An endless hierarchy of identical entities or operations, such as the reiterated images of a mirror reflected in a mirror or the segments of a curve of the snowflake type.

Integer. Any member of the set

$$\{ \cdots, -4, -3, -2, -1, 0, +1, +2, +3, +4, \cdots \}.$$

Also, in the proper context, a natural number, a whole number, or a positive integer.

Integer, peak. An integer with digits that, reading from the left, steadily increase to a maximum and then steadily decrease to a final right-hand digit, as in 234631. [*J.R.M.* 4:170; July 1971.]

Integer, regular peak. A peak integer with digits on each slope in arithmetic progression, as in 159753. [*J.R.M.* 4:170; July 1971.]

Integer, plateau. An integer with all like intermediate digits, which differ from its like end digits, as in 47774. [*J.R.M.* 4:169; July 1971.]

Integer, valley. An integer with digits that, reading from the left, steadily decrease to a minimum and then steadily increase to a final right-hand digit, as in 985234. [*J.R.M.* 4:170; July 1971.]

Integer, regular valley. A valley integer with digits on each slope in arithmetic progression, as in 864234. [*J.R.M.* 4:170; July 1971.]

Integer, undulating. An integer in which the alternate digits are consistently greater than or less than the digits adjacent to them, as in 415362. [*J.R.M.* 4:169; July 1971.]

Integer, smoothly undulating. An undulating integer in which only two distinct digits are present, as in 2525252. [*J.R.M.* 4:169; July 1971.]

Instant Insanity. Trade name of a popular puzzle consisting of four multi-colored unit cubes, each of which has its faces painted red, blue, white, or green in a definite manner. The puzzle is to assemble the four cubes into a 1 × 1 × 4 rectangular prism such that all four colors appear on each of the four long faces of the prism. Of 82,944 possible rectangular prisms that can be arranged from them, only two distinct arrangements satisfy the required conditions.

Irregular operation. See *Illegal operation.*

Jeu de Baguenaudier. See *Chinese rings.*

Jeu du Taquin. The Fifteen, or Boss, puzzle; also known as *Diablotin* in France, and sometimes called *Imp.*

Jordan curve. Any simple plane curve. See also *Jordan's theorem; simple curve.*

Jordan's theorem. In a plane, every closed curve that does not cross itself divides the plane into one interior region and one exterior region. Such a curve is called a simple curve. Any continuous line connecting a point in the interior with a point in the exterior (such as *PQ* in the figure shown) must intersect the curve. Every simple curve in the plane is topologically equivalent to a circle.

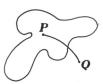

Jourdain's card paradox. A well-known logical paradox: One side of a card reads, "The sentence on the other side of this card is TRUE"; the other side of the card reads, "The sentence on the other side of this card is FALSE."

Kakeya needle problem. What is the plane figure of least area in which a line segment of unit length can be rotated 360°? [Sôichi Kakeya, Japan, 1917.]

Kalah. An African board game somewhat like Oware; in addition to the twelve compartments there is a larger oval compartment (*kalah*) at either end of the board. The purpose of the game is to accumulate as many playing pieces as possible in the large oval kalah at the right.

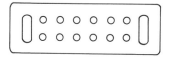

Kaprekar's constant. The unique self-reproducing integer 6,174, which terminates Kaprekar's routine when this routine is applied to any four-digit integer (not all four digits alike) in decimal notation. [*Scrip.M.* 15:244; 1949.]

Kaprekar's routine. Consists of rearranging the digits (not all alike) of an integer, N_0, to form the largest and smallest possible integers, finding their difference, N_1, and applying the ordering-subtraction operation to N_1 and to the subsequent differences until a self-producing integer or a regenerative loop is obtained. [*M.Mag.* 45:121; May 1972.]

Kepler's star polyhedra. Three-dimensional star polyhedra formed by extending the edges of an icosahedron or those of a pentadodecahedron.

Kirkman's schoolgirls problem. As originally enunciated, to arrange fifteen things in different sets of triplets. [*Lady's and Gentleman's Diary,* 1850.]

Kiss Precise. The title of a poem by Frederick Soddy (1936) in which he gives, in verse and without symbols, the relationship between the radii of mutually tangent circles. The relationship in question is $\alpha^2 + \beta^2 + \gamma^2 + \delta^2 = \frac{1}{2} (\alpha + \beta + \gamma + \delta)^2$, where α, β, γ are the curvatures of three given circles A, B, and C expressed in terms of the sides a, b, c, of $\triangle ABC$, and δ is the curvature of the inner circle whose radius is r; thus $\delta = 1/r$, and $\alpha = 1/(s - a)$, $\beta = 1/(s - b)$, and $\gamma = 1/(s - c)$, where $2s = a + b + c$.

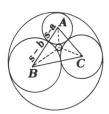

Klein bottle. A bottle-shaped, one-sided surface with no edges and no "inside" and no "outside"; it can be formed by inserting the small end of a tapering tube through one side of the tube and then spreading it so as to join the other end.

Knight's tour. A classic chessboard problem calling for a path formed by moving the knight in such a way that it will move successively onto every possible cell once and only once. If the knight can move from the last cell reached to the initial cell, then the tour is called a *re-entrant* path.

Knot. A simple closed curve in three-dimensional space. Both in a plane and in four-dimensional space all simple closed curves can be deformed, without crossing themselves, into circles; but in three-dimensional space some curves forming a knot cannot be so deformed.

Königsberg bridges. A classical problem. Is it possible to traverse a specific pattern of seven bridges in such a way as to cross each bridge once and only once? The problem was shown to be impossible by Euler, who, in generalizing it, laid the foundation of modern network (graph) theory.

Labyrinth. See *Maze*.

Latin square. A Latin square of the nth order is an array of n^2 cells, in n rows and n columns, in which n letters consisting of n a's, n b's, and so on, are arranged in the cells so that the n letters in each row and each column are different.

Lattice. A lattice is a set of points with integral coordinates, in a plane or in space, with respect to a Cartesian reference system. The points belonging to this set are called *lattice points*. Two fundamental properties of a plane lattice are these:

1. It is possible to draw through any given lattice point infinitely many lines that do not pass through any other lattice point.
2. Any straight line through two given lattice points must pass through an infinity of other lattice points.

Lehmer's photoelectric number-sieve. An electronic device that factorizes large numbers with unbelievable rapidity.

Life. A sophisticated solitaire recreation invented by John H. Conway that simulates population changes by using "genetic laws" relating to births, deaths, and survivals; played on a large checkerboard or a Go-board with a large number of counters of two colors.

Linkage. A mathematical or drawing device consisting of a combination of bars or pieces pivoted together so as to turn about one another, usually in parallel planes; often used for transmitting motion.

Lissajous's figures. This refers to the family of curves that are described by a point whose motion is the resultant of two simple harmonic motions in perpendicular directions. Since the motions have different periods and different amplitudes, the variety of interesting patterns obtainable is seemingly endless. Lissajous's figures can be produced mechanically by suitably arranged swinging pendulums (harmonograph), by means of differential rotating gear wheels (spirograph), or by means of an electrical device (oscillogram).

Loculus of Archimedes. An ancient tangram puzzle consisting of fourteen tiles made by dissecting a rectangle as shown in the figure, the length of the original rectangle being twice its width; M, N, L, J, I, and H are mid-points, and $\overline{IK}$ extended passes through A.

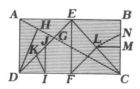

Logic machine. In general, an electronic computer designed or programmed to manipulate the symbols of thought; for example, to translate from one language to another, to play a game of checkers or Nim, to prove theorems in symbolic logic, and so on.

Logic problems. See *Inferential problems.*

Lucas numbers. The Lucas sequence $\{L_n\}$ is defined by $L_1 = 1, L_2 = 3,$ $L_n = L_{n-1} + L_{n-2}$ for $n \geq 3$. Thus $\{L_n\} = \{1, 3, 4, 7, 11, 18, \cdots\}$.

Lunes of Hippocrates. The two lunes, or crescents, formed by semicircles having the legs and hypotenuse of a right triangle as diameters. The sum of the areas of the two lunes is equal to the area of the triangle.

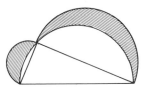

McKay's theorem. Given $a/b < c/d$, where a, b, c, and d are integers, then $(a + b)/(b + d)$ is between a/b and c/d.

Magic circles. Circles so constructed that their points of intersection can be numbered in such a way that the sum of the integers lying on any given circle is equal to the sum of the integers lying on each of the other circles.

Magic constant. The constant sum of the numbers in each row, column, and main diagonal of a magic square. For a normal magic square the constant is given by $\frac{1}{2}n(n^2 + 1)$.

Magic cube. An $n \times n \times n$ magic cube consists of a series of integers so arranged that any column or row of n integers and the four main diagonals (each containing n integers) through the center of the cube add up to the same magic constant.

Magic hexagon. A unique configuration of nineteen hexagonal cells arranged contiguously to form an overall hexagonal shape. The cells are numbered with the integers 1–19 in such a way that the sum of the integers in any straight line of edge-joined cells is 38.

Magic square. A square array of n numbers such that the sum of the n numbers lying in any row, column, or main diagonal is some constant. The numbers may be positive or negative integers, or fractions. Generally, magic squares are formed from the first n natural numbers, in which case they are called normal magic squares.

Magic star. A five-pointed star (pentagram) with its five points of intersection and its five "points" so numbered that the sum of the magic constant for each straight line is 24. The numbers used are the integers 1 through 12, with the 7 and the 11 omitted.

Malfatti problem. To determine the sizes of three nonoverlapping circles of the greatest combined area which could be cut from a given triangle. [1803.]

The converse problem is to find the triangle of least area which can enclose three nonoverlapping circles of given radii. (The converse problem was presumably not considered by Malfatti.)

Map coloring. A generalization of the four-color map problem, which seeks to determine the smallest number of colors sufficient for coloring the countries of a given map. It is known that all possible maps with thirty-eight or fewer countries in the plane or on a sphere can be colored with just four colors. A general proof that four colors are sufficient for all possible maps in the plane has not as yet been found.

Marelle. See *Nine Men's Morris*.

Martingale. Specifically, a system of betting such that in a sequence of bets, losses are recovered by progressively increasing the stakes.

Mascheroni constructions. Problems of geometric construction calling for the use of the Euclidean compasses (collapsible) only.

Masculine numbers. See *Feminine numbers*.

Maxigon. The maximum-sided polygonal face possible in a member of a V-family of polyhedra (q.v.). Each member will have its own maxigon, varying in the number of sides, and the largest of the family will occur in that member in which $n - 1$ vertices lie in a plane and one outside it. The vertices of the plane define this maxigon. [John McClellan, *J.R.M.* 3:58–60; Jan. 1970.]

Maze. Specifically, a complex network of intercommunicating paths or passages; idealized, the paths are the branches of an Euler graph or network, and the places where two or more paths meet are *nodes*.

Mersenne numbers. Numbers of the form $2^n - 1$, where n is an integer.

Mill. See *Nine Men's Morris*.

Misère. A term sometimes applied to games when the object is to try to *avoid* the customary win; for example, Nim, pebbles, losing checkers, or ticktacktoe (forcing the opponent to make a straight line).

Möbius band. If one edge of a long strip of paper with parallel edges is twisted through 180° and the ends of the strip are then fastened, the resulting surface is a Möbius band; it has only one "side" and only one bounding edge. Any point on the strip can be joined to any other point on the strip by a curve lying wholly on the strip and not crossing the bounding edge. See also *Paradromic rings*.

Moiré pattern. In general, a pattern produced whenever two periodic structures are overlapped. The interacting figures often consist of straight lines, curves, or dots, but not necessarily; the basic requirement is that the figures have some sort of solid regions and some open regions (cf. *Moiré silk*).

Monomino. A single-square polyomino.

Morley's theorem. If the trisectors of the angles of a triangle are drawn so that those adjacent to each side intersect, the intersections are the vertices of an equilateral triangle. [The theorem was enunciated by Frank Morley in 1899 and proved fifteen years later by W. E. Philip.]

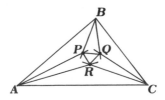

Mosaic. A surface decoration made by inlaying in patterns small pieces of colored glass, stone, or wood, such as in tiled or parquet floors. Many mosaics are tessellations, although the basic requirement is that they cover the plane completely.

Multigrade. A multigrade is a particular relationship between sets of numbers and their powers. For example:

a) $1^2 + 6^2 + 8^2 = 2^2 + 4^2 + 9^2$
b) $1^3 + 6^3 + 7^3 + 17^3 + 18^3 + 23^3 = 2^3 + 3^3 + 11^3 + 13^3 + 21^3 + 22^3$

Multimagic squares. A magic square is multimagic of degree p if the square formed by replacing each element by its kth power is magic, for every k from 1 to p.

Multiperfect numbers. Any integer such that the sum of its divisors plus the given integer is equal to an integral multiple of the integer itself. For example, the sum of the factors of 120 is 240, and $240 + 120 = 360 = 3(120)$. In general, $s(N) + N = kN$, where $s(N)$ represents the sum of the divisors of N and k is an integer greater than 1.

Mutession. A tiling relationship in which the plane is covered by pairs of polygons such that each polygon in the pair tessellates the other in the sense that a finite number of congruent polygons that are similar to one of the two polygons can be arranged in a nonoverlapping way to form the other polygon. [R. W. Meyer, *M.Tchg.*, no. 56, pp. 24–27; Autumn 1971.]

Mutuabola. Name designating the graphs of $y^x = x^y$ and $x \log y = y \log x$. [R. R. Rowe, *J.R.M.* 3:176–78; July 1970.]

Mystic hexagram. Refers to the famous theorem of projective geometry, first enunciated by Pascal: If a hexagon be inscribed in a conic, then the points of intersection of the three pairs of opposite sides are collinear, and conversely.

Napoleon's problem. A classical Mascheroni construction problem: Given two diagonally opposite corners of a square, find the other two corners using only a compass.

Narcissistic number. Any number that can be represented in some way by a mathematical manipulation of the digits of the number itself. Many varieties are possible, including digital invariants and visible representations. Examples of narcissistic numbers would include the following:

$$371 = 3^3 + 7^3 + 1^3$$
$$407 = 4^3 + 0^3 + 7^3$$

Nasik magic square. Same as a diabolic, panmagic, or pandiagonal square.

Natural number. Any member of the infinite set $\{1, 2, 3, 4, \cdots\}$.

Necklace. A closed circular chain of beads, usually of two colors. [Dudeney; Gardner, *New Mathematical Pastimes from Scientific American*, p. 240.] Cf. also, *necklet*, as in Frederick Soddy's poem *The Hexlet*, which speaks of spheres as "a necklet of graded beads" (1936).

Net. A plane figure that can be "folded" into a three-dimensional model of a given polyhedron.

Network. See *Graph*.

Nim. In its most general form, a game for two players in which any number of counters are divided arbitrarily into several piles. Playing alternately, each player selects one of the piles and withdraws any number of counters, but at least one; the player drawing the last counter (or counters) wins. [C. L. Bouton, 1902.]

Nimatron. An electronic machine (computer) designed to play a perfect game of Nim by virtue of the fact that it operates on the binary system. [Edward U. Condon, 1940.]

Nimrod. An improved Nim-playing robot machine developed about 1951.

Nine Men's Morris. An old board game (also known as *triple hopscotch, Marelle,* and *Mill*) for two players, on a board as shown. Each player begins with nine counters; the object is to place three pieces in a row, which allows him to confiscate a piece from his opponent. The first player reduced to two pieces loses.

Normal magic square. Any magic square formed from the first n^2 natural number.

Normal number. Any number in whose decimal expansion all digits occur with equal frequency and all blocks of digits of the same length occur with equal frequency.

Normal piling. See *Spherical close-packing.*

Noughts and crosses. See *Ticktacktoe.*

Number base. A numeral used as the basis of any ciphered numeration system that uses the principle of position. If the base numeral is designated as b, then the system in base b will require the use of exactly b digits, viz., 0, 1, 2, 3, $\cdots$ $(b-1)$. Any number N in this system may be expressed as the sum of successive powers of the base b: thus $N = a_0 (b)^0 + a_1 (b)^1 + a_2 (b)^2 + a_3 (b)^3 + \cdots$, where the coefficients $a_0, a_1, a_2, a_3, \cdots$ represent any of the b digits is used in the system.

Number giants. Although "large" is clearly a relative term, extraordinarily large numbers are encountered in the physical sciences and astronomy. Such numbers are sometimes referred to as number giants; for example, the *googolplex,* $10^{(10^{100})}$, or *Skewe's number,* $10^{10^{10^{34}}}$.

Number mysticism. A somewhat loose term embracing numerology, ancient and medieval beliefs in the esoteric qualities of numbers (e.g., Gematria), the humor of Martin Gardner's Dr. Matrix, and other number curiosities and coincidences.

Number pleasantries. A broad term often used to include number oddities, curiosities, patterns, and paradoxes; number tricks; digital variations and identities; multigrades; palindromes; illegal operations; and so on.

Numeral. Any symbol or group of symbols used to designate a number or a constitutent of a number; specifically, any one of the so-called Hindu-Arabic numeral symbols, that is, 0, 1, 2, 3, 4, 5, 6, 7, 8, and 9.

Numerology. The pseudoscientific study of numbers; a spurious art, akin to astrology, in which numbers and number relations can allegedly be used to foretell the future, influence events, explain coincidences, reveal character, and so forth.

Oblong numbers. See *Rectangular numbers.*

Octahedron. A convex octahedron is a solid figure bounded by eight plane polygons. Thus a hexagonal prism or the frustum of a hexagonal pyramid are octahedrons. A *regular* octahedron is bounded by eight congruent equilateral triangles; it has 6 vertices, 8 faces, and 12 edges.

Octonary numeration. A numeration system with base eight, or on the scale of eight; also known as *octic arithmetic.*

Optical illusion. As used in recreational mathematics, any diagram or drawing that creates a false mental image, invites a misinterpretation, or depicts an "impossible" physical reality.

Origami. Originally, the art of folding realistic animals, birds, fish, and other objects from a single sheet of paper without cutting, pasting, or adding decorations. In recent times these restrictions are sometimes overlooked. Paper folding of regular polygons and other geometric figures, although not unrelated, is strictly not a part of classical Origami.

Oware. A popular board game played by native children and adults mostly in West Africa. The game requires considerable skill and is played on a board divided into twelve compartments. Initially, each compartment contains four small objects. Sometimes twelve small holes are dug in the ground. The two players, using 48 pebbles, sit on opposite sides of the board or holes, using the stones as with Kalah.

Packing. A packing of convex bodies is an arrangement in which no two of the bodies have common interior points. Packing problems are encountered in crystallography, botany, virology, and other areas of physical science, as well as in the theory of numbers and information theory. See also *Close packing; Tessellations.*

Palindrome. Any number, symbol, word, or sentence that reads the same from left to right and vice versa. For example: 24942; · — — ·; 1,5,10,10,5,1; level; noon; "Madam, I'm Adam"; "Able was I ere I saw Elba."

Palindromic number. An integer symmetrical to its middle. Otherwise, an integer that coincides with its reverse, as do 121 and 483384. Its coincidence ratio is 1.

Pandiagonal magic square. Any magic square in which all the broken diagonals as well as the main diagonals add up to the magic constant.

Pangram. An old form of playing with words in which the goal is to get the maximum number of different letters into the shortest possible sentence.

Panmagic square. Same as a pandiagonal or nasik square.

Pantograph. An instrument used for enlarging or reducing a given diagram, map, and so on. In essence, it is a linkage as here shown. Points *M, E,* and *A* are collinear; *BCDE* is a parallelogram; and the ratio $AE/EM = AB/BC =$ constant. If any one of the points *M, E,* or *A* is kept fixed, the other two describe similar curves.

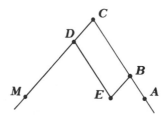

Paper folding. The practice of folding paper to form (1) specified geometric figures or (2) desired objects or toys. In the latter instance the art is called *Origami* (q.v.) and permits the use of scissors and other gadgets to assist and embellish forming the end product.

Paradox. A statement or situation that either is self-contradictory or contradicts a previously accepted axiom, theorem, or principle. In logic, *paradox* is generally regarded as synonymous with antinomy, although the term *paradox* is also correctly used in a broader sense to include intuitive contradictions such as optical illusions, "illegal" arithmetical operations, fallacious proofs in geometry or algebra, and unexpected properties of geometric figures.

Paradromic rings. A modification of the familiar Möbius band, given m half-twists (i.e., when one end of the original strip is turned through an angle of $m\pi$ radians). When m is even, a surface with two sides and two edges is obtained; when cut along the center line, this surface yields two rings each having m half-twists and linked together $m/2$ times. When m is odd, the surface obtained has only one side and one edge; when cut along its center this surface yields only one ring, which has $2m + 2$ half-twists (if $m > 1$, the ring is knotted).

Parhexagon. A parhexagon is a hexagon in which any side is both equal and parallel to the side opposite it.

Parity. Two integers are said to have the same parity if they are both even or both odd; if one is odd and the other is even, they are said to have different parity.

A "parity check" refers to a reasoning process that in some way depends on identification with odd and even numbers.

Parquet. Essentially the same as a tessellation; some parquets are not as "restricted" as a tessellation, but a parquet always covers the plane completely.

Partition (of an integer). The number of partitions $p(n)$ of an integer n is the number of ways n can be written as a sum of positive integers, $n = a_1 + a_2 + \cdots + a_k$, where k is a positive integer and $a_1 \geq a_2 \geq a_3 \geq \cdots \geq a_k$.

Pascal's triangle. A triangular array of numbers consisting of the coefficients of the expansion of $(a + b)^n$, for $n = 0, 1, 2, 3, \cdots$.

Path. A route in a graph that passes through no edge more than once.

Pathological curve. Any curve regarded as the limit of a sequence of polygons or a sequence of numbers; for example, the snowflake curve, the in-and-out curve, the crisscross curve, space-filling curves, and dragon curves.

Peasant multiplication. A method for multiplying any two integers by halving and doubling, rejecting remainders, as here shown.

39	53
19	106
9	212
4	424
2	848
1	1696

Only those numbers in the second column that correspond to odd numbers in the first column are added. Thus

$$39 \times 53 = 53 + 106 + 212 + 1696 = 2067.$$

The explanation of the algorithm rests on the properties of numbers expressed in the binary scale.

Pebbles. A game for two players. At the start of the game, an odd number of pebbles is placed in a pile. Taking turns, each player draws one, two, or three pebbles from this common pile. When all the pebbles have been drawn, the player who has an odd number of them in his possession is declared the winner.

Peg solitaire. A popular board game in England, the United States, and the USSR, where the board consists of thirty-three square cells arranged in the form of a Maltese cross. It is usually played with marbles. In France a 37-cell board is used, whereas in other countries both boards are in use.

Pendulum patterns. Intricate patterns traced by a ray of light through a tiny hole at the bottom of a compound pendulum as it swings over a sheet of photographic paper. Sometimes the oscillating pendulum is fitted with a pen. The traceries formed resemble Lissajous's figures.

Pentacubes. The 29 pieces formed by putting five congruent cubes together in all possible ways. [Theodore Katsanis, ca. 1960.]

Pentagonal numbers. A class of polygonal numbers defined by the geometric figure they represent; thus for a pentagon:

They may also be defined as sums of special arithmetical sequences:

$$1 + 4 + 7 + 10 + \cdots + (3n - 2) = \frac{n(3n - 1)}{2}.$$

Pentagram. A regular star-shaped figure formed by joining each vertex of a regular pentagon with every other vertex and then deleting the sides of the pentagon. Regarded by the Pythagoreans as a symbol of their order, it was presumed to possess magic qualities.

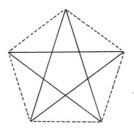

Pentomino. A five-square polyomino.

Perfect digital invariant. Any integer that is equal to the sum of the nth power of its integers for some n; for example:

$$1634 = 1^4 + 6^4 + 3^4 + 4^4.$$

Perfect number. Any integer, the sum of whose divisors, excluding the given integer, is equal to the integer itself. The two smallest perfect numbers are $6 = 1 + 2 + 3$, and $28 = 1 + 2 + 4 + 7 + 14$.

In all, by 1971, twenty-three perfect numbers have been found, some with the aid of electronic computers. It has been shown that any number of the form $2^{n-1} (2^n - 1)$ is a perfect number, provided that $(2^n - 1)$ is a prime number.

Perfectly odd square. A perfectly odd square of order n is an $n \times n$ array of ones and zeros such that the sum along each row, each column, and all diagonals is odd. A 1×1 array consisting of the element 1 is a trivial example; perfectly odd squares of order 2, 3, and 4 do not exist.

1	1	0	0	1
0	1	1	0	1
0	1	1	0	1
1	0	0	1	1
1	0	1	0	1

Periodic decimal. See *Repeating decimal.*

Permutation. Any ordered arrangement that can be formed by using some or all of a finite set of entities.

Petersburg paradox. See *St. Petersburg paradox.*

Petrie polygon. A skew polygon or a zigzag in which the first and second edges are sides of one face of a regular polyhedron, the second and third edges are sides of another face of the given polyhedron, and so on around.

Phi. Known also as the golden mean, or golden number. It is usually denoted by the Greek letters phi (ϕ) or tau (τ), where $\phi = \frac{1}{2}(\sqrt{5} + 1) = 1.61803 \cdots$ and $1/\phi = \frac{1}{2}(\sqrt{5} - 1) = .61803 \cdots$. If a line is divided in accordance with the golden section, one part is ϕ times the other, or $1/\phi$ part of the whole.

Photoelectric factoring machine. Invented jointly by D. H. Lehmer and D. N. Lehmer (University of California, ca. 1933); a sophisticated mechanism, involving gears and photoelectric cells, that identifies the factors of huge numbers in a matter of minutes.

Phyllotaxis. A botanical phenomenon in the arrangement of leaves on a tree, the florets of a sunflower, the helical whorls of a fir cone or a pineapple, and so on, where the arrangements involve fractions whose numerators and denominators are Fibonacci numbers.

Pick's theorem. The area enclosed by a polygon on a lattice or geoboard equals one-half the number of border nails plus the number of interior nails minus 1.

Piling. See *Ball-piling.*

Plateau's problem. To find the surface of least area spanning a given contour. For practical purposes, any specific solution can be obtained, approximately, by fashioning a wire frame in the shape of the desired contour and dipping it in a solution of soap and glycerine.

Platonic solids. The five regular Platonic polyhedra include the *tetrahedron* (4 triangular faces), the *cube* (6 square faces), the *octahedron* (8 triangular faces), the *dodecahedron* (12 regular pentagons), and the *icosahedron* (20 triangular faces). These five only were known to the ancient Greeks.

In addition, four other regular polyhedra are now known—the so-called *stellated polyhedra*, two with star vertices and two with star faces. None of these four is a convex figure.

Polyaboloes. Flat shapes consisting of specified numbers of congruent isosceles right triangles joined edge to edge. They embrace diaboloes, triaboloes, tetraboloes, and so on. [*New Scientist* (England) 12:706; Dec. 1961.]

Polycube. A polyhedron formed by joining unit cubes.

Polygonal knot. If a strip of paper is knotted once and carefully pressed flat, the folds will form a regular pentagon. All polygons with an odd number of sides may be produced in this manner.

Polygonal numbers. Polygonal numbers are a special kind of figurate numbers. They are characterized by their "shape."

Triangular numbers:

Square numbers:

Also, *oblong numbers*, which are the sums of successive even numbers:

The theory is extended to include pentagonal, hexagonal, heptagonal, octagonal, etc., numbers. See also *Figurate numbers.*

Polyhexes. Flat shapes consisting of specified numbers of congruent hexagons joined edge to edge. They embrace trihexes, tetrahexes, pentahexes, and so on. [*Sci.Am.* 216:124; June 1967.]

Polyiamonds. Flat shapes consisting of specified numbers of congruent equilateral triangles joined edge to edge. They embrace diamonds, triamonds, tetramonds, and so on. [*New Scientist* (England) 12:316; Nov. 1961.]

Polyominoes. Flat shapes consisting of specified numbers of congruent squares joined edge to edge. Thus a domino consists of two congruent attached squares; a three-square figure is called a tromino, a four-square figure is a tetromino, a five-square figure is a pentomino, and so on. [Solomon Golomb, *A.M.M.* 61:672; Dec. 1954.]

Polytope. The bounded intersection of a finite number of closed half-spaces; or, technically, a subset of a Euclidean space that is the convex hull of a finite set of points. In a narrower sense, a regular figure in a space on n dimensions, $n > 3$.

Prime number. A positive integer greater than 1 that has no proper factors; or, more generally, an integer with absolute value greater than 1 that has no integral divisors or factors except itself and $\pm$ 1. Examples of prime numbers are 2, 5, 13, 79, 227. The number 1 is regarded as neither prime nor composite.

Primitive Pythagorean triple. If any two terms of a Pythagorean triple are relatively prime, then it is a primitive Pythagorean triple. For example: 3, 4, 5; 5, 12, 13; and 8, 15, 17.

Primitive semiperfect numbers. A number is primitive semiperfect if it is semiperfect but not divisible by any other semiperfect number. There are infinitely many primitive semiperfect numbers.

Prismoid. See *Antiprism.*

Probability board. See *Galton board.*

Probability curve. The well-known bell-shaped curve representing random-chance distribution or normal binomial frequency distribution; known also as the *Gaussian curve* or the curve of errors. One form of its equation is $y = ae^{-kx^2}$.

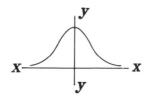

Proper divisors. The proper divisors of an integer comprise all its integral divisors, excluding the integer itself. Thus the proper divisors of 24 are {1, 2, 3, 4, 6, 8, 12}. They are also called *aliquot* divisors. (q.v.)

Pseudomath. A term coined by Augustus De Morgan to identify amateur or self-styled mathematicians, particularly circle-squarers, angle-trisectors, and cube-duplicators, although it can be extended to include those who deny the validity of non-Euclidean geometries. The typical pseudomath has but little mathematical training and insight, is not interested in the results of orthodox mathematics, has complete faith in his own capabilities, and resents the indifference of professional mathematicians.

Pyramidal numbers. "Solid" three-dimensional figurate numbers formed by summing polygonal-number series:

With a triangular base: 1, 4, 10, 20, 35, $\cdots$ $r(r+1)(r+2)/6$.

With a square base: 1, 5, 14, 30, 55, $\cdots$ $r(r+1)(2r+1)/6$.

Pyramidal numbers with triangular and square bases may represent pyramidal piles of symmetrical objects, say, spheres, where each layer represents a triangular or square number, respectively, and the pyramid is "uniformly solid." This is not true of pyramidal numbers with other bases, which will have one or more holes in the several layers of spheres.

Pythagorean triple. A set of three integers a, b, and c, that satisfies the identity $a^2 + b^2 = c^2$.

Quadratrix. A transcendental (i.e., nonalgebraic) curve, invented by Hippias (ca. 425 B.C.), which enables one to multisect an angle and to square the circle. One form of the Cartesian equation of this curve is $y = x \tan(\pi y/2)$.

Quadrature of the circle. One of the three famous problems of antiquity, it called for constructing a square equal in area to a given circle by means of Euclidean tools only, that is, straightedge and compasses. The solution is impossible under the specified conditions, as shown when Lindemann proved in 1882 that π is a nonalgebraic number.

Quadrille. A pattern of dominoes in which like numbers of dots are arranged in groups of four.

Queens problem. A chess problem that requires placing eight queens on a chessboard so that no one of them can take any other in a single move.

Quincunx. The Latin term for the familiar $\vdots \cdot \vdots$ pattern for "five" as it appears on dice and dominoes. Also used to designate the Galton probability board.

Rabbatment. Same as a *Schlegel diagram* (q.v.).

Radix. The base of any given numeration system or scale of notation.

Random clumping. Refers to questions such as, When objects are scattered at random, how many are hidden behind others? How many clumps of two or more will be formed?

Random digits. If, in a number of n digits, each of the ten digits 0, 1, 2, $\cdot$ $\cdot$ $\cdot$, 9 occurs approximately 10 percent of the time, the number is said to consist of random digits.

Recurring decimal. See *Repeating decimal.*

Recurring digital invariant. A sequence of sums of powers of a number ending with the original number. For example:

$$55: 5^3 + 5^3 = 250$$
$$250: 2^3 + 5^3 + 0^3 = 133$$
$$133: 1^3 + 3^3 + 3^3 = 55$$

Redundant number. Same as *Abundant number.*

Reflexible. A figure is reflexible if it is superposable with its image in a plane mirror. This is the ordinary meaning of the term *symmetrical.*

Repdigit. An integer composed of like digits, such as 77,777. [*J.R.M.* 5:123; Apr. 1972.]

Repeating decimal. A decimal in which all the digits (after a certain one) consist of a set of one or more digits repeated indefinitely; for example, .666 $\cdot$ $\cdot$ $\cdot$ or .01797979 $\cdot$ $\cdot$ $\cdot$. Every terminating decimal may be regarded as a repeating decimal; thus .25 = .25000 $\cdot$ $\cdot$ $\cdot$, and so on.

Repeating designs. Certain types of decorative design developed by repeating the same figure at regular intervals in the plane. They may or may not be tessellations and are often found in mosaics and parquets.

Rep-tile. A tile is a rep-tile of order n if exactly n copies of the tile may be used to form a pattern of the same shape as the tile.

Repunit. An integer consisting only of ones, such as 111 or 111,111. [*J.R.M.* 2:139; July 1969.]

Repunit prime. A prime number consisting only of ones, such as 11, or 1,111,111. Numbers consisting only of ones may be represented by the formula $\dfrac{10^n - 1}{9}$, where n gives the number of ones. To yield a repunit prime, a necessary—but not a sufficient—condition is that n be a prime.

Retrograde analysis. In chess problems, a technique of determining, from a given position, what has happened earlier in the game.

Reuleaux triangle. The simplest noncircular curve of constant width; it can rotate "snugly" within a square, maintaining contact continuously with all four sides of the square. [Franz Reuleaux, 1829–1905.]

Reversi. An old game played on a standard chessboard but in no way similar to checkers or chess. It is played with 64 counters having contrasting colors on their opposite sides, each player starting with 32 counters.

Rithomachy. Also known as *Rithmomachia;* a medieval number game, possibly of Greek origin. It was played on a double chessboard (8×16) and involved relations such as $42 = 36 + \dfrac{1}{6}$ of 36 and $81 = 72 + \dfrac{1}{8}$ of 72. Popular during the fourteenth and fifteenth centuries.

Rose curves. Curves whose polar equations are of the form $r = a \cos n\theta$ and $r = a \sin n\theta$, where n may be any positive real number.

Rotor. Any convex figure that can be rotated inside a polygon or polyhedron while constantly touching every side or face. [Michael Goldberg.]

Roulette. The curve generated by a fixed point on a curve as the curve rolls on another fixed curve (or straight line); for example, cycloids and trochoids.

Round robin. A tournament in which all the entrants play each other at least once, failure to win a contest not resulting in elimination from the tournament.

Rubber sheet geometry. A colloquial term that loosely describes topology from the layman's viewpoint.

Russell's paradox. In a town that boasts of only one barber, all the men fall into one of two sets: those men who are shaved by the barber and those who shave themselves. To which set does the barber belong?

St. Petersburg paradox. A classic problem in probability theory. A penny is tossed until heads appears. If this occurs at the first throw, the bank pays the player £1; otherwise, the player throws again. If heads appears at the second throw, the bank pays £2; if at the third throw, £4; and so on, doubling every time. Thus, if the coin does not come down heads until the nth throw, the player then receives £2^{n-1}. What should the player pay the bank for the privilege of playing this game?

Scale of notation. See *Number base.*

Schläfli symbol (polyhedron). A polyhedron may be characterized by a Schläfli symbol $\{p, q\}$, which means that it has p-gonal faces, q at each vertex.

Schläfli symbol (tessellation). A symbolic representation specifying the nature of a semiregular tessellation by naming the polygons occurring at any vertex in the order in which they appear.

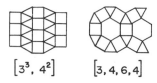

$$\left[3^3, 4^2\right] \qquad \left[3, 4, 6, 4\right]$$

Schlegel diagram. A two-dimensional diagrammatic device that is intended to preserve the essential characteristics of a three-dimensional structure; also known as a *rabbatment.* Schlegel diagrams arise in connection with the study of polytopes and in the theory of graphs.

Sectio aurea. See *Golden section.*

Self-replicating digits. A set of n digits, no two alike, such that when they are arranged in descending order and reversed and the new number is subtracted from the original number, the same n digits reappear in the result. [Martin Gardner, *Sci.Am.*, Jan. 1965, p. 112.]

Semimagic square. A square that fails to be magic only because one or both of the main diagonal sums differs from the orthogonal sums.

Semiperfect numbers. A natural number n is called semiperfect if there is a collection of distinct proper divisors of n whose sum is n. In order that n be semiperfect, it is necessary, but not sufficient, that it be perfect or abundant.

A number is *primitive* semiperfect if it is semiperfect but not divisible by any other semiperfect number.

Semiregular solids. These are the thirteen *Archimedean solids* (q.v.).

Shoemaker's knife. See *Arbelos.*

Sickle of Archimedes. See *Arbelos.*

Sierpinski curve. A remarkable "pathological" curve that contains every interior point of a square and is nevertheless unicursal; its area is less than half that of the square.

Sieve of Eratosthenes. A procedure for identifying prime numbers, attributed to Eratosthenes (ca. 200 B.C.). Thus, from the set of natural numbers—

1. begin with 2, and delete all its multiples except itself;
2. find the next greater number not deleted, that is, 3, and delete all its multiples except itself;
3. find the next greater number not deleted, that is, 5, and delete all its multiples except itself;
4. continue in the same manner as far as desired.

Those numbers not deleted are prime numbers.

As a practical method for identifying the primes, this procedure obviously has serious limitations.

Sim. A game for two people played on the six vertices of a regular hexagon. [Invented by Gustavus J. Simmons; see *Sci.Am.*, Jan. 1973, in Martin Gardner's column.]

Simple curve. A simple curve in a plane is a closed curve that does not cross itself; it has an interior and an exterior and thus separates the plane into two distinct regions. Hence—

1. as in the figure shown, any curve that contains both a point in the interior and a point in the exterior $(\overline{PQ})$ of a simple closed curve must of necessity intersect the given closed curve;
2. any two points in the interior (A,B) or in the exterior (R,S), may be joined by a broken-line curve that does not intersect the given closed curve.

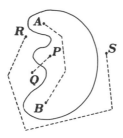

Skeleton division. A long division in which most or all of the digits have been replaced by the same arbitrary symbol (such as $\times$ or $*$) to form a cryptarithm.

Skew polygon. A polygon whose vertices do not all lie in the same plane.

Snowball primes. A set of prime numbers whose digits follow a definite pattern. For example:

409; 4099; 40993; 409933; 4099339; 40993391;

and so on, which may or may not terminate.

Snowflake curve. Consider an equilateral triangle. Trisect each side and replace the center third of each by two sides of an equilateral triangle described on it outwards. Treat the resulting curve in the same way; continue this pattern indefinitely. The result is Von Koch's snowflake curve, which is infinitely long, has a finite area, and at no point possesses a tangent.

Sociable number. A number such that if after a certain number of steps in the process of successive additions of the divisors of the number, the original number is obtained. For example, Madachy gives the 19 divisors of 12,496 as 1, 2, 4, 8, 11, 16, 22, 44, 71, · · ·, 3,124, and 6,248; their sum is 14,288. There are 19 divisors of 14,288, and their sum is 15,472. Further, 15,472 has 9 divisors, whose sum is 14,536; this has 15 divisors, whose sum is 14,264; this has 7 divisors, whose sum is 12,496. [J. S. Madachy, *Mathematics on Vacation*, pp. 145–46; 1966.]

Soma cubes. The seven Soma pieces, created by Piet Hein, include all the different irregular, nonconvex polycubes that can be made by joining three or four unit cubes at their faces. The seven Soma pieces can be assembled into a solid cube, $3 \times 3 \times 3$.

Soma pieces. A subset of polycubes, namely, all the solid figures that can be formed by joining four unit cubes at their faces, yielding eight so-called tetracubes. Another subset consists of twenty-nine pentacubes.

Sophism. A fallacy in which faulty reasoning has been knowingly or deliberately injected. Zeon's so-called paradoxes are essentially mathematical sophisms.

Sorites. In logic, a form of argument involving several premises and one conclusion and admits of resolution into a chain of syllogisms, the conclusion of each of which is a premise of the next.

Spherical close-packing. A particular way of placing equal spheres in a box so that they are in horizontal layers and so arranged that each sphere is in contact with four spheres in the next lower layer, with four in the same layer, and with four in the next higher layer. Such an arrangement is also known as *normal piling;* it gives the greatest number of spheres with which the box can be filled.

Spirograph. A set of drawing instruments consisting essentially of a fixed plastic ring pinned to a drawing board and several smaller plastic disks whose teeth mesh with those of the fixed ring. A pencil inserted in a small hole in one of the small disks allows the disk to be rotated against the inner edge of the fixed ring and produces interesting curves and loops similar to Lissajous's figures.

Spirolateral. A geometric configuration derived from a logically constructed set of rules with the aid of conventional graph paper and appropriate rotations. [Frank C. Odds, *Math.Tchr.*, Feb. 1973, p. 121.]

Sprouts. A pencil and paper game, beginning with n spots on a sheet of paper. A move consists of drawing a line that joins one spot to another or to itself and then placing a new spot somewhere along the line. Lines may have any shape but must not cross lines or pass through previously made spots; no spot may have more than three lines emanating from it; the winner is the last person able to play. [J. H. Conway and M. S. Paterson, ca. 1966.]

Square numbers. A class of polygonal numbers that may be defined by the geometric figure they represent; thus for a square:

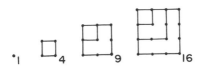

They may also be defined as sums of a special arithmetic sequence:
$$1 + 3 + 5 + 7 + \cdots + (2n - 1) = n^2.$$
It can be shown that every integer is the sum of at most four square numbers, not necessarily all different. See also *Gnomon; Polygonal numbers*.

Squared rectangle. Any rectangle that can be subdivided into unequal squares is known as a "perfect" rectangle. A squared rectangle is one that can be cut up into two or more squares, not necessarily unequal. "Squaring the square" means subdividing a given square into smaller squares, no two of which are alike.

Squaring the circle. See *Quadrature of the circle.*

Squaring the square. See *Squared rectangle.*

Stellated polyhedra. Polyhedra whose faces or vertex figures are "star polygons," that is, polygons with equal sides and angles, but not convex.

The term applies to some of the regular polyhedra as well as Archimedean polyhedra (with star-faces or star-vertices, or both).

Stomachion. See *Loculus of Archimedes.*

Street flexagon. A special type of flexagon whose faces, numbered 1, 2, 3, · · ·, *n*, may be made to appear in sequential order. [J. S. Madachy, *Mathematics on Vacation*, p. 73; 1966.]

String figure. A design or configuration made by taking a piece of flexible string from six to seven feet long, knotting the ends to form a closed loop, and then "weaving" or twisting this loop on the fingers to produce a desired configuration.

Strobogrammatic number. A number that is unchanged by plane rotation through 180°, such as 16891. [*M.Mag.* 34:182; Jan. 1961.]

Subfactorial. The subfactorial of an integer *n* is

$$n! \times \left[\frac{1}{2!} - \frac{1}{3!} + \frac{1}{4!} - \cdots \frac{(-1)^n}{n!} \right].$$

For example, subfactorial 5 is $(120) \left(\frac{1}{2} - \frac{1}{6} + \frac{1}{24} - \frac{1}{120} \right)$
= 44.

Superellipse. A curve having the same equation as an ellipse except that the exponent of the variables is $2\frac{1}{2}$ instead of 2. Created by Piet Hein. The three-dimensional form is known as a *superegg*.

Supertask. A problem situation or query leading to a paradox involving the concept of infinity or of infinite cardinals.

Symmetric. A figure is said to be symmetric if it admits of a certain number of symmetries (q.v.).

Symmetry. A symmetry, or a symmetry operation, is any combination of motions and reflections that leaves the figure unchanged as a whole. Any rotation or translation may be regarded as a combination of two reflections.

Tablut. An elaborate board game of Swedish origin; uses black and white pieces (king and warriors), all of which are moved like a rook in chess. [Martin Gardner, *Sci.Am.* 209:126; Oct. 1963.]

Tac Tix. A particular variation of Nim in which 16 counters are arranged in a 4 × 4 square. [Piet Hein, ca. 1950.]

Talisman hexagons, rectangles, and triangles. Number arrays similar to talisman squares.

Talisman square. An $n \times n$ array of the integers from 1 to n^2 such that the difference between any integer and its immediate neighbor (horizontally, vertically, or diagonally) is greater than some given constant.

Tangram. The Chinese tangram, an ancient geometric puzzle over four thousand years old, consists of seven pieces or tiles cut from a square as shown, where E, F, G, and H are, respectively, midpoints. The object of the tangram is to assemble the seven pieces to form common objects in silhouette. See also *Loculus of Archimedes.*

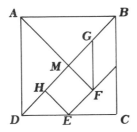

Tarry-Escott problem. The Tarry-Escott problem is that of finding two sets of integers, which may be assumed to be equal in number (since zero is allowed), such that those in each set have the same sum, the same sum of squares, and so on, up to and including the same sum of the kth powers.

Task problem. In chess, any problem that has maximum or minimum characteristics in relation to its space, medium, limitations, and thematic features. [T. R. Dawson, *Ultimate Themes,* 1938.]

Tau. An alternative symbol (τ) for the golden number

$$\phi = \frac{1}{2} \left(\sqrt{5} + 1 \right) = 1.61803 \cdots$$

Tautochrone. The curve traced by a body moving without friction under the force of gravity such that the time required to reach a fixed point is the same regardless of the starting point.

Taxicab geometry. A variety of non-Euclidean geometry based on a lattice of points where the shortest "distance" between two points is not unique.

Teeko. A modification of ticktacktoe using a 5×5 board and four counters. [John Scarne, ca. 1950.]

Ternary numeration. A numeration system having base 3, or on the scale of 3, and therefore requiring only three digits: 0, 1, 2.

Base 10	Base 3
0	0
1	1
2	2
3	10
4	11
5	12
6	20
7	21
8	22
9	100
10	101
11	102
12	110
.	.
.	.
.	.

Tessellation. A plane tessellation is a collection of polygonal tiles that fit together with no overlapping or voids to cover the plane entirely. Or, it may be described as a two-dimensional honeycomb, that is, an infinite set of polygons fitting together to cover the entire plane exactly once, so that every side of each polygon belongs also to one other polygon; in short, a map with infinitely many faces.

Tessellation, regular. A tessellation consisting entirely of regular polygons, all exactly alike and meeting corner to corner, that is, no vertex of one polygon touches the side of another. There are exactly three possible regular tessellations.

Tessellation, semiregular. One in which two or more kinds of regular polygons are fitted together corner to corner in such a way that the same polygons, in the same cyclic order, surround every vertex. There are exactly eight semiregular tessellations.

Tesseract. See *Hypercube.*

Tetraflexagons. A group of four-sided paper structures similar to a hexaflexagon. The simplest tetraflexagon is a three-faced structure appropriately designated as a tri-tetraflexagon. There are at least six types of four-faced tetraflexagons, known as tetra-tetraflexagons. A hexa-tetra-flexagon has also been described.

Tetraflexatube. A flat, square-shaped flexagon that can be opened into a tube. By appropriate flexing along the boundaries of the right triangles, the tube can be turned completely inside out.

Tetrahedron. A convex tetrahedron is a solid figure bounded by four triangular faces; it is the simplest three-dimensional simplex. A regular tetrahedron is bounded by four congruent equilateral triangles; it has 4 faces, 4 vertices, and 6 edges.

Tetriamond. A polyiamond consisting of four triangles.

Tetromino. A four-square polyomino.

Ticktacktoe. A well-known game in which one player marks down only crosses and the other only ciphers, each alternating in filling in his mark in any one of nine cells in a square array. The player who first fills in three of his marks in a row, column, or diagonal is the winner. The game is simple; the strategy is not.

Tiling. See *Mosaic*.

Toetacktick. A modification of ticktacktoe in which the first player to get three in a row *loses*. [Mike Shodell.]

Tomahawk. A simple mechanical device by means of which an approximate trisection of an arbitrary angle can be effected. Although such a trisection is approximate, the tomahawk itself can be constructed with straightedge and compasses only.

Topology. A branch of geometry that deals with those properties of geometric figures that remain invariant under certain types of distortion or deformation; for example, a transformation that shrinks, twists, and so on, in any way without tearing.

Torus. Known also as an *anchor ring*, a circular torus is a doughnut-shaped three-dimensional "solid" figure produced by revolving a circle about an axis lying in its plane but not cutting the circle.

Tower of Hanoi. A classical puzzle presumably due to Lucas (1883) that consists of three pegs or spindles and eight circular disks of different diameters, each with a hole in the center. Initially, the eight disks are placed on one spindle so that the largest is on the bottom and the successive disks decrease in diameter with the smallest on top. It is required to shift the disks from one spindle to another in such a way that no disk shall ever rest on a disk smaller than itself and thus to transfer the original "tower" to another spindle with the disks finally arranged as they were on the initial tower.

Traveling salesman problem. If required to visit each of a given set of cities once, what route should a salesman take to make the total distance traveled a minimum?

Tree. A connected graph without circuits.

Triamond. A polyiamond consisting of three triangles.

Triangular numbers. A class of polygonal numbers that may be defined by the geometric figure they represent. Thus for a triangle:

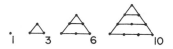

They may also be defined as sums of a special arithmetic sequence:

$$1 + 2 + 3 + 4 + \cdots + n = \frac{n(n + 1)}{2}.$$

It can be shown that every integer is either a triangular number or the sum of two (not necessarily different) or at most three triangular numbers. See also *Polygonal numbers*.

Trisection problem. Probably the best known of the three famous problems of antiquity—the others being the duplication of the cube and the squaring of the circle. An arbitrary angle cannot be trisected by using only the straightedge and compasses, although it can be done with the aid of conics, higher-plane curves, and transcendental curves.

Tromino. A three-square polyomino.

Twin primes. Successive primes with a difference of two, such as 17 and 19, or 821 and 823. They become relatively rare as primes get larger.

Unexpected egg paradox. A logical paradox similar to the paradox of the "unexpected hanging" (q.v.). [Michael Scrivin, *Mind*, vol. 60, July 1951; Martin Gardner, *The Unexpected Hanging and Other Mathematical Diversions*, pp. 11–23; 1963.]

Unexpected hanging paradox. A controversial logical paradox in which a judge sentences a prisoner on Saturday. "The hanging", says he, "will take place at noon on one of the seven days of next week. But you will not know which day it is until you are so informed on the morning of the day of the hanging." Assuming that the judge always kept his word, the prisoner's lawyer contended that the sentence could not possibly be carried out. Was he correct? [Ca. 1940; Michael Scrivin, *Mind*, vol. 60, July 1951.]

Unicursal curve. The path followed in tracing a given geometrical figure so that every line in it is traversed once and only once, although it is permitted to pass through any point of intersection (node) more than once.

Uniform polyhedrons. A polyhedron that has regular faces and that admits of symmetries which will transform a given vertex into every other vertex in turn. The Platonic polyhedra are uniform; so are the right regular prisms and antiprisms whose lateral faces are squares and equilateral triangles, respectively. There are exactly thirteen finite, convex uniform polyhedra; these are the Archimedean solids (q.v.).

Unique factorization theorem. Every integer greater than 1 can be represented in one and only one way as a product of prime numbers, disregarding the order of multiplication.

Unit fraction. Any fraction whose numerator is 1 and whose denominator is a positive integer $\neq 0$; for example,

$$\frac{1}{2} \, , \frac{1}{5} \, , \frac{1}{32}, \text{ and so on.}$$

V-family. A group of polyhedra having a like number of vertices. When these polyhedra differ as to the number of faces, F, each is called a *member* of the V-family. [John McClellan, *J.R.M.* 3:58–60; Jan. 1970.]

Venn diagrams. Diagrams employing overlapping and enclosing circles to show relationships between sets. [John Venn, 1834–1923.]

Versum. The sum of an integer and its reverse. Reiteration of the reversal-addition operation produces a *versum sequence*. [*M.Mag.* 45:186; Sept. 1972.]

Vertex. Either an endpoint of an edge or an isolated point of a graph.

Visible representation numbers. Any number that equals the sum of the squares (or cubes) of its digits taken in pairs or in halves, the sum of the factorials of its digits, and so on. For example:

$$1233 = 12^2 + 33^2$$
$$145 = 1! + 4! + 5!$$

Von Koch curve. See *Snowflake curve.*

Vux triangle. A triangle in which the measure of one of its three angles is one-half the measure of another of its angles. No vux triangle is equilateral; only two vux triangles are isosceles. [F. Cheney, *M.T.* 63:407; May 1970.]

Waring's problem. To show that for any integer n, there is an integer $K(n)$ such that any integer can be represented as the sum of not more than $K(n)$ numbers, each of which is an nth power of an integer. In particular, any integer can be represented as the sum of not more than four squares and as the sum of not more than nine cubes. The problem was solved in 1909.

Weird numbers. A weird number is an abundant number that is not semiperfect. There are infinitely many weird numbers; actually, the set of weird numbers has positive density. [S. Benkoski, *Am.M.Mo.* 79:774; Aug.–Sept. 1972.]

WFF'N PROOF. Trade name of a collection of twenty-one games of logic, ranging from very easy to rather challenging games. [Laymen E. Allen.]

Whirling squares. A golden rectangle has the property that the removal of a square from one end of the rectangle leaves a similar rectangle, turned through 90°. If this process is continued indefinitely, a nest of squares is formed converging on a point P which is the pole of an equiangular (approximately) spiral passing through the points of division; hence, "whirling squares."

Wilson's theorem. This states that the number $(p - 1)! + 1$ is divisible by p if and only if p is a prime; for example, $6! + 1 = 721$ is divisible by 7, whereas $7! + 1 = 5,041$ is not divisible by 8.

Wythoff's game. A modification of Nim in which there are exactly two piles of counters; in each draw the player may select counters from either one or both piles, but in the latter event he must draw the same number from each pile. The player taking the last counter wins.

Yin and Yang. In Chinese religion and philosophy, Yin and Yang refer to two principles: Yin = dark, negative, and feminine; Yang = bright, positive, and masculine. The geometric pattern representing Yin and

Yang (shown below) has been used as a trademark as well as for decorative purposes.

Zeno's paradoxes. The arguments adduced by Zeno of Elea (ca. 450 B.C.) to prove that motion is impossible, regardless of whether distance or time is held to be infinitely divisible or to be made up of a large number of small, indivisible atomic parts. The four paradoxes include (1) the *Dichotomy*, (2) the *Achilles and the Tortoise*, (3) the *Arrow*, and (4) the *Stade*.

Zonahedra. Three-dimensional projections of n-dimensional hypercubes; their edges are all equal, and their faces are generally rhombs.